美国世界建筑文物保护基金会资助项目

国家"985工程二期"清华大学本科人才培养建设项目资助

故宫博物院宁寿宫花园历史研究与文物保护规划

乾隆遗珍

Qianlong's Collector's

The Studies and Master Conservation Plan for Qianlong Garden

刘畅　　　　　　王时伟　　　　　　张淑娴

Liu Chang　　　　Wang Shiwei　　　　Zhang Shuxian

清华大学出版社　Tsinghua University Press

序（一）

　　自 1965 年创建之始，世界建筑文物保护基金会（WMF，曾用中文名称：世界文化遗产基金会，以下简称基金会）已经在世界上 80 多个国家针对具有重要历史文化价值的艺术和建筑的保护工作给予支持。基金会在中国的工作属于优先策略对象之列。

　　基金会在故宫的工作始于 2001 年对紫禁城倦勤斋的保护与复原。这项工作很快建立了基金会与故宫博物院的合作伙伴关系，进而形成了基金会在国际范围内最紧密、最重要的合作关系，并已经成为文化遗产保护领域国际合作的一种模式。

　　宁寿宫花园（乾隆花园）历史研究与文物保护规划的制定，始自倦勤斋并覆盖倦勤斋保护项目，反映出基金会与故宫博物院合作的加强，反映出双方深化国际合作、推进中国文化遗产保护的共同承诺。

　　基金会愉快而荣幸地应邀参与到故宫博物院保护、展示宁寿宫花园的工作中来。这个项目的独特之处在于宁寿宫花园是紫禁城内未经人为干预、富有历史意义的最大遗址之一。此外，宁寿宫花园保护规划的实施，将提供更多的公众教育机会，也能够向更多的人士解读中国建筑和皇家历史。该项目同时使基金会和故宫博物院在倦勤斋项目中得到的收获运用到花园中的其他建筑中，并且为中美文物保护和博物馆领域的技术、文化合作与交流提供更多的机会。

　　基金会参与宁寿宫花园保护规划项目得到了一些国际捐赠者的慷慨支持。为首者是福利曼基金会，为该项目提供资金支持的还有罗伯特·威尔逊先生发起的"保护我们的遗产"挑战基金、美国的布朗基金会、美国的斯达基金会、英国的英美烟草公司、美国的蒂芙尼基金会，以及基莫曼夫妇。

邦尼·博纳姆

美国世界建筑文物保护基金会总裁

2006 年 2 月

Preface 1

Since its founding in 1965, the World Monuments Fund (WMF) has worked internationally in over 80 countries to support the conservation and preservation of culturally and historically significant works of art and architecture. WMF's work in China is one of its highest institutional priorities.

WMF's work in the Forbidden City began in 2001 with the Restoration and Preservation of the Lodge of Retirement. This work quickly developed into one of WMF's strongest and most important partnerships worldwide, and has become a model of international cooperation in the field of cultural heritage conservation.

The creation of this Master Plan for restoration of the entire Qianlong Garden (Ningshou Gong Garden) in which the Lodge is located, reflects the strength of WMF's partnership with the Palace Museum and a mutual commitment to furthering the spirit of international cooperation to advance the conservation of cultural heritage in China.

WMF is pleased and honored to be invited to cooperate with the Palace Museum on the preservation and interpretation of the Qianlong Garden. This unique site is one of the largest relatively untouched sites of historic significance remaining within the Forbidden City. In addition, the implementation of this Master Plan will provide opportunities for public education and interpretation of key aspects of China's architectural and imperial history to expanding audiences. It will also allow the work of WMF and the Palace Museum at the Lodge of Retirement to benefit the other buildings and sites located in the Qianlong Garden, and expand opportunities for international technical and cultural exchange among conservation and museum professionals in the U.S. and China.

WMF's participation in the Qianlong Master Plan is made possible by the extraordinary generosity of international donors lead by the Freeman Foundation, with additional support from the Robert W. Wilson Challenge to Conserve our Heritage, the Brown Foundation (USA), the Starr Foundation (USA), British American Tobacco (UK), The Tiffany & Co. Foundation (USA), and Mr. and Mrs. Kimmelman.

Bonnie Burnham

President
World Monuments Fund
2006.2

序（二）

乾隆皇帝真是位有魅力的皇帝。他很自豪于自己的文治武功，也很得意于自己的长寿和家族的兴旺。他把他的自豪和得意之情留在了4万多首诗里，也留在了他亲自提议兴造的园林和建筑群中，传达到今天，传达给我们。应该说乾隆花园（官方称宁寿宫花园）是乾隆皇帝直接指挥建设的，他深厚的文化修养使他把诗情与画意、皇家园林与私家园林、北方与南方工艺、古代传统与当代成就举重若轻地融汇在一起。每当我漫步在乾隆花园，总是能想见这位太上皇享受着这文化艺术与工艺技术相结合的成果，耄耋之年仍旧意气风发，不知老之将至的样子。

但是现在的乾隆花园太陈旧了，200多年前的辉煌掩藏在尘封里，留在记录中；各类材料的老化使得原本优雅的室内外空间与环境面目全非。如何保护乾隆花园，并且有限度地向公众开放，是故宫保护事业中的一个重要课题。2001年8月，美国世界建筑文物保护基金会与故宫博物院合作，开始了共同保护乾隆花园中的建筑——倦勤斋的项目。经过一年多细致的调查研究，写出了调研报告、施工方案和项目预算文本，并分别经过双方领导的审查和认可。2003年3月20日，双方正式签署协议，保护工程进入实施阶段。共同的工作加深了双方的了解。双方对扩大合作规模，在保护倦勤斋的基础上保护整座乾隆花园一拍即合。清华大学建筑学院的刘畅先生、故宫博物院古建部的王时伟先生和张淑娴女士又经过一年的努力，于是产生了这本书。

为不可移动文物制定保护规划在中国是一个新的要求。2002年修订颁布的《中华人民共和国文物保护法》第十条和第十六条规定，中国的各级人民政府要把文物保护事业纳入本行政区域的国民经济规划和社会发展规划；把对文物保护单位的保护措施纳入建设规划。2003年中国文化部颁布的《文物保护工程管理办法》第四条规定："文物保护单位应当制定专项的总体保护规划，文物保护工程应当依据批准的规划进行"。2004年9月，中国国家文物局发布《全国重点文物保护单位保护规划编制要求》，提出了保护规划应该包括的10项基本内容。《乾隆遗珍——故宫博物院宁寿宫花园历史研究与文物保护规划》（以下简称《规划》）的编制符合中国法律和法规的要求，是我们进行乾隆花园保护必须要做的前期工作。

另一方面，《规划》编制时国家文物局的文件还没有发布，因此规划的编制带有一定的探索性质。刘先生和王先生列举了一系列国内外对于遗产地保护的宪章性文件，包括1931年的雅典宪章，1964年的威尼斯宪章，1983年的加拿大阿普来顿宪章，1979年的澳大利亚巴拉宪章，2002年中国的文物古迹保护准则——承德宪章，来作为编制规划的依据，以此使规划符合文化遗产保护的普遍原则。

保护文化遗产的历史真实性和完整性，全面继承它的文化价值，是文化遗产保护永恒的主题。要实现这个主题，首先要确定保护工作的程序。《中国文物古迹保护准则》规定：文物古迹的保护工作总体上分为六步，依次是文物调查、评估、确定各级保护单位，制订保护规划，实施保护规划，定期检查规划。《规划》根据乾隆花园的情况，编排了这样一个程序：查阅历史文献，调研原有结构，写出报告；提出保护目标和对策；编制总体规划；编制行动计划；为实施程序的全过程进行培训和教育。我认为这个程序是恰当的。我还注意到这个程序中有几步内容特别值得称道。

首先，查阅历史档案和文献做到了尽可能详尽，而且提出了明确的目标，就是力图通过查阅文献，判断古人是如何作出总体计划决策的。《规划》所查阅的文献分别收藏在故宫博物院、中国第一历史档案馆、中国国家图书馆、清华大学等多家机构，钩沉辑录，困难自不必说；而多种档案的罗列排比，把自乾隆三十五年到乾隆四十四年间宁寿宫花园修建过程，像画卷一样清晰地展现在我们面前：君臣之间的反复沟通交流，从呈送烫样，估工估料，从后向前次第完成土建，添配硬木装修，创作书画，通景画，建筑油漆彩画，制作露天和室内陈设、帐幔铺陈，直到制作匾额，工程有条不紊。《规划》还把目光扩展到圆明园等同时期皇家园林的资料和乾隆皇帝本人的诗作，通过对比研究，复原作为私人空间的乾隆花园的历史面貌；进而从乾隆花园的建造中抽象出一种建筑格局、一种园林风格——乾隆风格，即清代中期皇家

Preface 2

development of their administrative areas, and protection of the cultural relics into the construction plan. According to Article 4 of the *Regulatory Measures for Projects for Protection of Cultural Relics* that the Ministry of Culture of China issued in 2003, "The institutions for protection of cultural relics shall develop overall protection plans, and the projects for protection of cultural relics shall be implemented in accordance with the approved plans." In September 2004, the State Cultural Relics Bureau issued the *Requirements for Development of Plans for Protection of the Cultural Relics of National Importance*, which stipulates that a protection plan shall comprise ten basic contents. The *Study and Master Conservation Plan for Qianlong Garden* (hereinafter referred to as the "Master Plan") fulfils the requirements of the relevant Chinese laws and regulations, and it is a job that must be done to develop this Master Plan. On the other hand, State Cultural Relics Bureau didn't issue the document when the Master Plan was developed, so it was somewhat a kind of exploration. Mr. Liu and Mr. Wang presented a number of foreign and domestic charters for protection of heritage sites, including the Athens Charter of 1931, the Venice Charter of 1964, the Appleton Charter of 1983, the Burra Charter of 1979, and Chengde Charter of 2002, i.e. Principles for the Conservation of Heritage Sites in China, and took them as the foundations for developing the Master Plan, so it could conform to the common rules for protection of cultural heritages.

It is an eternal theme in protection of cultural heritages to protect the historic facility and integrity of cultural heritages and inherit their cultural values in an all-round way. To achieve this theme, the procedures for protection shall be first defined. Principles for the Conservation of Heritage Sites in China offers six steps for protection of cultural relics and historic sites, which are survey of cultural relics, appraisal of cultural relics, determination of protection level, stipulation of protection plan, implementation of protection plan, and regular inspection on protection plan. The Master Plan provided such a procedure for Qianlong Garden: consulting historical documents, research on the original structures, and work out a report; put forward the objectives of and measures for protection; develop an overall plan; develop an action plan; and carry out training and education for implementing the whole procedure. I believe this is a

It is truly true to say that Emperor Qianlong was enchanting. He was quite proud of his outstanding statecraft and brilliant military exploits, as well as his long life and growing family. His over 40 000poems reflected this pride and complacency, which were also incorporated in the gardens and architectures he ordered to construct, and delivered to us. It should say that Qianlong Garden (official named Ningshou Gong Garden) was constructed directly under the leadership of Emperor Qianlong, who got profound cultural mastery and easily combined poetic charm with artistic conception, loyal garden with private gardens, northern craftwork with southern craftwork, and ancient traditions with temporal achievements. Whenever wandering in Qianlong Garden, I could imagine this emperor's father who abdicated in favor of his son was enjoying this achievement embodying culture and craftwork, forgetting his agedness, and still highly spirited and vigorous.

Now Qianlong Garden looks quite shabby, and the resplendence over 200 years ago is covered with dust and kept in history. The various materials are aged; the originally elegant indoor and outdoor space and environment are damaged beyond recognition. It is an important subject in the Palace Museum conservation that how we can properly protect Qianlong Garden while opening it to the public with certain restrictions. In August 2001, the World Monuments Fund and the Palace Museum started to work together to protect the Lodge of Retirement, an architecture in Qianlong Garden. Over one year of delicate survey and study, a study report, a construction plan, and a project budget have been worked out, and reviewed and approved by the leaders of both parties. On March 20, 2003, an agreement was officially executed between the two parties, and the conservation project stepped into the phase of implementation. Upon further understanding of each other during cooperation, both parties fitted in with each other to expand their cooperation to the whole Qianlong Garden. Mr. Liu Chang of the School of Architecture, Tsinghua University, and Mr. Wang Shiwei of the Department of Ancient Architectures, Palace Museum, over one more year of hard work, jointly produced *The Study and Master Conservation Plan for Ningshou Gong Garden*.

It is a new requirement to develop conservation plans for immovable cultural relics in China. According to Articles 10 and 16 of the *Law of People's Republic of China on Protection of Cultural Relics* modified and issued in 2002, the governments at all levels shall include protection of cultural relics into the plan of national economy and social

园林的主导风格。还要提及，清代建筑文献的门类极其丰富，《规划》引用的有御制诗集，官方史书，方志，匠作则例，私人笔记，清宫有关衙署的档案如奏销档、奏案，内务府活计档，陈设档，画样，烫样，宫廷画家作品等。正是这些文献，使我们对清代建筑名物制度和乾隆风格有了更为生动的认识。

其次，《规划》摸索和开创了对故宫内檐装修进行调研记录的方法。故宫博物院与美国世界遗产基金会在选择合作目标时，就已经锁定了倦勤斋的内装修。故宫宫殿建筑群，总体壮丽恢弘，代表了封建国家以及皇帝的最高礼仪空间和政务活动空间的标准。但是它同时也是私人空间，也要为皇帝和他的众多家庭成员提供生活、教育、祭祀、宗教信仰、游豫、鉴赏、休息等空间。这些地方的建筑外观遵守着基本统一的制度，如何使室内空间形成特色是个大问题，康熙、雍正皇帝都曾经亲自讨论。乾隆皇帝则直接指挥了乾隆花园建筑的内装修工程。他喜爱江南的风光，用移天缩地的气魄把一些江南著名景点仿造到北京来；他也让两淮盐政为乾隆花园定做硬木内装修，于是江南工匠的手艺连同他们的灵气一起进入了紫禁城。不用说每一个室内空间的分隔布置都充分满足了需要，只是分隔技巧和各种隔断样式，加上隔断上的镶嵌，就让我们无法凭空想象其何等丰富、儒雅与富贵了。看去平整的挂檐，表面竟然是由竹木细丝拼合的图案；在沉静的紫檀裙板上，凸显的素雅山水画是用"竹黄"浮雕的。"通景画"、"线法画"，这种诞生在欧洲的艺术被移植到玉粹轩、遂初堂，倦勤斋通景画的藤萝造就了永远的春天。这些空间目前较少对公众开放，也不为社会所了解。虽然保持了养在深闺的神秘，却也实实在在造成和加速了自然力对它的侵害。既然全面保护内装修是一个新课题，如何调研并准确记录它们也是前人没有做、而保护前必须完成的任务。《规划》为每一种类型的内装修设计了图例，标注在建筑平面图上。然后规定了残损的三个级别，划定了四级工艺难度，也用不同的颜色标注。重要的是，这些带有标注的图纸只是索引，将来调查完成时，大量的表格、照片、细节，构成了乾隆花园内装修的数据库。作者还正在研究引用"GIS"（地理信息系统）的方法，利用数字技术储存和管理这些数据，成为乾隆花园永久保存的档案。

再次，《规划》注意到，对于文物保护项目，经过了历史研究、现场调研评估、提出对策之后，还应该进行基础技术的试验与研究，并把它列入实施计划。这一点至关重要：不仅仅是为了一些新技术的引进，也不单单是为了表现工作细致与否，更为重要的是，在中国传统的古建筑"维修"概念中，强化不可移动文物保护的观念。在故宫这样一个有着近600年历史的古建筑群里，在中国这样一个有着几千年木结构建筑发展史的国家，对建筑的建造、保养维护、更新，早就形成了完整的经验和管理制度，成功地保证和延长了建筑的使用价值，维持了建筑应

Yongzheng both ever talked about it in person. Emperor Qianlong even directly took care of the interior fitments and decorations of the architectures in Qianlong Garden. He loved the scenes in the south of the lower reaches of Yangtze River, and bravely copied some famous scenic spots from there to Beijing. He also ordered the Salt Official in charge of Huainan and Huaibei to customize iron wood fitment and decoration for Qianlong Garden, so some craftsmen from the south of the lower reaches of Yangtze River and their intelligence entered the Forbidden City. The compartments of each indoor space fulfilled the needs of course, but it is hard for us to imagine how abundant, how elegant and how glorious the techniques and styles of the compartments as well as the inlays on the compartments were. The surfaces of the hanging eaves, which look flat and smooth, are actually patterns of bamboo threads incorporating marcquetry; the simple but elegant landscape paintings on the red sandal wood bottom panel are relief sculptures of bamboo inner husks. "Panoramic mural" or "landscape", an art born in Europe, was transplanted to the Pavilion of Jade Purity, and the Hall of Original Wish Fulfilment, and the wisteria on the panoramic mural Tromp l'oeil of the Lodge of Retirement created an ever-lasting spring. These spaces are seldom opened to the public today, and not understood much by people. The mystery of these spaces is well kept, but they are really trespassed by the natural force. Overall protection of the interior finish work is a brand new subject, and investigating and correctly recording them is a mission that our predecessors haven't done but must be done before protection. The Master Plan defines legends for each type of interior finish work, and puts them on the layouts of the architectures. It also provides three levels of damage and incompleteness, and four levels of technical difficulties, which are indicated with different colors. What's more important, the drawings with the legends and signs are just indices, and when the survey is completed in the future, a large number of sheets, photos, and details will constitute a database of the interior finish work of Qianlong Garden. The authors are researching on the introduction of "GIS" (geographic information system) and utilization of digital technologies to store and manage these data, so that they become permanently saved archives of Qianlong Garden.

Third, the Master Plan notices that, for protection projects of cultural relics, experiments and studies of basic technologies shall also be conducted after historical research, field appraisal and provision of countermeasures, and shall be included in the action plan. This is extremely critical, not only because of the introduction of new technologies or delicacy of jobs, but also the idea of protection of immovable cultural relics in Chinese traditional concept of

proper procedure, and I also notice that some contents of this procedure are praiseworthy.

First of all, historical documents and archives are consulted in detail, and clear objective is put forward. That is, great efforts have been made in consulting historical documents, so as to tell how the ancient people made the overall plan. The documents referred to by the Master Plan are separately kept in the Palace Museum, the First Historical Archives of China, the National Library of China, Tsinghua University and some other institutions. It is not necessary to say how difficult it is to find the profound truths. The various documents and archives that are ranged and arranged clearly show us the whole process of construction of Ningshou Gong Garden from Qianlong Year 35 through Qianlong Year 44, which is really a magnificent spiracle before us: the Emperor and the ministers communicated and exchanged ideas repeatedly, involving submission of architectural models, estimation of manhours and materials, completion of civil construction from rear to front, addition of iron wood decoration and fitment, production of paintings and calligraphies, panoramic murals, and architectural color paintings, production of open-air and indoor displaying and veiling, and manufacturing of steles, and everything went on in an orderly way. The Master Plan also paid attention to the data about some contemporaneous imperial gardens as the Old Summer Palace (Yuanming Yuan) as well as the poems and essays of Emperor Qianlong. Through comparative study, they were recovered as the historical visage of Qianlong Garden, a private space. Thus, an architectural pattern, or a garden style, the Qianlong style, which was a leading style for the imperial gardens in the middle Qing Dynasty, was abstracted from Qianlong Garden. What's also worth mentioning is that Qing Dynasty extremely abounded with various documents relating to architecture. The Master Plan cited emperor's poem collections, official history records, local history records, Standardization and Exemplification for Handiworks, private notes, and archives of the relevant agencies of Qing Government, such as memorial archives, archives on household handiworks, historic archives on interior displaying, architectural drawing, architectural model, works of court painters, etc. It is right these documents and archives that enable us to clearly understand the system of things and their names as well as Qianlong style in the Qing Dynasty.

Second, the Master Plan explores a new method for investigating and recording the interior finish work of the Palace Museum. When determining the objective of cooperation, the Palace Museum and the World Monument Fund focused on the interior fitment of the Lodge of Retirement. The architectures in the Palace Museum are splendor and grand as a whole, and represent the standards for the highest amenity space and governmental activity space of the feudal states and the emperors. At the same time, however, it was also a private space, where the emperors and their numerous family members lived, were educated, sacrificed, held religious activities, walked, appreciated things, and rested. The appearances of these architectures comply with a basic uniform system. It was a big issue how to produce unique features for the indoor spaces, and Emperor Kangxi and Emperor

有的外貌和景观的美学特征。唯独这些工作的着眼点首先在于使用，在于用建筑表现制度，一座不能再使用的建筑就失去了存在的理由。这与当代不可移动文物保护的目标存在巨大差异。如何继承传统经验，比如明清皇宫按时进行岁修保养，屋顶按季节除草清垒，及时清理雨水沟（淘沟），补抹灰皮等；比如对于传统的油漆彩画，维修、大修，甚至落架，是否可以成为文物保护的手段之一，是否可以按新的要求做一些改变，老一辈文物保护工作者已经进行了几十年的实践，并作了一些理论总结。但是有时候经验也会产生惯性，某些经验做法可能与文物保护的目标背道而驰，需要我们特别小心地去避免。随着当今世界各国文物保护事业的交流发展，随着科学技术的突飞猛进，我们可以在前人的基础上再进一步。在倦勤斋的实践（参见《倦勤斋保护工作阶段报告——通景画部分》）中，大家已经通过对保护通景画的各阶段和多种工艺、材料的试验研究，把传统技术与文物保护观念很好地结合起来。强化保护观念，最终要建立一系列标准和制度。《规划》不可能完成这个任务，但是以保护内装修为重点的乾隆花园项目，为建立标准进行了有益的尝试。

　　作者要我为本书作序，拜读一遍，收获良多。规划是为了指导实践的，良好的规划是成功的开端。按照《规划》所建议的实施和培训计划，每一个技术细节都要经过试验，每一个措施都要从局部成功再推广。故宫博物院与美国世界遗产基金会的合作也正是从一座建筑扩展到整座建筑群和乾隆花园的全部空间。我因此相信，我们共同保护乾隆花园的计划一定会取得预期的成功。

晋宏逵

故宫博物院副院长
2005 年 10 月

"maintenance" of ancient architectures. For the ancient architectures of the Palace Museum, which is nearly 600 years old, and in China, a country maintaining several thousand years of history of wooden structure architectures, complete experiences and management systems have been developed for construction, maintenance and update of architectures for long. Thus, it successfully ensures and prolongs the service values of the architectures, and maintains the aesthetic features of their appearance and landscape. However, all jobs were for use of the architectures to represent systems, and the architecture that isn't used any more would lose its reason to survive. This is terribly different from today's objective of protection of immovable cultural relics. How shall we inherit some traditional experience? For instance, in the imperial palace in the Ming Dynasty and Qing Dynasty, they conducted yearly maintenance, weeded and cleaned the tiled roof, cleared the rainwater pitches (cleaning out pitches), replastered walls, and conducted traditional colour painting, minor restoration, major restoration and major structure-disassembling. Can these methods become one of our tools for the protection of cultural relics? Or can some modifications be made to these methods as there are new requirements? The old generation protectors of cultural relics have practiced in this field for several decades, and conducted some theoretic summarization. Sometimes experience will keep their inertia, and some experience or methods may run counter to the objective of protection of cultural relics. We shall pay great attention to avoiding this. As the world states increasingly communicate and exchange experience in protection of cultural relics and sciences and technologies advance rapidly, it becomes possible for us to make further steps on the basis of the foundation that predecessors have laid. In the practice of the Lodge of Retirement (please refer to the Interim Report on the Conservation Work on the Quanqin Studio: The Panoramic Murals), they have, through experimental researches on the phases and craftwork and materials for protecting the panoramic murals, perfectly combined the traditional skills and the concept for protection of cultural relics. The concept of protection shall be reinforced, and a number of standards and systems shall be eventually set up. The Master Plan of course can't complete this mission, but Qianlong Garden project for protection of the interior finish work of Qianlong Garden has started a helpful experiment for standard establishment.

The authors asked me to write a preface for the Master Plan. I read it, and gained quite a lot. Plan is to guide practice, and a good plan is the starting point of success. According to the plans for implementation and training that are recommended by the Master Plan, each technical detail shall be tested, and each measure shall be spread after success in part. The cooperation between the Palace Museum and the World Monument Fund is right expanded from one architecture to all architectures and the whole space of Qianlong Garden. Therefore, we believe that our joint plan for protection of Qianlong Garden will surely succeed as expected.

Jin Hongkui

Deputy Director of the Palace Museum
2005.10

致谢

　　笔者身为"宁寿宫花园保护规划工作组"成员，诚挚地感谢所有为此项目的完成倾注了热忱与提供了帮助的组织和个人。

　　笔者首先向那些承诺并准备通过美国世界建筑文物保护遗产基金会为宁寿宫花园的保护提供资金支持的捐赠者致以敬意和谢意。没有他们的慷慨与关心，这个项目是不可能在短时间内提到日程上来的。故宫博物院——宁寿宫花园的直接管理者，是促成这个保护项目的根本；故宫博物院副院长晋宏逵先生，特别为规划工作、实施计划付出了无数心血，在任何需要帮助的情况下拨冗亲劳。对于故宫博物院和故宫博物院的领导，在此的区区数言已无法表达工作小组全体成员的感激之情。在此必须感谢的还有清华大学建筑学院吕舟教授和刘伯英教授的指导，以及清华大学、北京大学、中国林业大学的实验室工作人员的卓有成效的辛勤工作。可以说，正是这些帮助使得宁寿宫花园保护规划工作能够有一个坚实的基础。

　　最后，但无疑不是最次要的，必须说明，规划工作小组是由清华大学建筑学院、故宫博物院合作和美国世界文化遗产基金会委派人员和聘请专家组成的。作为工作小组负责成员，笔者认为，没有这个合作机制，没有其他成员的努力工作，就无法形成现在的规划成果。这里需要特别提名的有：故宫博物院的曹静楼先生、苑洪琪女士、傅连仲先生、赵仲华先生等；清华大学建筑学院的张荣先生、叶扬女士、魏青先生；美国世界文化遗产基金会的副总裁伍子兴先生、约翰·斯塔布斯、T.K.麦克林托克先生。本规划全过程和最终成果都融入了他们的智慧、知识和经验，在此并致谢忱。

刘畅　王时伟　张淑娴

ACKNOWLEDGEMENTS

It is a pleasure of the conservation team working on the Master Plan for Ningshou Gong Garden to thank the organizations or individual for their helpful and enthusiastic works in the Ningshou Gong Garden conservation project.

First please allow us to show our respects and appreciations to the donors and supporters of the project and the potential project of the preservation of the entire garden through New York based World Monuments Fund, without whom the international cooperative restoration project would not have come into being. The author owes thanks that cannot be presented here with words alone to the Palace Museum, the chief party that decides and manages the whole project, and especially to the deputy director of the museum, Mr. Jin Hongkui, who has been giving the project the benefit of his wisdom despite the commitments to his time that a position of such responsibility demands. Thanks are also due to Professor Lü Zhou and Professor Liu Boying from School of Architecture of Tsinghua University, who have been paying close attention to the conservation plan and providing assistance whenever is called for. The fruitful and efficient efforts of the laboratories at Tsinghua University, Peking University and China Forestry University should also be noted here for their remarkable contribution to the fundamental result of the master plan.

Last but not least, this preliminary work could not be done without enormous contribution of all team members from the Palace Museum in Beijing and the World Monument Fund (WMF) in New York. To be specific, Mr. Cao Jinglou, Ms. Yuan Hongqi, Mr. Fu Lianzhong and Mr. Zhao Zhonghua from the Palace Museum, and Mr. Zhang Rong, Ms. Ye Yang, and Mr. Wei Qing from School of Architecture of Tsinghua University, and Mr. Henry NG Tzu and John H. Stubbs, both vice president of WMF, and Mr. T. K. McClintoch have been contributing their wisdom, knowledge and experience throughout the research phases.

Liu Chang, Wang Shiwei, Zhang Shuxian

翻译语言问题说明

对于这样一部为中美双方工作者、读者撰写的规划文本，翻译和语言无疑自始便已经成为一件棘手、而且在一些特殊情况下几乎无解的问题。本规划报告也因此共修改过四稿，其中两次修改都直接与语言问题有关。

回顾规划工作之初，这份由美国世界建筑文物保护基金会最先提出需求及委托的报告是用英文撰写的，而限于作者的英文水平，其中的诸多术语和叙述方式都存在很大的限制。在美方专家的帮助下总算形成了第二稿。随后，为了真正地将规划意见与保护设想在中国的文物工作中体现出来，作者又在英文稿的基础上翻译并改写成中、英对照文稿，这就是第三稿的规划报告。由于这一稿的规划报告已经长达数百页，中、英文的校对工作也因此再度成为了必需的工作。这项艰苦的工作最终经过规划工作小组内部人员的辛勤工作而基本完成了，但是必须指出，这一稿的中、英文对照也还有错误和遗漏——虽然这已经是我们的规划小组在现阶段能够做到的最大努力。WMF 副总裁约翰·斯塔布斯先生曾经作出非常精到的总结：规划工作永远是一个阶段性的成果，没有真正意义上的完成。

除了上述的诸多遗憾之外，还需要说明的问题有两个：

一是对于最基本的名称的翻译问题——关于"宁寿宫花园"的翻译方法问题。本规划英文文本中始终使用的是"Qianlong Garden"，而没有全部改为"Ningshou Gong Garden"。因为从美方设立项目之初，在所有的文件和公告中全部使用的就是"乾隆花园"的称谓。英文文本延续一些西方学者的翻译，能够使中外人士都能继续自己熟知的叫法。

二是对于诸多文物保护专业词汇的翻译问题。很多专业词汇中英文叫法都具有独特的含义，稍有差别意义就大相径庭。其中"restoration"便是典型的一例。《中国文物古迹保护准则》中对于文物建筑修缮的大修、小修、保养工程分别译作"major restoration"，"minor restoration"和"regular maintenance"。而该词英文的本意则偏重"修复"而不是"保守型保护"。"保护"做法则往往用"conservation"一词。本规划中提出的对宁寿宫花园建筑和内檐装修的保护措施主要综合的"修复"和"保守型保护"做法，故中文文本中的修缮和保护做法在英文文本中视该做法的实际倾向选择使用"restoration"或"conservation"。类似的问题还有一些，不赘。

刘　畅

STATE FOR LANGUAGE & TRANSLATION

For such a document prepared by Chinese and American operators and readers, translation and language have become a hard nut to crack from the very beginning, and even an issues that can't be resolved in some cases. This plan has been redrafted for four times, and two drafts were modified directly due to issues related to language.

Looking back to the initial stage of plan preparation, it was the World Monument Fund who first requested this report, but due to the authors' level of English language, there are quite a lot of problems related to technical terms and statements. With the help of some American experts, the second draft was issued. To embody the ideas and assumptions of protection in protection of Chinese cultural relics, the authors translated and rewrote the report, and this was the third draft, a Chinese-English bilingual draft. This draft comprised several hundred pages, and collating the Chinese and English languages of the draft was a job that must be done. This difficult task was basically completed through the painstaking work of some members of the work group. However, what must be pointed out is that it is impossible to eliminate each mistake or omission from the bilingual document, though the work group has done what they can. Mr. John Stubbs, vice president of WMF, once made a wonderful statement that planning would always lead to a periodical documentation, but never lead to real completion.

In addition to the said pities, there are still two issues that have to be explained:

One is the issue on translation of most basic name "Ningshou Gong Garden". The English copy of this plan always uses "Qianlong Garden" instead of using the direct translation. The American party has used the name "Qianlong Garden" in all relevant documents and bulletins from the initial stage of the project. Both Chinese and foreign friends can both understand their own terms given in the Chinese-English bilingual copy.

The other is the issue on translation of the technical terms related to protection of cultural relics. Many technical terms have their unique meanings in Chinese and English, which may be widely divergent from each other. "Restoration" is a typical example. In *Principles for the Conservation of Heritage Sites in China* uses such terms "major restoration", "minor restoration" and "regular maintenance", which lay particular stress on "renovation", not "conservative protection". It also uses the term "conservation". The protective measures for the interior finish work of Ningshou Gong Palace may combine the meanings of "restoration" or "conservation" in this plan, so either of them may be used in the English copy, which depends on the concrete situations. There are some other similar issues, which aren't explained one by one herein.

Liu Chang

目 录

CONTENTS

第一篇 | Part 1

指导原则与工作框架 | Guidelines & Outlines

第一章
宁寿宫花园保护的指导原则

1.1 关于项目重要性的陈述

(1) 宁寿宫花园位于紫禁城宁寿宫后部西路，共由四进院落组成。园中现存主要建筑二十九座，连接各座建筑的附属游廊、假山群组、园林植被、庭院陈设和铺装、室内多材质装饰装修，以及家具陈设等室内现存可移动文物。在造园艺术和装饰艺术方面是清代中期皇家园林代表，是故宫内现存的唯一的室内未受到当代系统人为干预的宫廷原状遗存，是清代帝王宫廷生活的生动体现。

(2) 宁寿宫花园的历史重要性首先体现在其保留了大量原始而真实的历史信息，虽经历种种历史变迁，包括在20世纪90年代进行的古建筑修缮工程，但是花园中的园林设施、建筑内檐装修、家具陈设自清代晚期至今还并未经过全面保护，也没有采取日常保养措施。

(3) 保护宁寿宫花园的重要性主要在于现存各类文物遗存，尤其是内檐装修，处于濒危状态，亟待采取恰当的保护措施。

(4) 宁寿宫花园及其建筑中所反映出的多种匠作工艺至今已经或正在失传，这些工艺必须结合保护工作进行重新发掘或抢救。

(5) 对于宁寿宫花园这一带有多重文化内含复杂的建筑群体系，文物利用工作面临说明阐释、开放路线设计、展陈布置等重要课题。只有在深入研究花园历史，逐一校核考证现存文物的基础上，才能真正全面理解并揭示宁寿宫花园中所携带的丰富历史内涵，才能更好地解说紫禁城文化。

1.2 项目任务陈述

宁寿宫花园的建筑和园林设施、室内和室外遗存相对完好地保留到了今日。就规模而言，宁寿宫花园属于大型建筑群落中的小型建筑群；就其环境条件而言，花园处在故宫这一独特的文化遗产范围之内，花园的保护规划应当服从故宫的总体保护规划；就其独特性而言，花园中园林设施、建筑中内檐装修布局和装饰是最具有代表性的，甚至是独一无二的。因此，宁寿宫花园的保护规划主要面临的挑战不是一般城市地段具有的一般问题，而是集中在如何全面发掘其历史价值和文物遗存，如何针对不同类型的遗存制订合理的、切实可行的研究保护计划，如何开放并全面有效地向公众介绍宁寿宫花园。本规划作为故宫保护总体规划中的局部建筑群的具有独特性的专项规划，立足于以下三项基本目标：

北京旧城区卫星地图　　资料来源：GOOGLE EARTH

北京旧城北部卫星地图　　资料来源：GOOGLE EARTH

北京皇城卫星地图　资料来源：GOOGLE EARTH

北京紫禁城周边卫星地图　资料来源：GOOGLE EARTH

1.1 Statement of the Project's Significance

(1) Qianlong Garden, formally entitled as Ningshougong Garden, is located in the rear west of the Ningshougong precinct, and is composed of four successive courtyards. There are 29 individual buildings, corridors linking the buildings, rockery, historical and modern plants, courtyard displays and pavements, interior settings, and furniture and other movable historical relics in the garden. From the view of gardening and decorative art, Qianlong Garden is the most representative one of Mid-Qing dynasty. Being the only one that remains untouched by modern human intervention, Qianlong Garden is a vivid interpretation of imperial court lives of Qing Dynasty. Furthermore Qianlong Garden is a mid-Qing period garden that represents highest imperial gardening and decoration skills, and most vivid private lives of Qing emperors.

(2) Even though buildings in Qianlong Garden have been repaired in the late-1990s, garden features and interior decorations and furniture have been neglected for decades without proper maintenance since the late Qing Dynasty and afterwards.

(3) The importance of preserving Qianlong Garden chiefly lies in protecting various kinds of relics in it, especially the interior settings in buildings which are in serious endangered condition and call for proper conservation treatments.

(4) Traditions in various fields of artisanry are now extinct or on the way to becoming so, which are represented in Qianlong Garden and its interiors. These can be discovered and rejuvenated through conservation treatments.

(5) Interpretation is a challenging in such a sophisticated and comprehensive complex of Qianlong Garden. Circulation and exhibit design based on sound research and genuine understanding will benefit profoundly the interpretation of Ningshou Gong precinct and that of the entire Forbidden City.

1.2 Mission Statement

Qianlong Garden is integrally preserved today in both its exterior and interior, and is especially renowned for its garden features and interior spacelayout and decorations. The master conservation plan for Qianlong Garden is based on the following three goals:

（1）在深入研究有关文献记载、图样、一切相关历史遗存及文物保护技术研究的基础上，维持、保护、修复宁寿宫花园和其中所有设施和附属文物；（2）突出该花园作为乾隆时期的建筑、园林代表的重要特点，强调乾隆时期的装饰艺术和匠作工艺传统；（3）展示花园及其功能的历史变化，展示乾隆皇帝及其继任者的私人生活。

为了实现以上目标，本规划制定了以下基本任务：

（1）开展相关历史研究工作，研究范围应涵盖从传统园林到匠作手工艺等多个门类；（2）开展教育培训传统工匠、文物保护工作者、博物馆员等基础工作；（3）保护、部分修复园中的园林设施、建筑构筑物及内檐装修与陈设；（4）在细致的历史文献、图档、实物的研究基础上，有效利用现代手段全面展示、揭示和介绍宁寿宫花园、建筑装饰艺术和展品的历史文化、科学、艺术内涵。

1.3 本规划所依据和借鉴的宪章和准则

（1）《中华人民共和国文物保护法》（2002年10月）；《中华人民共和国文物保护法实施条例》（2003年7月）；（2）威尼斯宪章（1964年）；（3）雅典宪章（1931年）；（4）关于保护改善建成环境的阿普来顿宪章（加拿大ICOMOS委员会，1983年）；（5）巴拉宪章（澳大利亚ICOMOS委员会，1979年，1981年、1988年修订）；（6）中国文物古迹保护准则（中国ICOMOS委员会，2002年）。

1.4 术语释义

1.4.1 保护/维护

总体而言保护/维护是指采取一定的保护措施，达到保存文物现状、材料与形式、历史信息，及其完整性的过程，具体做法包括防止破坏、加固、保养和修理等。针对宁寿宫花园保护规划而言，保护/维护措施主要适用于建筑物、园林设施和内檐装修。

1.4.2 修复

修复主要指按照历史特定阶段的特征加以精确表现的做法和过程。在对历史特征进行恢复的过程中，同时不可避免地对于其他历史时代留下的痕迹加以去除。乾隆花园中已经进行的（20世纪90年代）大木外檐彩画的复原工程便属于此类做法，恢复了乾隆中期的彩画特点。宁寿宫花园保护规划中也将采用这种方法。

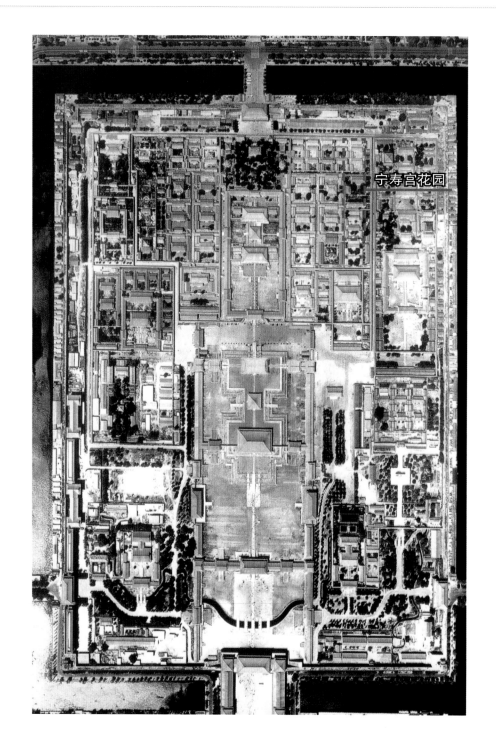

宁寿宫花园

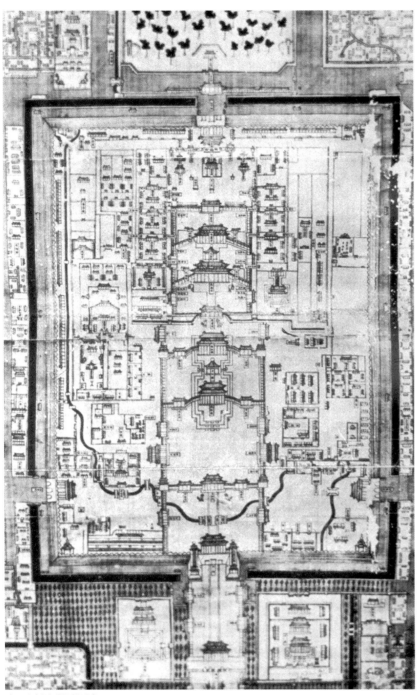

皇城衙署图局部 资料来源：《中国营造学社汇刊》

(1)Maintaining, conserving and restoring the Qianlong Garden and its contents and documentation based on historical and conservation research, (2)Presenting the garden as an example of architecture and gardening during the imperial period of Qianlong, and stress the related traditions of the decorative arts and artisanry, (3)Functioning as a window to the private lives of Emperor Qianlong and his followers.

The project of Qianlong Garden Conservation accomplishes the above objectives through,

(1) Support of research in related fields from traditional gardening to artisanry in decoration handiwork, (2) Educational programs in training artisans, conservators and curators, (3) The preservation and partial restoration of the garden features, building structures, and interior decorations, (4) Tracing historical documentations and taking advantage of modern means to exhibit and interpret the complex and interior objects.

1.3 Charter and Standard Guidelines

(1) China Legislation on Cultural Relics and Regulations for the Implementation of China Legislation on Cultural Relics. (2) International Charter for the Conservation and Restoration of Monuments and Sites (The Venice Charter), 1964. (3) The Athens Charter for the Restoration of Historical Monuments, 1931. (4) Appleton Charter for the Protection and Enhancement of the Built Environment (ICOMOS Canada), 1983. (5) The Australia ICOMOS Charter for the Conservation of Places of Cultural Significance (The Burra Charter), 1979, rev. 1981, 1988. (6) Principles for the Conservation of Heritage Sites in China (ICOMOS China Commitee), 2002

1.4 Definitions

1.4.1 Conservation /Preservation

Generally conservation/preservation is defined as the act or process of applying measures necessary to sustain the exsiting form, integrity, materials of a historical property, which historic information rests in and includes protection, stablization, maintenance and repair. In the Conservation Master Plan for Qianlong Garden, conservation/preservation chiefly refers to the proposed treatments to building structures, garden features and interior features.

1.4.2 Restoration

Restoration is defined as the act or process of accurately depicting the form, features, and characters of a property as it appeared at a particular period of time by means of the removal of features from other periods in its history and reconstruction of missing features from the restoration period. The previous treatments of timber components by repainting are restoration measures intented to reproduce Mid-Qing Dynasty relics. Restoration treatments will also be used judiciously in this conservation master plan.

1.4.3 改造利用

改造利用特指在保存文物建筑的主要部分及其历史特征和历史文化、艺术、科学价值的基础上，通过修缮、改造和添建，使之适合于新的使用功能的做法和过程。此外，在建筑中谨慎地增加有限的机械、电力及其他管线设施以使文物建筑适合于新的功能的做法也属于改造利用的概念范畴。本规划文本中，改造利用主要使用于以下两个方面：其一，广义而言，在文物建筑室内的历史环境中增加原状陈列展览；其二，将一些历史建筑，尤其是一些就其本身而言具有较低历史价值的建筑物，改造成为设备用房，以容纳现代机械、电力、服务等设施。

1.4.4 原状

规划制定者认为，每项文物保护工作都应在深入考察评估的基础上确定该项目文物原状的内容。宁寿宫花园文物原状主要指该建筑群，及其中的园林设施、建筑物、内檐装修作为皇家园林的原有使用状况，主要反映乾隆年间建成后到嘉庆时期的历史。本规划同时关注嘉庆之后的历史，认为末代皇帝离开故宫之前的历史时期里，皇家对该建筑群所做出的调整同样具有历史重要性，保留至今的历史痕迹应当按照文物原状对待。

1.4.5 基础设施

宁寿宫花园中的基础设施主要指花园中现存的文物建筑的基础设施，包括古建筑基础、排水系统、地炕系统等。规划在花园中添加的现代设施系统主要在第二篇第六章中陈述。

1.4.6 园林设施

宁寿宫花园中的园林设施主要包括花园中的假山、小品雕刻及陈设座、种植土壤层、绿化植被、水景等。其中土壤处理与植物复壮等问题由于其复杂性和丰富性应当引起特别关注。

1.4.7 建筑与构筑物

宁寿宫花园中，建筑与构筑物主要指花园中所有的楼阁、厅堂、轩、亭座、门庑、游廊等。在考察这些建筑/构筑物时，主要目标是考察其主体结构、外檐装修、地面铺装、屋面构造及其他室外装饰等部分。

1.4.8 内檐装修

宁寿宫花园中，内檐装修为一广义概念，主要指的是文物建筑室内罩隔、平台、楼梯、装饰板墙、顶棚、匾联、通景画、贴落和墙纸等。

新陬潭珑
故宫博物院宁寿宫花园历史研究与文物保护规划

宁寿宫花园

资料来源: La chine a Terr et en ballon

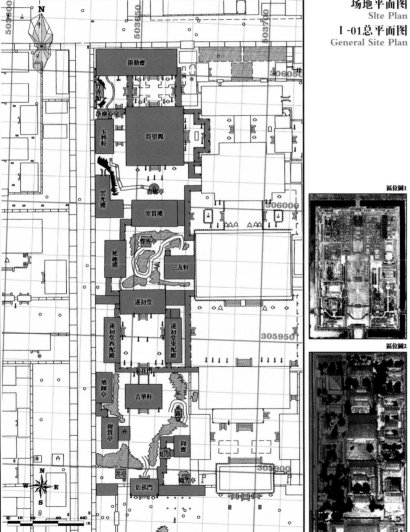

乾隆花园文物保护规划
Master Conservation Plan for Qianlong Garden

清华大学文化遗产保护研究所
故宫博物院

Part I

场地平面图
Slte Plan

I -01总平面图
General Site Plan

區位圖1

區位圖2

1.4.3 Rehabilitation

Rehabilitation is defined as the act or process of making possible a compatible use of a property through repair, alternation and additions while preserving the portions and features which conveys its historical, cultural or artistic values. The limited and sensitive upgrading of mechanical, electrical, and plumbing system and other code-required work to make the property functional are also appropriate treatment within the definition of rehabilitation. The term is used in this context chiefly for two purposes, a) accomodating broad means of exhibitions in historic interior spaces, and b) using some historic structures of minor historic importance as rooms for modern mechanical, electrical, plombing system, other required devices, and as service spaces.

1.4.4 Original

In the case of Qianlong Garden, original is defined as the complex and its garden features, buidling structures and interior contents when it was used as a private garden especially during Qianlong and Jiaqing periods in Qing Dynasty (after completion of the final interior construction in 1779 to 1820). It is also recognized that modifications made to the complex and its changes in its contents from 1820 to 1924, after Jiaqing period till the last emperor's departure from the palace, are of considerable cultural significance.

1.4.5 Infrastructure

Infrastructure, in the case of Qianlong Garden, chiefly refers to the original fundations, drainage system, and underground heating system in the present complex. Modern systems to be added to the complex are stipulated in Chapter 6, Circulation, Interpretation & Facilities.

1.4.6 Garden Features

Garden Features chiefly refers here to rockery, rails and posts, courtyard pavement, sculptures and bases, and soil and horticultural items. The survey and treatment of the soil and horticultural items are discussed separately on account of the complexity and contents.

1.4.7 Buildings and Structures

Buildings and structures chiefly refers here to buildings, halls, pavilions, chambers, corridors, and their openings, such as window and door, pavement and roof, exterior decorations, etc.

1.4.8 Interior Features

Interior features chiefly refer here to interior screens, platforms, stairs, decorative wall boards and ceilings, hanging tablets, tromp l'oeil murals, Tieluo paintings (decorative silk / paper paintings mounted directly on to wallpaper), and wallpaper.

1.5 工作流程

1.5.1 记录工作

　　档案记录工作，包括历史资料和本次规划勘察阶段的资料，主要由草图、建筑图、绘画、照片、文档、调研表格组成。这些资料将按照规划流程分别按建筑整理成帙。规划过程中的各级别的决策将同样得到足够的关注和记录。

1.5.2 保护措施与人员培训

　　1. 保护/修复/改造利用方面的教育培训：鉴于宁寿宫花园保护工作的基本出发点是保存历史信息，表现清帝宫廷生活，当今以保护为出发点的工作应当建立在可逆性、真实性和可读性的基础上。对于保护工作者的培训应当首先强调文物保护理论理论素质的提高。

　　2. 宁寿宫花园保护规划的实施阶段应当按照以下步骤逐步进行，因而对参与人员的教育培训工作也有以下不同的侧重点。

　　(1) 规划设计阶段：历史研究+现状勘察+保护原则与基本措施+基本保护技术研究；强调各学科的综合与协作。(2)实施方案阶段：技术方案研究+试验性操作；强调专业分工，强调文物保护技师培训。(3)工程/实施阶段：分阶段实施；强调文物保护技师培训与管理强调，强调展陈设计人员与讲解人员的培训。

　　3. 为了保证规划目标的实现，对于不同的参与人员应当逐步建立下列培训制度：(1)传统工艺匠师：建立师徒传承制度。(2)文物保护技术人员：建立在中国、美国等地的学院或博物馆中的基础理论和实践培训制度。(3)文物保护科研人员：建立在中国、美国等地的学院或博物馆中的理论和实验室基础培训制度。(4)文博馆员：建立在中国、美国等地的博物馆中展陈理论与实务的培训。

1.5.3 文物展示与说明

　　本规划在第六章中提出了宁寿宫花园文物展示与说明的基本建议。随着保护规划的实施，还必须将此基本建议深化完善，形成展示和说明的具体方案。同时，对于制定和执行此具体方案的博物馆员和解说人员的教育培训工作将对最终的展示与说明效果提供莫大帮助。

1.5.4 规划分期与长期保养

　　本规划在第五章中提出了宁寿宫花园保护工作分期设想和长期保养的工作计划。

宁寿宫花园鸟瞰　　资料来源：天津大学建筑系，《清代内廷宫苑》

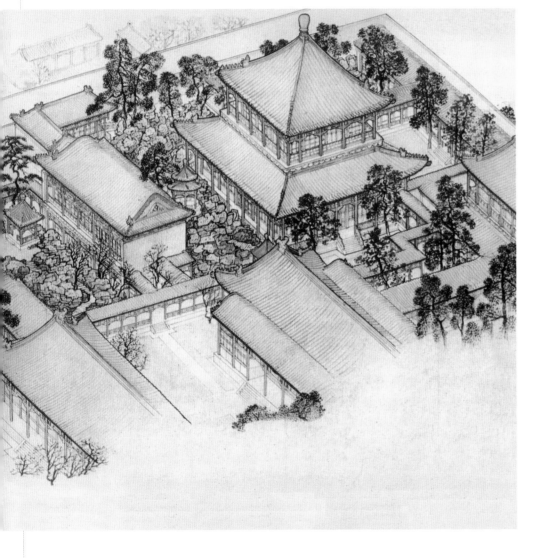

1.5 Procedure

1.5.1 Documentation

Documentations, consisting of sketches, paintings, measured drawings, photographs, written descriptions, condition assessment tables, both historical and made during current surveys and planning, will be compiled as part of the historic structure report process. Special attention will be given to documenting the decision making process of the master plan.

1.5.2 Proposed Treatment & Education

1. Conservation + Restoration + Rehabilitation: The basic goal of the treatment is to present the original garden complex as the private space for Qing emperors. Therefore, to the greatest extent possible, interventions should be carried out in a manner that is reversible, authentic to the original, and legible.

2. Implementation of the Master Plan should follow the procedure as,

(1) Master Plan: Studies on History + Site Survey + Proposed Remedies + Fundamental Technique Researches. (2) Action Plan: Technique Researches + Experimental Treatment . (3) Implementation: Identifying phases; Emphasizing education, management and cooperation among different disciplines.

3. In order to achieve the goal of the master plan, education should be stressed,

(1) For traditional artisanry: establishing master+apprentice system. (2) For long-term monitoring, with WMF help: training conservator in academies and museums in China and USA. (3) For conservation technical solutions: educating conservation scientists in academies and museum laboratories in China and USA. (4) For interpretation: educating curators in academies and museums in China and USA.

1.5.3 New System for Interpretation and Circulation

The master plan provides a primary plan for interpretation and circulation in Chapter 6. It is also important that an action plan should be made revising the relevant part of the master plan. It is certain that future work will benefit remarkably from the educational program for curators.

1.5.4 Proposed Phases & Future Maintenance

The master plan provides plan for working phases and future maintenance in Chapter 5.

一期工作前的研究阶段（2008年10月–2009年10月）

(1)继续修复倦勤斋，撰写纸张、木作、丝绸、油饰保护总结报告；(2)宁寿宫花园中现存文物材料学、工艺学调研，保护修复研究与试验；(3)编制宁寿宫花园现存文物总数据库及分支数据库；(4)制定一期工作计划和实施方案。

一期工作（2009年5月–2013年05月）

(1)全面整修宁寿宫花园排水系统，制定日常维护制度；(2)开展宁寿宫花园植物复壮与土壤改良工作；(3)实施对第四进院落（碧螺亭所在院落）的假山保护；(4)按照实施方案规定的进度修复竹香馆、玉粹轩、符望阁、云光楼内檐装修，对碧螺亭进行建筑保护；(5)制定第四进院落的展示和说明方案；(6)准备并实施第四进院落的展示和说明方案，开放第四进院落；(7)至2008年初，应当初步完成玉粹轩和竹香馆的室内外保护工作，为2008年中期开放第四进院落北半部做好准备；(8)建立和维护第四进院落现存文物总数据库及分支数据库；(9)制定第二期工作计划和实施方案。

二期工作（2013年6月–2016年6月）

(1)各院落植物维护与土壤改良工作；(2)实施对第三进院落（耸秀亭所在院落）的假山保护；(3)按照实施方案规定的进度修复萃赏楼、延趣楼、三友轩内檐装修，对耸秀亭进行建筑保护；(4)制定第三进院落的展示和说明方案；(5)准备并实施第三进院落的展示和说明方案，开放第三进院落；(6)建立和维护第三进院落现存文物总数据库及分支数据库；(7)制定第三期工作计划和实施方案。

三期工作（2016年7月–2019年7月）

(1)各院落植物维护与土壤改良工作；(2)实施对第一、二进院落的假山保护；(3)按照实施方案规定的进度修复第一、二进院落中遂初堂、古华轩、旭辉庭、抑斋等建筑的内檐装修，对其他建筑进行保护；(4)制定第一、二进院落的展示和说明方案；(5)准备并实施第一、二进院落的展示和说明方案，开放第一、二进院落；(6)建立和维护第一、二进院落现存文物总数据库及分支数据库。

Research Phase, 2008/10-2009/10

(1) Implement and summarize the conservation in the Lodge of Retirement which serves as a pilot project for that of the entire garden. (2) Study on basic technical solution and experimental processes for the relics in the garden; (3) Organize and design the information system for Qianlong Garden relics. (4) Prepare the conservation action plan for phase I.

Phase I, 2009/05-2013/05

(1) Renovate the drainage system. (2) Start maintaining the plants and improve the soil in all courtyards. (3) Preserve the rockery in the fourth courtyard. (4) Restore the exterior and interior of the Chamber of Bamboo Fragrance, the Pavilion of Jade Purity, the Building of Wish and Reality in Accordance, the Building of Cloud Light. (5) Interpret and exhibit exterior and interior features. (6) Mobilize for opening of the fourth courtyard. (7) Aim for 2008, Restoration of the exterior and interior of the Chamber of Bamboo Fragrance and the Pavilion of Jade Purity would be possibly completed, to allow for the north part of the fourth courtyard would be ready to open for special visit during the Olympic Games. (8) Establish, fill-in and maintain the Cultural Relics Information System (CHIS) of the fourth courtyard of the garden. (9) Draw conservation action plan for phase II.

Phase II, 2013/06-2016/06

(1) Regularly maintain the plants and improve the soil in all courtyards. (2) Preserve the rockery in the third courtyard. (3) Restore the exterior and interior of the Building of Collection and Appreciation, the Building of Extended Delight, the Pavilion Three Friendship and the Pavilion of Aloft Bueaty. (4) Interpret and exhibit exterior and interior features. (5) Mobilize for opening of the third courtyard. (6) Establish, fill-in and maintain CHIS of the third courtyard of the garden. (7) Draw conservation action plan for phase III.

Phase III, 2016/07-2019/07

(1) Regularly maintain the plants and improve the soil in all courtyards. (2) Preserve the rockery in the first and second courtyard. (3) Restore the exterior and interior of buildings in the first and second courtyards, including interior conservation of the Hall of Fulfillment of Original Wishes, the Pavilion of Ancient Flower and the Chamber of Self-Constraint should be stressed. (4) Interpret and exhibit exterior and interior features. (5) Mobilize for opening of the first and second courtyards. (6) Establish, fill-in and maintain CHIS of the first two courtyards of the garden.

第二章
宁寿宫花园保护规划工作概要

2.1 关注点·责任·框架图

2.2 规划分期与经费估算

　　宁寿宫花园保护规划基于故宫博物院与美世界文化遗产基金会合作意向的前提，合作涵盖保护经费和技术支持两部分基本内容。前文所述主要涉及工作任务和技术内容，兹一并将宁寿宫花园保护规划各期工作与对应的所需经费加以整理，作为规划工作总体框架的一部分。经费估算明细详见第二篇第七章。

研究阶段经费估算

2008/10-2009/10

项目编号	项目名称	项目内容	经费估算（元）
I	研究项目		610 000
I-a	古建筑生物破坏防治		50 000
I-b	古建筑彩画检测与保护方法检验		50 000
I-c	假山叠石做法研究与结构安全勘察		200 000
I-d	室内罩隔精细镶嵌雕刻工艺与破坏机理研究		200 000
I-e	漆器破坏机理与保护方法研究		100 000
I-f	倦勤斋绘画类文物保护方法总结		10 000
II	保护方案设计、项目启动与前期准备		1 000 000
II-d	建立专题保护工作室		1 000 000
IX	不可预见费	专题项目合计 *10%	161 000
研究阶段总额			**1 771 000** **USD 215 976**

第一期保护经费估算

2009/05-2013/05

项目编号	项目名称	项目内容	经费估算（元）
II	项目启动与前期准备		224 000
II-a	申报与组织审议	保护工作立项、方案审批	4 000
II-b	现场准备		20 000

Chapter 2
Master Plan Outlines

2.1 Main Concerns & Responsibilities

2.2 Phase Laying & Budget

The master conservation plan for Ningshou Gong Garden was developed based on the intention of cooperation of the Palace Museum and the World Monuments Fund. The cooperation covers financial and technical aspects. Text in above sections mainly exlicates the technical tasks and contents, and the following charter is on required fund corresponding to the tasks. Technical tasks and the budget together form the outline and guideline of the master plan. As envisaged tasks and technical requirements are identified above, phase laying and budget are listed below.

Budget for Research Phase

2008/10-2009/10

Item	Sub-item	Explanation	Estimation of Cost (Yuan)
I	Research Project		610 000
I-a	Bio-deterioration in structure		50 000
I-b	Analyses and Proposed Treatments to Remaining Architectural Color Paintings on Beams		50 000
I-c	Structural safety of rockery		200 000
I-d	Interdisciplinary cooperation on Inlay & Marquetry		200 000
I-e	Lacquer works		100 000
I-f	Final Documentation Works on Paper and Silk in the Lodge of Retirement		10 000
II	Implementation Plan, Mobilization and Preparation		1 000 000
II-d	Additional Conservation Studio Set Up		1 000 000
IX	Contingency	Subtotal*10%	161 000
Research Phase TOTAL			**1 771 000** **USD 215 976**

Budget for Phase I

2009/05-2013/05

Item	Sub-item	Explanation	Estimation of Cost (Yuan)
II	Mobilization and Preparation		224 000
II-a	Permits	For setup of the project and approval of the conservation plan	4 000
II-b	Site Preparation		20 000

项目编号	项目名称	项目内容	经费估算（元）
IV-a	假山叠石		250 000
IV-b	庭院地面铺装		960 000
IV-c	陈设与陈设座		65 000
IV-d	土壤改良与古树复壮		100 000
V	古建筑		7 544 450
VI-Bldng ID	内檐装修		27 009 800
VII	杂项		700 000
VII-a	记录		100 000
VII-b	展陈与解说		600 000
VIII	管理费		300 000
	小计		43 328 250
IX	不可预见费	为无法预见的问题及可能必须临时设立的培训与教育项目等	4 332 825
第一期总额			**47 661 075** **USD 5 812 326**

第二期保护经费估算

2013/06-2016/06

项目编号	项目名称	项目内容	经费估算（元）
II	项目启动与前期准备		684 000
II-a	申报与组织审议		4 000
II-b	现场准备		20 000
II-c	脚手架		160 000
II-d	建立专题保护工作室		500 000
III	基础设施		5 060 000
III-a	排水设施		100 000
III-b	地炕设施		160 000
III-c	电力设施（照明、警报、通信等）		4 800 000
IV	园林设施		1 610 000
IV-a	假山叠石		450 000
IV-b	庭院地面铺装		960 000
IV-c	陈设与陈设座		100 000
IV-d	土壤改良与古树复壮		100 000
V	古建筑		4 126 467
VI-Bldng ID	内檐装修		9 033 250

项目编号	项目名称	项目内容	经费估算（元）
VII	杂项		700 000
VII-a	记录		100 000
VII-b	展陈与解说		600 000
VIII	管理费		250 000
	小计		21 463 717
IX	不可预见费	为无法预见的问题及可能必须临时设立的培训与教育项目等	2 146 372
第二期总额			**23 610 089** **USD 2 879 279**

第三期保护经费估算

2016/07-2019/07

项目编号	项目名称	项目内容	经费估算（元）
II	项目启动与前期准备		524 000
II-a	申报与组织审议		4 000
II-b	现场准备		20 000
II-c	脚手架		500 000
III	基础设施		3 900 000
III-a	排水设施		200 000
III-b	地炕设施		100 000
III-c	电力设施（照明、警报、通信等）		3 600 000
IV	园林设施		2 670 000
IV-a	假山叠石		350 000
IV-b	庭院地面铺装		1 920 000
IV-c	陈设与陈设座		200 000
IV-d	土壤改良与古树复壮		200 000
V	古建筑		6 473 667
VI-Bldng ID	内檐装修		7 537 500
VII	杂项		1 400 000
VII-a	记录		200 000
VII-b	展陈与解说		1 200 000
VIII	管理费		250 000
	小计		22 755 167
IX	不可预见费	为无法预见的问题及可能必须临时设立的培训与教育项目等	2 275 517
第三期总额			**25 030 684** **USD 3 052 522**

Item	Sub-item	Explanation	Estimation of Cost (Yuan)
III-a	Drainage		75 000
III-b	Underground Heating		100 000
III-c	Electrical (Including Security Telecom etc.)		6 000 000
IV	Garden Features		1 375 000
IV-a	Rockery		250 000
IV-b	Courtyard Paving		960 000
IV-c	Sculptures and Bases		65 000
IV-d	Soil Enhancement & Plant Retention/Supplementation		100 000
V	Building ID		7 544 450
VI-Bldng ID	Interior Items		27 009 800
VII	Miscellaneous		700 000
VII-a	Documentation		100 000
VII-b	Opening Exhibit/Presentation		600 000
VIII	Overhead and Management		300 000
	SUBTOTAL		43 328 250
IX	Contingency	For problems unpredicable, and training and education programs	4 332 825
Phase I TOTAL			**47 661 075** **USD 5 812 326**

Budget for Phase II

2013/06-2016/06

Item	Sub-item	Explanation	Estimation of Cost (Yuan)
II	Mobilization and Preparation		684 000
II-a	Permits		4 000
II-b	Site preparation		20 000
II-c	Scaffolding		160 000
II-d	Additional Conservation Studio Set Up		500 000
III	Infrastructure		5 060 000
III-a	Drainage		100 000
III-b	Underground Heating		160 000
III-c	Electrical (Including Security Telecom etc.)		4 800 000
IV	Garden Features		1 610 000
IV-a	Rockery		450 000
IV-b	Courtyard Paving		960 000
IV-c	Sculptures and Bases		100 000
IV-d	Soil Enhancement & Plant Retention/Supplementation		100 000

Item	Sub-item	Explanation	Estimation of Cost (Yuan)
V	Building ID		4 126 467
VI-Bldng ID	Interior Items		9 033 250
VII	Miscellaneous		700 000
VII-a	Documentation		100 000
VII-b	Opening Exhibit/Presentation		600 000
VIII	Overhead and Management		250 000
	SUBTOTAL		21 463 717
IX	Contingency	For problems unpredicable, and training and education programs	2 146 372
Phase II TOTAL			**23 610 089** **USD 2 879 279**

Budget for Phase III

2016/07-2019/07

Item	Sub-item	Explanation	Estimation of Cost (Yuan)
II	Mobilization and Preparation		524 000
II-a	Permits		4 000
II-b	Site preparation		20 000
II-c	Scaffolding		500 000
III	Infrastructure		3 900 000
III-a	Drainage		200 000
III-b	Underground Heating		100 000
III-c	Electrical (Including Security Telecom etc.)		3 600 000
IV	Garden Features		2 670 000
IV-a	Rockery		350 000
IV-b	Courtyard Paving		1 920 000
IV-c	Sculptures and Bases		200 000
IV-d	Soil Enhancement & Plant Retention/Supplementation		200 000
V	Building ID		6 473 667
VI-Bldng ID	Interior Items		7 537 500
VII	Miscellaneous		1 400 000
VII-a	Documentation		200 000
VII-b	Opening Exhibit/Presentation		1 200 000
VIII	Overhead and Management		250 000
	SUBTOTAL		22 755 167
IX	Contingency	For problems unpredicable, and training and education programs	2 275 517
Phase III TOTAL			**25 030 684** **USD 3 052 522**

第二篇

研究·评估·保护

Part 2

Researches, Assessments & Remedies

第三章
历史研究

宁寿宫花园，又称乾隆花园，坐落于紫禁城东北的宁寿宫内西路。宁寿宫是乾隆三十六年至四十一年间（1771—1776年），为乾隆皇帝在位60年后归政养老时所建，是中国唯一现存的太上皇宫。在乾隆之前，此地曾为皇太后居所，明代曾有仁寿宫、哕鸾宫、喈凤宫等宫殿，清康熙二十八年（1689年）改建为宁寿宫。乾隆皇帝年幼时深受康熙皇帝钟爱，为日后登极打下基础。乾隆帝即位之初便对天发誓，如果上天保佑他像其祖父康熙皇帝一样在位60年，他就传位给儿子。乾隆三十六年（1771年），开始兴建太上皇宫殿，以备归位后享用。乾隆四十一年（1776年）新宫建成，历时五年，耗银巨万，虽仍名宁寿宫，但规模超过以往[1]。宁寿宫花园是宁寿宫的点睛之笔。在长160余米、宽不足40米、南北狭长的地带里，克服了种种不利条件，巧妙构思，于规整中见变化，融南北造园风格于一体，博采众家之长，显示出高超的造园艺术水准。

3.1 历史资料的类型

针对现存的种类丰富、内容全面的历史资料开展研究工作，校雠文字、图档、实物自身的和其间的差异、变化，研究者和保护工作者无疑可以对宁寿宫花园的历史价值、艺术价值和科学价值有更深刻的认识，从而更加明确保护工作的重点和方向。

总体上说，关于宁寿宫花园的历史文献大致可以分为由印行著作、宫廷档案构成的文字档案和由部分外围绘画、图档构成的形象资料两大类。具体而言，文字档案涵盖的类型十分复杂，仅宫廷档案一项就涉及奏折、奏销档、活计档、陈设档等多类，形象资料同样如此。值得注意的是，其中历史图档一类主要来自清宫各地工程处的样式房，究其绘制时期虽为清中期以后，大都是修缮前朝遗构的工程，也不直接关乎宁寿宫花园，但是同样能够对今天更深入地理解花园的历史渊源有很大的帮助作用。当然，本规划现阶段的历史研究工作仅仅是开端性的，需要日后研究者更广泛地参与和更深入地解读。

此外，清代宫廷建筑的历史文献同时包含详尽的甚至有些重复冗长的建筑工程、庭院绿化工程、陈设制作、内檐装修工程等方面的做法、工料信息，所憾相当一部分史料在历史中漫灭无存。下文中特对所见史料罗列骈比以方便日后补正。

3.1.1 印行著作

今日常见的涉及宁寿宫花园的史料是《国朝宫史续编》、《日下旧闻考》等。另有当代学者章乃炜编著的《清宫述闻》可以作为一种史资长编看待，是今天研究的线索和引导。

现将历史及当代的印行著作中关于宁寿宫花园的章节、章节大致内容整理见下表。

著 作	有关章节	内 容
国朝宫史续编 [2]	宫殿九 内廷六，卷之五十九	记载室内匾联情况
日下旧闻考 [3]	第一册，国朝宫史，卷十八	记载部分匾联、御制诗情况
清宫述闻 [4]	内廷三	记载戏院及其上表演岔曲等情况
清帝御制诗 [5]	（1）《清高宗御制诗四集》卷三十三、四十五、五十五、六十一、七十七 （2）《清高宗御制诗五集》卷二十八、四十三、五十一、六十、七十七、八十六、九十三 （3）《清仁宗御制诗二集》卷四十二 （4）《清仁宗御制诗二集》卷四十二、四十七	帝王诗集、乾隆御制诗文选中关于宁寿宫花园及其缘起的记述

3.1.2 宫廷档案

清代宫廷档案系手书史料，详尽记载了内务府主管的各项工作，涵盖了建筑、装饰装修的建造、改造等多方面信息。今天的学者们应当感谢以罗振玉为代表的历史人物，没有民国时代一大批枵腹从公的爱国人士的拯救，这些珍贵的历史档案便不可能流传至今[6]。

为方便分类归纳，本规划将清代宫廷内务府档案分成以下名目：奏销档，活计档，陈设档，匠作则例[7]等，详见下页表。

1. 章乃炜，《清宫述闻》（初续合编本），849页：转引《乾隆三十七年总管内务府福隆安折》，北京：紫禁城出版社，1990年。
2. [清]庆桂等编，《国朝宫史续编》，北京：北京古籍出版社，1994年。
3. [清]于敏中等编，《日下旧闻考》，北京：北京古籍出版社，1981年。
4. 章乃炜，《清宫述闻》。
5. 《清高宗御制诗文全集》，北京：中国人民大学出版社，1993年。
6. 单士魁，《清代档案丛谈》，北京：紫禁城出版社，1987年。
7. 则例，"聚已成之事，勒定编次之也"，王世襄先生称为"规章制度丛抄"，匠作则例相当于古代的工程定额。现存则例主要收藏于中国国家图书馆、中国文物研究所、清华大学图书馆、北京大学图书馆、首都图书馆等处。

3.1.1 Printed Works

Concerning imperial palaces and gardens, we can still read today some official prints that contain paragraphs describing Qianlong Garden and building within it, which are *Continuation of History of Imperial Palace*（国朝宫史续编）and *Textual Research of Historic Records of the Capital of Beijing*（日下旧闻考）, and we can find abound poems composed by Qing emperor chant the garden buildings among which those written by Emperor Qianlong are regarded as diaries of the dominant monarch. What is more, *Qing Palace Review*（清宫述闻）by Mr. Zhang Naiwei in Min'guo period, can not be overestimated for its insight into abundant historical records of these writings.

In the following list, specific relevant section numbers and the contents are compiled for the convenience of research.

Works	Relevant Section	Contents
Continuation of History of Imperial Palace[2]	Palace 9, Inner Court 6, Book 59	Containing records of the interior plaque and couplets
Textual Research on Historic Records of the Capital of Beijing[3]	Volume 1, History of Imperial Palace, Book 18	Containing records of the interior plaque and couplets
Qing Palace Review[4]	Inner Court 3	Containing records on theatrical space in the Lodge and the performance
Poetry Anthologies by Qing Emperors[5]	Poetry by Emperors Qianlong, Anthologies IV, Volume 33, 45, 55, 61, 77 Poetry by Emperors Qianlong, Anthologies V, Volume 28, 43, 51, 60, 77, 86, 93 Poetry by Emperors Jiaqing, Anthologies II Volume 42, 47	Emperors' poems, Qianlong's poetry Anthologies were regarded as his diary

3.1.2 Imperial Archives

Hand-copied rather than printed, imperial household archives contain the most detailed and comprehensive information about construction, furnishing and changes to the palaces and gardens. These were contained in 8000 sacks which were rescued by Mr. Luo Zhenyu (罗振玉) from those waiting to be paper-pulped in Min'guo period[6].

The imperial household archives can be further classified into Cost Memorial to the Throne, Royal Edict for Handiworks, Furnishing Inventories, Exemplification and Regulation for Constructions[7] ect, we can see the selected malerial. in the table below (Month refers to Lunar Carlendar).

Ningshou Gong Garden, popularly referred as Qianlong Garden, is located in Ningshou Gong Precinct in the northeast of the Forbidden City. The precinct was reconstructed during the 36th and 41st year (1771-1776) of Emperor Qianlong's reign, which is the only remaining complex dedicated to the emperor's retired life in China. Before the reconstruction in Qianlong period, buildings served for empress dowagers' in Ming Dynasty and the early periods of Qing Dynasty, and the new title of Ningshou Gong was given after rebuilding in the 28th year of Kangxi period. Emperor Qianlong made a vow that if the Heaven blessed him to be on the throne for 60 years, he would hand over his crown to his son. The work that was wholly for fulfilling his promise commenced in 1771 and was completed in 1776, and cost 1.4 million Liang of silver. The title being remained, the building scale far more exceeded the precedent. Qianlong Garden is the diamond on the top of the crown of Ningshou Gong precinct. With a length of 160m and width of less than 40m, the gardener well arranged the building complex and garden features into the narrow site by overcoming the shortage with colorful changes of design, and by composing the imperial garden with local and exotic influences. Both design and construction of the garden represent a superb level of artistic accomplishment.

3.1 Types of Historical Records on Qianlong Garden

It is acknowledged that a thorough-as-possible investigation into the extant incredibly rich and colorful imperial records of Qing Dynasty would be all indispensable foundation for understanding and preserving Qianlong Garden.

Generally, the extant historic documents can be classified into two families, i.e. literal materials and protracted-rendered drawings. To be specific, literal materials are rich resource and range from official prints, emperors' poetry anthology, imperial household archives, and official or private transcriptions of official building norms. The historic architectural drawings are mainly from Yangshi-Fang (Architectural Pattern Office in Imperial Construction Agency), and are indirectly concerned with the buildings in Qianlong Garden, and moreover were drawn in the successive era after Qianlong period. Nevertheless all the remaining documentation has profound significance for current and future study .

Additionally the historic documentation includes cost and construction of the buildings, horticultural items, courtyard furnishings, and interior features, which are detailed and somewhat prolix and repetitive while some were effaced or lost in the lapse of time. The various sorts of historic material and contemporary studies are enumerated and indexed in the following text.

乾隆瀚琦
故宫博物院宁寿宫花园历史研究与文物保护规划

档案类型[1]	相关目录
内务府奏销档	胶片 94，乾隆三十五年十一月，记载工程基本内容
	胶片 95，乾隆三十六年正月
	胶片 97，乾隆三十六年十一月
	胶片 98，乾隆三十七年六月
	胶片 99，乾隆三十七年十一月
	胶片 101，乾隆三十八年十一月
	胶片 103，乾隆三十九年八月
	胶片 105，乾隆四十年五月
	胶片 107，乾隆四十一年十一月
	胶片 108，乾隆四十二年七月
	胶片 109，乾隆四十四年三月
	胶片 114，乾隆四十七年正月
	403-203，乾隆五十二年
	812-091/163，光绪十三年；胶片 184，839-147，光绪十八年十二月
内务府奏案	208 包、311 包，乾隆三十七年；221 包，乾隆四十年五月；233 包，乾隆四十二年七月至九月。记载工程基本内容
	484 包，嘉庆五年；533 包、540 包，嘉庆十三年；563 包，嘉庆十七年；588-592 包，嘉庆二十二年；597 包，嘉庆二十三年；602 包，嘉庆二十四年
	993，光绪十九年
内务府堂谕堂交	第一包，乾隆五十八年八月。谕如意馆及早完成藤萝天顶画
汉文录副奏折	档号 0133-091，乾隆三十八年十月六日
	档号 0704-025，乾隆三十八年四月八日
	李质颖宁寿宫装修工程奏折四件[2]
内务府活计档	胶片 127，乾隆三十九年，如意馆
	胶片 128，乾隆三十九年，行文
	胶片 129，乾隆三十九年，金玉作
	胶片 129，乾隆四十年三月，如意馆
	胶片 129，乾隆四十年十一月，如意馆
	胶片 130，乾隆四十年十月，灯裁作
	胶片 130，乾隆四十年十月，油木作
	胶片 130，乾隆四十年闰十月，钱粮库
	胶片 131，乾隆四十一年，灯裁作
	胶片 132，乾隆四十一年五月，匣裱作
	胶片 133，乾隆四十二年六月，如意馆
	胶片 134，乾隆四十二年十月，油木作
	胶片 134，乾隆四十三年七月，记事录
	胶片 136，乾隆四十三年，铜镀作
	胶片 138，乾隆四十四年十一月，如意馆
	胶片 139，乾隆四十五年十月，金玉作
	胶片 139，乾隆四十五年十月，铸炉处
	胶片 141，乾隆四十六年二月，灯裁作
	胶片 141，乾隆四十六年五月，灯裁作
	胶片 145，乾隆五十年，行文
	胶片 146，乾隆五十一年，铜镀作
	胶片 152，乾隆五十七年，铜镀作
	胶片 152，乾隆五十八年，记事录

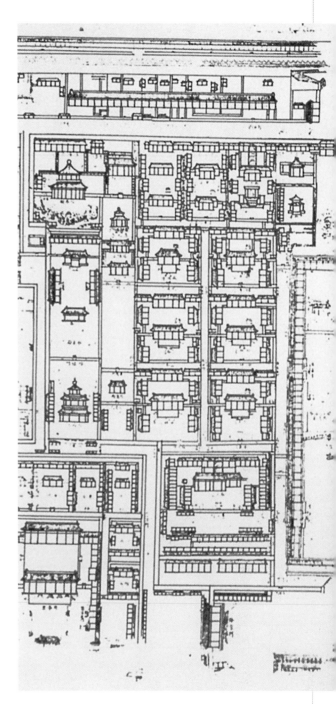

乾隆京城图局部

资料来源：《加摹乾隆京城全图》，北京燕山出版社

1. 今皇家档案主要收藏于中国第一历史档案馆。
2. 载于：《宫中档乾隆朝奏折》第三十四、三十五辑，中国台湾：国立故宫博物院印行。

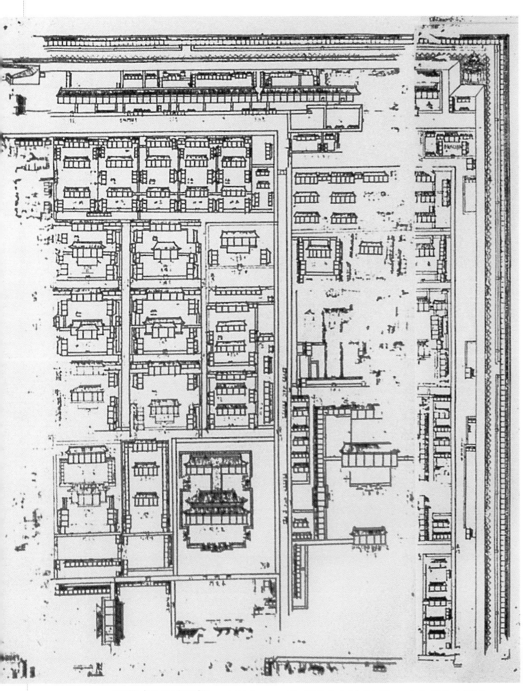

乾隆京城图局部 资料来源：《加摹乾隆京城全图》，北京燕山出版社

Archive	Relevant Section/Version
Archive on Imperial Household Expenditure	Film 94, 11th month, 1770. On basic information of the works
	Film 95, 1st month, 1771.
	Film 97, 11th month, 1771.
	Film 98, 6th month, 1772.
	Film 99, 11th month, 1772.
	Film 101, 11th month, 1773.
	Film 103, 8th month, 1774.
	Film 105, 5th month, 1775.
	Film 107, 11th month, 1776.
	Film 108, 7th month, 1777.
	Film 109, 3rd month, 1779.
	Film 114, 1st month, 1782.
	403-203, 1787.
	Codex 812-091/163, 1887; Film 184, Codex 839-147, 12th month, 1892
Imperial Household Archive of Memorials	Package 208, 311, 1772; Package 221, 5th month, 1775; Package 233, 7th to 9th Month, 1777. On basic information of the works
	Package 484, 1800; Package 533,540, 1808; Package 563, 1812; Package 588-592, 1817; Package 597, 1818; Package 602, 1819.
	Package 993, 1893
Archive on Imperial Household Dept. Instructions	Package 1, 8th month, 1793. On commanding the Hall of Ruyi (Painters' Office) to finish wisteria-ceiling paintings immediately.
Memorial Ectypes in Mandarin	No. 0133-091, 10th month, 1773. Making interior screens in South etc.
	No. 0704-025, 4th month, 1773.
	Four memorials to the throne on constructions of Ningshou Gong Garden by Li Zhiying, Qianlong period
Archives on Imperial Household Handiworks	Film 127, 1774. Orders to the Hall of Ruyi (Painters' department)
	Film 128, 1774. On missive between departments
	Film 129, 1774. Orders on gold and jade works
	Film 129, 3rd month 1775. On the Hall of Ruyi
	Film 129, 11th month, 1775. Orders to the Hall of Ruyi
	Film 130, 10th month, 1775. Orders on leather and sewing works
	Film 130, 10th month, 1775.Orders on wood and painting works
	Film 130, 10th-plus month, 1775. Orders on storeroom for daily use and cost
	Film 131, 1776. Orders on leather and sewing works
	Film 132, 5th month, 1776. Order on box making and paper mounting
	Film 133, 6th month, 1777. Orders to the Hall of Ruyi
	Film 134, 10th month,1777. Orders On wood and painting works
	Film 134, 7th month, 1778. On basic note and records
	Film 136, 1778. On copper and plating works
	Film 138, 11th month, 1779. Orders to the Hall of Ruyi
	Film 139, 10th month, 1780. Orders on gold and jade works
	Film 139, 10th month, 1780. Orders on making stoves and burners
	Film 141, 2nd month, 1781. Orders on leather and sewing works
	Film 141, 5th month, 1781. Orders on leather and sewing works
	Film 145, 1785. On missive between departments
	Film 146, 1786. Orders on copper and plating works
	Film 152, 1792. Orders on copper and plating works
	Film 152, 1793. On basic note and records

档案类型	相关目录
旨意底档 旨意题头底档	3731 号，乾隆四十一年，皮裁作
	3738 号，乾隆四十三年二月，铜镀作
	3746 号，乾隆四十三年十一月，匣裱作
内务府陈设档	陈 494，嘉庆十九年抄本
	道光十七年《陈设档》抄本
	光绪二十三年《陈设档》抄本
清代匠作则例[1]	《总管内务府现行则例》，清刻本，清华大学藏
	《圆明园现行工程则例》（14、15、16、18 卷本），清抄本，清华大学藏
	《热河工程则例》（存十七卷），清抄本，中国国家图书馆
	《热河园庭现行则例》（十二卷）清抄本，中国国家图书馆
	《万寿山工程则例》（十九卷），清抄本，中国国家图书馆
	《圆明园万寿山内庭汇同则例》（三十五卷），抄本，中国国家图书馆藏
	《内庭圆明园内工诸作现行则例》，中国文物研究所藏
	《圆明园万寿山内庭三处汇同则例》，北京大学藏
	（散帙，于高家档案中），清抄本，清华大学建筑学院藏
	（散帙，于样式雷档案中），清抄本，中国国家图书馆藏
	[清] 史贻直，《工部则例》，清乾隆刻本

3.1.3 舆图和建筑图样

　　一般认为，样式雷世家是清代宫廷建筑师。本规划不就此展开过多评论，同时也承认样式雷世家在宫廷工程中扮演着非常重要的角色。应当特别强调的是，现存清宫建筑图样主要出自于清末和清覆后，因雷家衰败而出售的祖传秘藏，资料中无一处题写"样式雷"，反而屡屡落款"样式房"，可见雷家发挥设计本领有这样一个前提——必须遵照清宫内务府机构上层官员的领导，并符合皇家规制。尽管现存图样主要是乾隆后所成，但样式雷家族在历史上还承接过不少早期的图档，同时也注意搜集整理自己经手的测绘、设计资料，因此这些反映清代中早期建筑和这些建筑在清代晚期逐步演变的图样便成为今日研究宁寿宫花园和同类研究工作不可缺少的基本参考。同样地，尽管今天尚未发现关于宁寿宫花园的图样，但是我们可以找到相当数量与宁寿宫花园始建密切相关的其他花园的资料，我们甚至可以断言，这些资料充分地表明宁寿宫花园的设计是以其他一些皇家园林建筑为母本的。

　　此外，我们还必须提到《乾隆京城全图》和《圆明园四十景图》。它们虽然不是建筑制图，却携带大量的建筑学信息；虽然不够准确，但信息丰富而形象。

　　本规划所参考的舆图、建筑图样等形象资料可归纳见下页表。

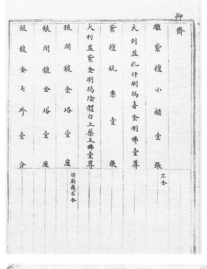

清宫内务府档案　资料来源：故宫博物院

1.《内庭圆明园内工诸作现行则例》、《圆明园万寿山内庭三处汇同则例》二帙则例参见王世襄主编：《清代匠作则例》卷一、二，北京：大众出版社，2000 年。

Archive	Relevant Section/Version
Archives on Imperial Household Handiworks	No. 3731, 1776. Orders on leather and sewing works.
	No. 3738, 2nd month, 1778. Orders on copper and plating works
	No. 3746, 11th month, 1778. Orders on box making and paper mounting
Archives on Imperial Household Collection & Displaying (AICD)	AICD No. 494, 1814. Jiaqing period Inventory
	AICD of Juanqin Zhai, 1837. Daoguang period Inventory
	AICD of Juanqin Zhai, 1897. Guangxu period Inventory
Imperial or Official Exemplification and Regulation for Handiwork and Constructional Works (E&R)	Present E&R of Imperial Household Department.
	Present E&R of Yuanming Yuan Works
	E&R for Rehe Construction Works
	Present E&R for Rehe Garden Works
	Present E&R for Mnt. Wanshou
	Present E&R for Yuanming Yuan, Mnt. Wanshou & inner Court
	Present E&R for Inner Court
	Present E&R for Yuanming Yuan, Mnt. Wanshou & Inner Court
	Present E&R in Cost Control Office Archive, Archives of late Qing period
	Present E&R in Pattern Design Office Archive, Archives of late Qing period
	Present E&R on Handiworks for Ministry of Construction

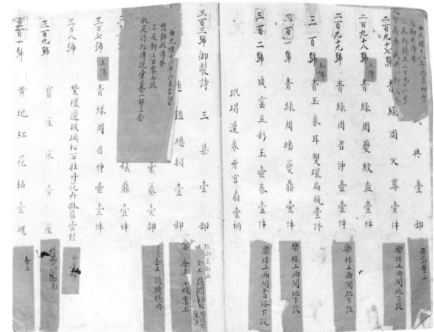

清宫内务府档案 资料来源：故宫博物院

3.1.3 Historical Architectural Representations

A popularly accepted view believes that a Yangshi-Lei family (Yangshi for Pattern Design, and Lei is the family name) can be defined as architects in Qing Court. While there is some debate about this view, the author accedes that the family had been playing an important role in the late Qing Dynasty, and it is worth stressing that the extant collections of architecture representations mostly come from the family collections that were sold out after the fall of Qing Dynasty. Despite that the drawing time of the works was later than Qianlong period, the family were very designed to collect some previous works during the declining stage of the family career in Qing Court, which is absolutely profoundly significant for today's studies. Notwithstanding drawings on Qianlong Garden cannot yet be found in the remaining architectural representations, no one can deny that those on relative gardens and buildings once used as prototypes for Qianglong Garden are so revealing that they should be included in this compilation of materials.

Besides, we must also count in a cartological achievement of *the Qianlong Map of the Capital* (乾隆京城全图) which depicts the courtyards and buildings in the capital before the construction of the Qianlong Garden, and a series of *the 40 scenes in Yuanmingyuan* (圆明园四十景图), that vividly render Qiang emperors' favourite gardens among which some were selected as inspirations or even models for designing Ningshou Gong Garden.

相关绘画、图样	与宁寿宫花园建筑内檐装修的关系
乾隆京城全图[1]	涉及乾隆年间改造宁寿宫前该宫的大致情况
圆明园四十景图[2]	坦坦荡荡、坐石临流分别是宁寿宫花园倦勤斋、禊赏亭的设计参照
中国国家图书馆藏，（圆明园坦坦荡荡）素心堂半亩院地盘画样[3]	半亩园室内设计是倦勤斋室内戏院空间的设计参照
故宫博物院藏，建福宫花园立样[4]	建福宫花园是宁寿宫花园第四院落的设计参照
中国国家图书馆藏，故宫博物院藏（长春园）含经堂地盘画样	含经堂淳化轩以西园林建筑是宁寿宫乐寿堂以西园林建筑的设计参照

3.1.4 当代研究现状

由于宁寿宫花园的巨大魅力与深厚的历史背景，现当代学者曾经花费大量精力开展相关研究。然而即便是《清代内廷宫苑》一类的集中讨论紫禁城园林的专著也无法将这座花园全面展现，无法将历史问题逐一剖析解答。另外由于其他当代研究的专业领域的限制，现有研究至今仍未针对宁寿宫花园形成有体系的、全面的揭示。

兹将笔者所见当代研究论著整理见下表。

作者	题目	出处
天津大学建筑系	清代内廷宫苑	天津大学出版社，1986 年
赵光华	禊赏亭之"禊"源流小考	《故宫博物院院刊》1979 年第 3 期
于倬云 傅连兴	乾隆花园的造园艺术	《故宫博物院院刊》1980 年第 3 期
徐启宪 周南泉	《大禹治水图》玉山	《故宫博物院院刊》1980 年第 4 期
傅连仲	乾隆花园点滴	《故宫博物院院刊》1980 年第 4 期
万 依	乾隆花园的园囿	《故宫博物院院刊》1984 年第 2 期
许以林	宁寿宫的花园庭院	《故宫博物院院刊》1987 年第 1 期
朱 杰	长春园淳化轩与故宫乐寿堂考辨	《故宫博物院院刊》1999 年第 2 期
罗文华	清宫六品佛楼模式的形成	《故宫博物院院刊》2000 年第 4 期
聂崇正	故宫倦勤斋天顶画、全景画探究	《区域与网络——近千年来中国美术史研究国际学术讨论会论文集》抽印本，台湾大学艺术史研究所发行，2001
刘 畅	清代宫廷和苑囿中的室内戏台述略	《故宫博物院院刊》2003 年第 2 期
张淑娴	倦勤斋建筑略考	《故宫博物院院刊》2003 年第 3 期
倦勤斋工作组 刘 畅 等执笔	倦勤斋保护工作阶段报告	《故宫博物院院刊》2004 年第 1 期
李福敏 整理	故宫《倦勤斋陈设档》之一	《故宫博物院院刊》2004 年第 2 期
李福敏	关于《倦勤斋陈设档》的几点认识	《故宫博物院院刊》2004 年第 2 期

圆明园四十景图 资料来源：法国国家图书馆

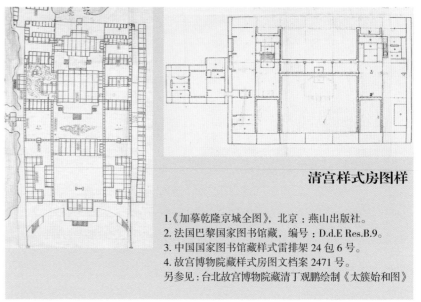

清宫样式房图样

1.《加摹乾隆京城全图》，北京：燕山出版社。
2. 法国巴黎国家图书馆藏，编号：D.d.E Res.B.9。
3. 中国国家图书馆藏样式雷排架 24 包 6 号。
4. 故宫博物院藏样式房图文档案 2471 号。
另参见：台北故宫博物院藏清丁观鹏绘制《太簇始和图》

Archive	Relevant Section	Contents
Court Paintings, Maps and Imperial Architectural Representation for Construction Works	Captical Map of Qianlong Period1	Ningshou Gong before Qianlong's renovation
	Paintings of the 40 scenery sites in Yuanming Yuan	Used as conceptual models for Qianlong Garden
	Architectural drawings on scenery sites of Tantan Dangdang in Yuanming Yuan	Used as spacial models for the Lodge of Retirement in Qianlong Garden
	Architectural representation for Jianfu Gong Garden	Used as spacial models for the 4th quatyard in Qianlong Garden
	Drawings of Hanjing Tang in Changchun Yuan	Drawings of Hanjing Tang in Changchun Yuan

3.1.4 Contemporary Studies

It is understandable that architectural historians have been spending great energy in unscramble the charming and mysterious garden in Ningshou Gong precinct. But the topics of appeal are so rich that comprehensive volume such as *Imperial Inner Court Gardens of Qing Dynasty* (《清代内廷宫苑》) cannot comb out a systematic structure for relics in the Garden, and multi-disciplinary knowledge background is so indispensably required that contemporary studies have left great many questions to be explained more fully.

We can list the most representative studies as follows.

Author	Tile	Publication Provenance
Fclt. of Acht, Tianjin Univ.	Inner Court Gardens of Qiang Dynasty	Tianjin: Tianjin Univ. Press, 1986
Zhao, Guanghua	Research on the Character Xi in Xishang Pavilion	Journal of the Palace Museum, 1979(3)
Yu, Zhuoyun Fu, Lianxing	Art of Gardening of Qianlong Garden	Journal of the Palace Museum, 1980(3)
Xu, Qixian Zhou, Nanquan	Carved Jade Mount on Da-Yu's Controlling Flood	Journal of the Palace Museum, 1980(4)
Fu, Lianzhong	Random Historic Materials on Qianlong Garden	Journal of the Palace Museum, 1980(4)
Wan, Yi	Gardening Art of Qianlong Garden	Journal of the Palace Museum, 1984(2)
Xu, Yilin	Courtyard Settings in Ningshou Gong Garden	Journal of the Palace Museum, 1987(1)
Zhu, Jie	Chunhua Xuan in Changchun Yuanand Leshou Tang in the Forbidden City	Journal of the Palace Museum, 1999(2)
Luo, Wenhua	On formation of Hexa-Buddhist-Building in Qing Court	Journal of the Palace Museum, 2000(4)
Nie, Chongzheng	Study on interior Mural and Ceiling Paintings in the Lodge of Retirement in the Palace Museum	Region & Net: International Conference on Chinese History of Art, Taipei: Taiwan Univ. 2001
Liu, Chang	Narration and Commentary on Interior Theatres in Gardens and Palaces of Qing Dynasty	Journal of the Palace Museum, 2003(2)
Zhang, Shuxian	Preliminary Studies of the Lodge of Retirement	Journal of the Palace Museum, 2003(3)
Liu, Chang et al.	Periodical Report of Conservation Works in the Lodge of Retirement	Journal of the Palace Museum, 2004(1)
Compilation: Li, Fumin	Collection of Displaying Archives of the Lodge of Retirement	Journal of the Palace Museum, 2004(2)
Li, Fumin	Commentaries on Displaying Archives of the Lodge of Retirement	Journal of the Palace Museum, 2004(2)

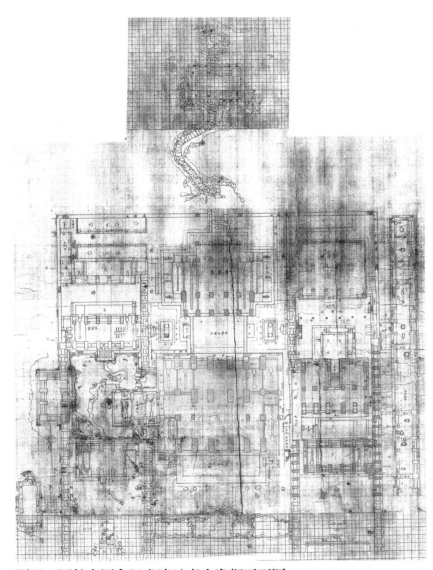

圆明三园长春园含经堂遗址考古发掘平面图
资料来源：北京市文物研究所 圆明园管理处

3.2 对宁寿宫花园的进一步理解

如上文所述，当代学者关于宁寿宫花园的研究成果尚遗留不少问题。本节所叙述的内容不是针对所有的问题给出答案，而是根据园林设计从总体布局到局部构造和装饰设计的线索，将问题系统化、条理化。

3.2.1 地段概况

与故宫平面布局相似，宁寿宫建筑也分为前后两部分，其主要殿宇形制也多仿自故宫原有建筑，尤其是重要建筑。如皇极殿仿乾清宫、宁寿宫仿坤宁宫、养性殿仿养心殿、符望阁仿延春阁、景福宫仿静怡轩、梵华楼和佛日楼仿慧曜楼和吉云楼、倦勤斋仿敬胜斋……诸如此类，宁寿宫仿佛是故宫的缩影。

宁寿宫花园是宁寿宫中最为独特的院落，常被学者们称为该建筑群的点睛之笔。在长160米，宽不足40米，南北狭长的地带里，宁寿宫花园克服了种种不利条件，巧妙构思，于规整中见变化，融南北造园风格为一体，博采众家之长，显示出高超的造园艺术水准。宁寿宫花园自南而北划分为四个院落，形成风格各异的四个景区。

第一进院落迎门为一带假山，以"曲径通幽"的手法将游人引入古木参天、山石环抱的院内。院内正中是一座敞轩，名古华轩，因轩前一株古楸而得名。轩内施以简洁明快的落地罩，使内外景致隔而不断，追求一种物我一体的境界。轩前以西侧的禊赏亭和东侧的假山露台互为对景。禊赏亭内于地面开凿流杯渠，仿晋人王羲之《兰亭序》"曲水流觞"的故事为之。轩西堆石为山，山上建有旭辉庭，面迎朝阳，可赏日出。此进院落的东南角，以曲折的游廊围出一小院。游廊转角处建有一亭名"矩亭"，廊东连接面阔一间半的佛堂唤作"抑斋"。院内假山上建有撷芳亭。

古华轩后为一垂花门，其内为宁寿宫花园的第二进院落。这是一座一正两厢的住宅式院落，院中散点湖石，主体建筑遂初堂，取乾隆帝在位年后归政得遂初愿之意。

遂初堂后为第三进院落。此院落满堆石山，主峰上建有一亭，名耸秀亭，山下洞谷相通，蜿蜒曲折。山北有萃赏楼，山西有延趣楼。东南角有三友轩，即所谓松、竹、梅岁寒三友。轩内门窗装修及家具陈设皆以松竹梅为装饰图案，轩外植以松、竹、梅加以点缀，乾隆帝之风雅可见一斑。

第四进院落从建筑布局到形制均仿自乾隆登极之初所造的建福宫花园。华丽端庄的符望阁巍然屹立于院落正中。阁为重檐方殿，仿建福宫花园延春阁式样而建。阁前层峦叠嶂，峰峦上建有一亭，名碧螺亭。平面作梅花状，各种装饰也采用梅花图案，极为美观别致。建福宫花园有延春阁，阁前也有一丘石山，山上建有一方亭，名积翠亭。与符望阁、碧螺亭略有区别。符望阁西南有楼名云光楼，平面形同曲尺，仿自建福宫花园之玉壶冰。阁东有玉粹轩，仿建福宫花园之凝晖堂。其南为山石掩映的竹香馆，仿自建福宫花园之碧琳馆。阁后则为倦勤斋，仿自建福宫花园之敬胜斋[1]。

宁寿宫花园的布局紧凑多变，四进院落作为四个景区采用了不同的主题，形成了不同的景观。又以直廊、斜廊、曲廊、路径、洞谷、阁道、飞桥穿插联络，平直与曲折相结合，开阔与幽深交替，达到了引人入胜的艺术效果。宁寿宫花园的建筑形式灵活，绝无雷同之感。邻近宫墙的建筑，多采用楼阁将宫墙屏起，以避免生硬之感。邻近宫殿的建筑，则高低错落，以和宫殿互相因借，互为对景。

如果将宁寿宫花园放在乾隆时期的园林建筑设计的大背景下，我们还可以发现，这种丰富的园林效果的形成并不是该花园独有，而是宁寿宫花园吸取了乾隆中早期一些园林的特点而形成的，这与紫禁城中其他院落的规划设计、建筑风格和尺度大相径庭。尽管不是原创，但是在紫禁城中建设宁寿宫花园本身就带有更多的历史信息和回味余地。

3.2.2 园林设计手法

在当代学者研究宁寿宫花园的论著中，于倬云和傅连兴先生的《乾隆花园的造园艺术》一文特别探讨了清代造园艺术在宁寿宫花园中的反映。文章研讨深入且专精，相比涉及紫禁城内所有园圃的《清代内廷宫苑》及其他仅涉猎该花园某一方面的论述，则可谓达到了更高的水准。笔者在此主要借鉴这篇论文，着重讨论乾隆花园造园艺术的三个主要特点：空间轴线设计；叠山理水方法；建筑布局与设计。

宁寿宫花园占地0.59公顷，宽37米，长160米，总体长宽比例为4.6：1，呈狭长状。在宁寿宫后西路这个不大的空间中，把中轴线上的建筑安排进去以后，所剩空间已显湫隘，但是园林设计者却利用曲折、遮挡、隐约对视等手法将这个尺度问题巧妙地解决了。具体方法首先是将中轴线上的建筑处理成尺度上互相映衬的错动的韵律式排列，其次是使用假山营造出更小尺度的空间，用来反衬中尺度空间的宽敞，再有便是利用建筑和自然景观语汇遮挡封闭感很强的院墙。

很多研究表明，宁寿宫花园的轴线设计是建筑及其外围空间设计的重要特点。花园四进院落中前两个院落是共用一条主轴线的——起自花园

乾隆：《清高宗御制诗四集》卷三十三："敬胜依前式，倦勤卜后居"。注："此斋依建福宫中敬胜斋为之"。

Behind Guhua Xuan, a flora-pendant gate stands and opens to the second courtyard of vernacular residential style, plain and amiable. Decorated by spots of rockery works, the main hall of the yard, *Suichutang* (Hall of Fulfilling Original Wishes), was situated in the back on the axis, manifesting Qianlong's vow and fulfilling of the 60 years of reign.

The third yard, a hidden and astonishing scene, was composed of compact rockeries. A pavilion (Pavilion of Lofty Beauty) on the top of the hill overlooking the entire layout, caves, stone steps and verandas link the separated buildings, *Cuishanglou* (Building of Collection and Appreciation), Yan'qu'lou (Building for Extended Delight) and *Sanyouxuan* (Pavilion of Three Friends of Human Qualities). Interior features of the building are fantastic. Sanyou Xuan is representative. Motifs of pine, bamboo and plumb blossoms are used on screens and furniture in the room. Having the nature of resisting snow, these three plants are selected as metaphors for human qualities. Together with pine, bamboo and plum planted outside the chamber, Emperor Qianlong showed off his tastes and merits.

The fourth courtyard was designed after Jianfu Gong Garden, a Qianlong's favorite garden in the Forbidden City built in the early period of his reign. In the center is located Fuwang Ge (the Building of Wish and Reality in Accordance), with a hexastyle elevation in four directions, square in plan and with a double-eave on façade, imitating Yanchun Ge (the Building of Extended Spring). With a pyramidical roof, Fuwang Ge is the highest building in Qianlong Garden. The building is accompanied by a little pavilion on the rockery of plum motifs and of a plan shaped as a plum blossom, Biluo Ting (Pavilion of the Green Conch Shell). The little pavilion was designed to partially imitate a square pavilion Jicui Ting (Pavilion of Piling Emeralds) in Jianfu Gong Garden. Surrounding Fuwang Ge, an L-shaped Yunguang Lou (Building of Cloud Light) is situated in the southeast, and Yucui Xuan (Pavilion of Jade and Emerald) in the east, and Juanqin Zhai (Lodge of Retirement) that was aimed to imitate Jingsheng Zhai1, a lodge in Jianfu Gong Garden, is the rear row of the yard at the north. Through the verandas, people can access all the buildings from Fuwang Ge. To the west of Juanqin Zhai, inside the octagonal gate and in the shade of bamboos, is Zhuxiang Guan (the Chamber of Bamboo Fragrance), that is also linked with the Lodge through verandas.

3.2 Understanding Qianlong Garden

In the above-mentioned contemporary studies, there are kaleidoscopic pardahs for scholars to penetrate. The aim of this chapter is not to provide all answers to all questions but sort them according to a system from the subject of gardening methodology to the motives which directed the original design of the buildings and their decoration.

3.2.1 Site Description

Quite similar to the layout of the Forbidden City, that of Ningshou Gong Precinct is divided into two parts, the frontcourt area and the back residential area. To be manifesting, every important building in the precinct was designed after a most significant palace building elsewhere in the Forbidden City, e.g. Huangji Dian (the Hall of Supreme Empire) imitated Taihe Dian (the Hall of Supreme Harmony), Ningshou Gong (the Hall of Tranquility and Longevity) was after Kunning Gong (the Hall of Earthly Tranquility), Yangxing Dian (the Hall of Personal Nature Cultivation) was after Yangxin Dian (the Hall of Heart Cultivation), Fuwang Ge (the Building of Fulfilling Original Wishes) was after Yanchun Ge (the Building of Extended Spring), Jingfu Gong (the Palace of Scene and Felicity) was after Jingyi Xuan (the Pavilion of Peace and Delight), Fanhua Lou (the Building of Buddhist Flower) and Fori Lou (the Building of the Sun of Buddha) were after Huiyao Lou (the Building of Wisdom Light) and Jiyun Lou (the Building of Auspicious Cloud) respectively, Juanqin Zhai (the Lodge of Retirement) was after Jingsheng Zhai (the Lodge of Admiring Beautiful Scene), etc. In short, the design of the precinct epitomes the Forbidden City.

The most extraordinary setting in Ningshou Gong is the plan of Qianlong Garden, which is usually described as " *a crucial touch that brings life to the painted dragon* ". The site is narrow and long, approximately 40m × 160m. Not only was this restriction overcome by the garden designer, but it was also taken advantage of by merging together different styles of gardening, southern and northern. The unique coordination of the predominant styles illustrate both brilliant concept and supreme gardening skills. The garden is divided into four successive quadrangle yards with four specific tastes.

There is a rockery work right inside the gate of the first courtyard (Yanqi Men, the gate of Extended Felicity), hiding the scene inside. A small narrow and winding path was applied according to traditional methods of laying gardens, leading to a main pavilion of the yard at the visual center, Guhua Xuan (the Pavilion of Ancient Blossom) that was named after an ancient Chinese catalpa tree. Nothing but screens of casements was used in the pavilion to form a flexible space of the exterior and the interior. No egos but a feeling of unity of nature and being can be comprehended. To the southwest of the pavilion, facing the rockeries and platform in the east, is Xishangting (Pavilion for Enjoying Washing and Drinking), containing a mini canal where wine cups once had been floating on running water, and where poems had been floating from acute minds, alluding the story that the most famous ancient calligrapher Wang Xizhi once depicted in his master work *Lantingxu* (Prelude for the poem Pavilion of Cymbidium). Upper on the hill north to the pavilion, *Xuhuiting* (Chamber of the Morning Sun) was built facing the east, while a small garden with a pavilion called *Xiefangting* (Pavilion of Picking the Fragrance) enveloped by verandas was arranged in the southeast corner of the first courtyard.

南门延祺门，直至第二进院落的正殿遂初堂。随后这条轴线被弱化、错动了：第三进院落假山上的耸秀亭的中心轴线向东偏移了约1.1米（约合三尺四寸），第三进院落的后楼萃赏楼和第四进建筑的中轴线继续向东偏移动了约2.9米（约合九尺一寸）。而第三四进院落中的人行路线则须先后穿过曲折的假山下隧洞，并不似前两个院落中较为通达的行人路线。

中国园林中自然景观处理以叠山和理水为重。宁寿宫花园中的叠山做法使用得最为丰富，第一、三、四进院落中的假山上均设有登临路径，而第三、四院中的假山最为集中，更有穿山洞穴和隧道，为径，为室，为厅。但是由于紫禁城中用水受到极大限制，园中仅仅借鉴了最重要的中国传统园林观念之一——曲水流觞的做法，在第一进院中的禊赏亭中采用了曲折细流。一般而言，叠山往往用以营造野趣，屏蔽视线，而宁寿宫花园中的叠山则在这两个基本功能之外负担起了围合小尺度空间的作用，以便在空间规模受到很大限制的院中，在缺少水面配合的前提下，和其他尺度空间形成对比映衬，创造出一种无穷的空间变幻效果。

建筑布局与形式设计也是中国园林设计的基本要素。园中前两进院落，主要采用了单层建筑，形成基本方正，左右呼应的布局，仅有撷芳亭和旭辉庭设于不高的假山之上，追求较为活泼的效果。在后两进院落中，除了假山上的亭子和作为附属建筑的游廊、耳房，八座主要建筑中的五座都是两层以上的。在三座单层建筑——三友轩、玉粹轩、倦勤斋中，倦勤斋的室内还采用了仙楼做法，形成了两层的室内空间。如果我们看一看花园的整体剖面，便能够直观地体会建筑群乐章般的起伏的效果，及其背后铺陈和高潮的设计手法。

3.2.3 室内设计问题的讨论

除典雅的建筑本身之外，通观宁寿宫花园建筑的室内，檐装修隔断、室内壁画、家具陈设和室内文物多样而精美，毫不夸张地说，宁寿宫花园建筑本身就是一个内檐装修宝库。略作调查统计，我们就会发现，这些内檐装修语汇和装饰壁画既是丰富多彩的，又是自成系列的，其精美雕刻与镶嵌装饰远非通常所见的清宫隔扇可比。

宁寿宫花园建筑室内空间格局设计是具有变化和独特之处的。如果按照内檐装修手段的密集程度划分，大致可以将这些建筑归为三类：

第一类，亭轩等开敞空间，如矩亭、碧螺亭、古华轩等，室内部分不宜过分装饰，即便花园主轴线上的古华轩，亦仅做罩槅、天花，点缀匾联，并不曲折隔断再施淫巧。

第二类，次要的帝王活动空间，如抑斋、旭辉庭，及原状已遭较彻底改造的遂初堂东西配殿。另外遂初堂正殿内檐装修同样经历了历代削减，变化痕迹显著。这些空间尺度不大，其中所使用的内檐装修手段种类也不多。

第三类，主要的帝王活动空间，包括遂初堂原状、萃赏楼、三友轩、延趣楼、碧螺亭、符望阁、倦勤斋、云光楼、玉粹轩、竹香馆，这些建筑室内具有最丰富的空间划分和装修手段，不仅使用硬木装修、裱糊壁纸等，更引入了通景绘画、贴落等做法，鲜活地反映出帝王奢华的日常生活。

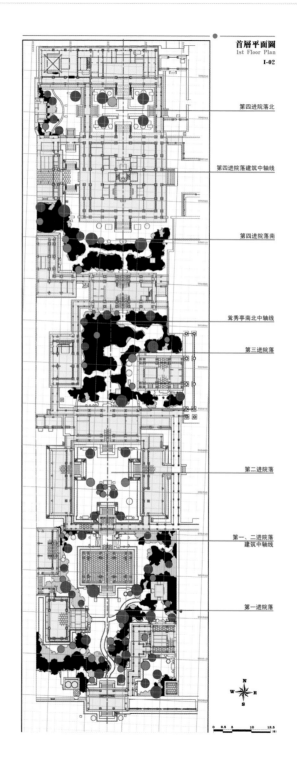

第四进院落北

第四进院落建筑中轴线

第四进院落南

耸秀亭南北中轴线

第三进院落

第二进院落

第一、二进院落
建筑中轴线

第一进院落

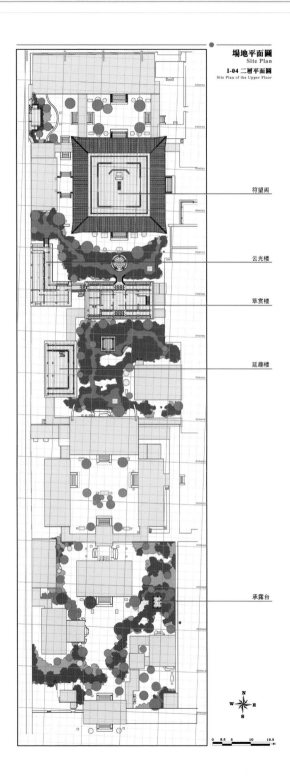

符望閣

云光楼

萃賞楼

延趣楼

承露台

Closer observing Qianlong Garden and considering the inspiration origins of the layout and design, one can definitely come into the understanding that the concept of planning is far different from that of most of other parts in the Forbidden City from the aspects of building layout, density of building and horticulture features, and spatial scale. Albeit Qianlong Garden was not a complete new creation at Qianlong's time, the location of the garden in the Forbidden City itself is rather a special event.

3.2.2 On General Design Concept

Among the extensive research on the Qianlong garden, Yu Zhuoyun and Fu Lianxing (于倬云,傅连兴) discussed from the view of garden design in their article *The Art of Gardening of Qianlong Garden* (乾隆花园的造园艺术). This article reached a higher level and is more purposive than the overall descriptions in *Imperial Inner Court Garden of Qing Dynasty* (清代内廷宫苑) and other discussions restricted in specific facets of the garden. In short, predecessor researchers had concentrated on three general design concepts of Qianlong Garden, i.e. spatial axis system, rock & water arrangement, and building disposal.

Qianlong Garden covers an area of 0.59ha., with a long and narrow plan at the ratio of 4.6:1, 160m long and 37m wide. Though the rear west route of Ningshou Gong precinct left was not spacious after arranging main middle route building in, the question of taking advantage of the zonary land was perfectly solved. The solutions include linking a series of courtyard with an axis system to forming a cascade of spaces, introducing substantial rockeries to build more private and cozy corners and to block the view of the high envelope wall of the precinct.

The axis system used to plan the garden has been revealed and discussed repeatedly as a most important factor. The front two courtyards are arranged along the same axis from the entrance gate of Yanqi Men (the Gate of Extended Felicity) to Suichu Tang (the Hall of Fulfilling Original Wishes, the main hall of the second yard), and the axis is weakened by a substantial rockery in the third courtyard and is yet extended and serpentine in to the caves in the manmade mountain. As a block of the front axis, the rockery also starts inside it the axis of the rear two courtyards with a rock maze of caves and a pavilion aloft on the top from which all the tricks of spaces are exposed. Starting from caves and then Cuishang Lou (the Building of Collection and Appreciation, the rear building in the third courtyard), the fourth courtyard is tandem concretely with corridors and abstractly with the rear axis system.

Piling rockery and disposing water surface are fundamental elements in Chinese gardening. Rockery is richly used in Qianlong Garden. Three of four courtyards have thick rockeries and moreover most of the rockeries have caves in it and stairs leading to the top while since the strict restriction of the surrounding water supply and the typical Sinicism concept of acclimation the only waterscape in the garden is merely a tiny stream in the Floating Cup Pavilion. Rockery is normally used to create a space of wildness and shadows, and here in Qianlong Garden, great more complicated was the rockeries design to be in order to form different series of tiny spaces and give a sense of endlessness and changefulness without accompany and assistance of water surface.

尤其在第三类建筑中，突出地反映出清中期室内设计特点——高明地营造室内环境气氛，灵活地运用装修语汇和设计技巧。这种技巧最基本的一点是张弛自如的室内空间划分。现将宁寿宫花园中内檐装修最为复杂的建筑中最大和最小的功能室内空间（过道和储藏空间不计）特征数据分别统计如下表所示：

建筑名称	房间名称	房间位置	空间高度	面积[1]（平方米）
萃赏楼	门厅	首层明间	一层	15.7
	佛堂内室	二层西进间北部	一层	4.8
三友轩	门厅	首层明间	一层	16.2
	书房	首层西次间	一层	11.7
延趣楼	二层大厅	二层	一层	36.7
	休息空间	北次间	一层	6.4
符望阁	顶层大厅	顶层	一层	114.1
	寝宫	首层中心	一层	4.0
倦勤斋	门厅	明三间	二层	38.5
	休息空间	下层东北部	一层	3.8
云光楼	罗汉堂	上层北部	一层	26.1
	寝宫	下层北部	一层	5.8
竹香馆	休息厅	下层中部	一层	8.0
	小休息空间	上层南部	一层	1.2

以倦勤斋为例，除过道之外，殿中最大空间面积达38.5平方米，二层总高度4米余（约合一丈五尺），最小空间面积仅3.8平方米，高度仅2米余（约合七尺），其他各空间尺度变化也十分丰富，用以满足不同的功能，营造不同的气氛，可谓张弛自如。这些空间组合在一起，抑扬起伏，即便未身临其境，也能够非常强烈地感受到殿内空间变化形成的丰富效果。

技巧的另一方面是仙楼空间的运用，即在单层建筑中营造两层空间。李斗在《扬州画舫录》中记载江南匠人有做小房子绝艺，就是在屋中造屋，层上加层[2]。仙楼的做法无疑使室内空间得到进一步利用，也使之更加丰富。花园中建有仙楼的建筑有符望阁、倦勤斋两座。

上述两个特点综合在一起，室内空间组织便达到了非常复杂的程度，需要设计人员创造性地运用空间想象力，同时使用多种技术手段。根据档案记载[3]：

乾隆三十九年四月 初四 日
奴才李质颖谨奏为奏闻事窃奴才于上年六七等月接奉内务府大臣英廉等寄信奉旨交办景福宫符望阁萃赏楼延趣楼倦勤斋五处装修并烫样五座画样一百二张等因为杨奴才随即遴派熟谙安商选购料物挑雇工匠择吉开工上紧成造奴才不时亲身查视详慎督办今已告成奴才逐件细看包裹装船于四月初四日开行专差家人小心运送进京除备文并造具清册呈送工程处逐件点收听候奏请安装外敬将装修五分镶嵌式样雕镂花纹绘图贴说先行恭呈御览谨缮折具奏伏乞皇上圣鉴谨奏。

宁寿宫花园第一进院落禊赏亭曲水流觞

宁寿宫花园耸秀亭下叠石

宁寿宫花园符望阁南叠石

1. 所有面积数值根据样式房图样、故宫博物院测绘资料等评估。
2. [清]李斗：《扬州画舫录》，北京：中华书局，1997年。卷十七，四二一页："大屋中施小屋。小屋上架小楼。谓之仙楼。江园工匠。有做小房子绝艺。"
3.《宫中档乾隆朝奏折》，第三十五辑，台湾：国立故宫博物院印行，第179页。

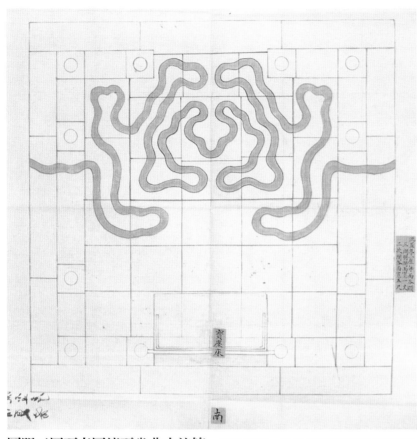

圆明三园万春园清夏堂曲水流觞　资料来源：中国国家图书馆样式雷排架

圆明园坐石临流曲水流觞遗迹

Building disposal and building structure are also elements in Chinese garden design. In the first two courtyards, all the buildings are single storeyed. Some buildings such as Pavilion of Embosoming Fragrance (撷芳亭) and Pavilion of Morning Splendour (旭辉庭) are built on top of rockeries to make inside elevation of the complex much richer. In the rear 2 courtyards, apart from the open pavilions on rockeries and auxiliary buildings including the corridors, 5 buildings of 8 are multi-storeyed. Among the one storey buildings, i.e. Pavilion of Three Friends (三友轩), Pavilion of Jade Purity (玉粹轩), the Lodge of Retirement (倦勤斋), the lodge has two storeys inside as the last building of the entire garden complex. Observing the cross section of the whole garden, one can easily appreciate the opus from the prelude in the front yard, then developing gradually along the axis to climax the soaring building and at last ending at the coda of the Lodge of Retirement.

3.2.3 What is Behind the Treasure Regalement

The murals and exceedingly thick inventory of interior furnishings along with the abundant interior spatial screenings are telling that Qianlong Garden can be described as a treasure regalement without any exaggeration. A survey finds a series of the most delicate interior spatial partitions, in comparison to the relatively plainer ones which are less delicately carved and lack inlay works of precious materials, and of the extant tromp l'oeil paintings in the garden.

Among all the interior spaces in the garden, interiors are not equal in design and can be classified into three groups in respect to the Density of interior features.

Group One, open spaces have plain interior vocabularies apart from the open corridors, such as Square Pavilion, Jade Conch Pavilion, and the Pavilion of Ancient Flower which yet was not over-decorated except that screens, tablets and ceiling are of rich expressions.

Group Two, spaces of less funtions for the Emperor, such as Chamber of Self-Constraint, Pavilion of Morning Light and the buildings that compose the courtyard of Fufilling Original Wishes, are of smaller spaces and less spacial partitions.

Group Three, some buildings have the most delicate decorations on the spatial partitions, and furniture and wall decorations were also recorded being specially made for the rooms. Among the 29 buildings, the most luxurious buildings are, from the front to the rear, Pavilion of Ancient Flower, Building of Collection and Appreciation, Pavilion of Three Friends, Building of Extended Delight, Building of Accomplished Wishes and Lodge of Retirement, Building of Cloud Light, Pavilion of Jade Purity and Chamber of Bamboo Fragrance, reflecting more vividly the life of the emperors.

Characteristics of interior design of Qing Court, especially scale of spaces, selection of decorative motifs and design techniques, are also best represented by the buidlings of Group Three. We can use scales of spaces as a clear illustration.

可见，在内檐装修设计阶段，样式房的工作在选择装饰主题、设计纹样之外，还包括平面功能的划分、罩槅形式的搭配选用等内容。由主管大臣审查确定后，发样交办，最后将制作人员的装饰纹样和工艺做法融入到细节设计当中。

说宁寿宫花园是内檐装修的宝库，首先是指其中精美绝伦的罩槅及其装饰做法。作为一个泱泱大国的君主，乾隆确实是非常的幸运，他的前辈已经把帝国带入了一个组织健全而稳定发展的阶段，而他，也确实遇到了可以缔造辉煌和享用辉煌的时候。几乎所有的研究都认为乾隆皇帝风度幽雅、好尚精美、热衷艺术，他在那个清代最为繁荣的历史阶段里，耗费了大量的财力，实现了自己的审美追求。如果我们追踪这位满族皇帝的生活轨迹，便不难发现他通过南巡和深入接触汉族士大夫，形成了颇有"汉风"和"南风"印记的工艺美术偏好。因此，将和平繁荣的帝国比喻成描绘这个内檐装修宝库的画布，而将汉族士大夫文化比喻成这张画最常用的色彩，应当是确有道理的。

历史资料还显示，在所有建筑室内空间中，那些内檐装修最为精美者，陈设和家具也全部是为这个空间量身定做的（详见下文）。在二十九座主要建筑中，带有内檐装修者共计14座，其中主要的帝王活动空间10座。这些建筑中家具尺寸是根据空间尺度而定，家具装饰是根据建筑装饰主题而定的。

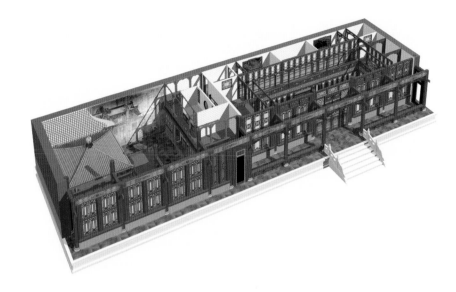

说宁寿宫花园是内檐装修的宝库，还指的是花园建筑中独特的通景画。所憾现存通景画仅仅存在于宁寿宫花园的第四个院落的建筑中。然而内务府活计档反映，宁寿宫花园原有通景画远不止如此。

对于现存的通景画，兹将有关历史记载摘录如下：

养和精舍云光楼：乾隆四十一年"十八日传旨宁寿宫转角楼明间西墙着王幼学等画线法画一张得时交造办处托贴钦此"[1]；

玉粹轩：乾隆四十年三月"初十日接得员外郎六格押帖一件内开二月二十二日太监胡世杰传旨宁寿宫玉粹轩明间罩内西墙着王幼学等画线法画一张。钦此"[2]；

乾隆四十年闰十月"十二日接得员外郎六格押帖内开十月二十一日首领董五经交宣纸一张传旨宁寿宫玉粹轩殿内明间罩内西墙通景画一张着姚文翰画。钦此"[3]；

倦勤斋：乾隆三十九年二月"二十日，接得郎中德魁等押帖一件，内开本月十一日太监胡世杰传旨，宁寿宫倦勤斋西三间内，四面墙、柱子、棚顶、坎墙俱着王幼学等照德日新殿内画法一样画。钦此"[4]；

另，乾隆四十二年六月"十六日，接得郎中图明阿押帖一件，内开六月十三日太监常宁传旨，宁寿宫倦勤斋仙楼上北墙线法画一张，着如意馆用绢画。钦此"[5]。

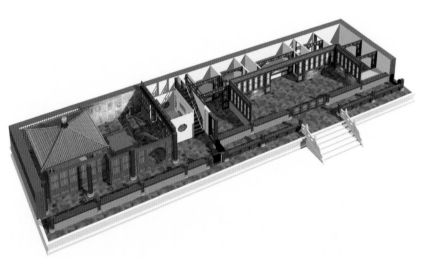

宁寿宫花园倦勤斋内檐装修布局示意图

1. 内务府活计档，中国第一历史档案馆藏，胶片 132。
2. 内务府活计档，中国第一历史档案馆藏，胶片 129。
3. 内务府活计档，中国第一历史档案馆藏，胶片 129。
4. 内务府活计档，中国第一历史档案馆藏，胶片 127。
5. 内务府活计档，中国第一历史档案馆藏，胶片 133。

宁寿宫花园倦勤斋内檐装修暨室内陈设复原想象图

资料来源：故宫博物院　　设计制图：刘　畅　　民望公司

Name of Bldgs	Room	Location	Height	Area(m²)
Bldg of Collection & Appreciation	Entrance Hall	Middle bay, Ground Floor	1 storey	15.7
	Buddhist Hall	Northwest, Upper Floor	1 storey	4.8
Pavilion of Three Friends	Entrance Hall	Middle bay, Ground Floor	1 storey	16.2
	Reading room	West bay, Ground Floor	1 storey	11.7
Bldg of Extended Delight	Hall	Upper Floor	1 storey	36.7
	Restroom	North, Ground Floor	1 storey	6.4
Bldg of Accomplished Wishes	Hall	Top Floor	1 storey	114.1
	Bedroom	Middle, Ground Floor	1 storey	4.0
Lodge of Retirement	Entrance Hall	Middle	2 storeys	38.5
	Restroom	Northeast, Ground Floor	1 storey	3.8
Bldg of Cloud Light	Buddhist Hall	North, Upper Floor	1 storey	26.1
	Bedroom	North, Ground Floor	1 storey	5.8
Bldg of Bamboo Fragrance	Restroom	Middle Bay, Ground Floor	1 storey	8.0
	Restroom	South, Upper Floor	1 storey	1.2

Taking the space arrangement in the Lodge of Retirement as an example, it can be calculated for the partitioned spaces other than passages, and it can be found that the most spacious covers 38.5 m² with a height of circus 4m (15 chi, convert to historic measurement), while the smallest one only covers 3.8 m² with a height of 2m (arround 7 chi). It is worth noting that other spaces are also rich in dimensional variety to accomodate various functions and to create various mood, which reflects sophistication of space arrangement. With the above mentioned numbers in mind, even one has not been to the spaces, he can also feel the contrast between the big halls and small room and sense of spatial richness one can have when wandering through the buildings.

Another important technique in interior space design is the creation of two levels in a single storey building. A Qing Dynasty literati, LI Dou described this technique in his *Recort in Painted Boat in Yangzhou*, how craftsmen in Jiangnan Rigion command the skill of building rooms and levels inside rooms, which is called the Immortals' Level[1]. The Immortals' Level further varies and enriches the design of how space is used. Two buildings in Qianlong Garden have Immortals' Levels, the Buidling of Accomplished Wishes and the Lodge of Retirement.

对于今已无存的通景画，兹将有关历史记载摘录如下：

遂初堂：乾隆三十九年十月"二十二日，接得员外郎图明阿押帖一件内开十月初七日太监胡世杰传旨宁寿宫遂初堂正殿西墙着王幼学画线法通景绢画一幅。钦此"[1]；

遂初堂东配殿：乾隆三十九年二月"二十三日接得郎中德魁等押帖一件内开本月十三日太监胡世杰传旨宁寿宫遂初堂东配殿五间内着艾启蒙照玉玲珑馆林光澹碧殿内西洋景改正线法着王幼学等画。钦此"[2]；

乾隆四十一年"十八日……传旨遂初堂明间后隔扇南墙用通景画一幅着方琮姚文瀚照奉三无私一样画。钦此"[3]；

倦勤斋东进间北墙：乾隆四十年十一月"十八日，接得员外郎图明阿押贴一件，内开十一月初三日太监胡世杰传旨，宁寿宫倦勤斋东进间北墙着王幼学等画线法画。钦此"[4]。

在中国宫廷画院史上，乾隆的如意馆是非常有特色、有"效率"的代表，至少比起他的父辈和祖辈，是尤其卓越的。这里我们也不应当忽视世界这个大视角，乾隆时代也恰好是中国在世界上的力量与地位转而下降的拐点。宁寿宫花园也反映出，乾隆个人对于西方的兴趣集中在艺术方面，而非科学技术。一则学者的评述值得回味[5]：

进入中国宫廷中的西方文化产品（物质的和精神的）大致可以分为科技、艺术和思想三个方面……我们发现，三个方面是依次进入和影响清宫的，而其依次占主导地位的时期，恰与清王朝历史发展相应；前期，清王朝兴起的时期，西方文化中的科技方面对清宫的影响最大；中期，清朝的鼎盛时期，西方文化中的艺术方面对清宫影响最大；末期，清朝的衰落时期，西方文化中的思想意识方面对清宫的影响最大。

简言之，乾隆的祖父康熙皇帝曾经下过大力气来学习西方的科学技术，乾隆则对外来的艺术情有独钟。当马葛尔尼和乔治·斯汤顿带领英国使团踏上大清帝国疆土的时候，乾隆对他们带来的19类590多件礼物，其中有行天仪、太阳系仪、天球图、地球图和反射镜，此类仪器似乎无动于衷，而且在他看到一架战船模型上的有巨大杀伤力的火炮之时，没有像他的祖父康熙皇帝那样亲自考察试验炮火威力，没有在炎热的夏天邀请传教士到自己的花园里教授机械学和几何学，研究机械原理，反而批判了这种野蛮的武器——他无法预见，百年后这些大炮对清政府的致命打击。

三友轩定制家具

云光楼通景画

1. 内务府活计档，中国第一历史档案馆藏，胶片 128。
2. 内务府活计档，中国第一历史档案馆藏，胶片 127。
3. 内务府活计档，中国第一历史档案馆藏，胶片 132。
4. 内务府活计档，中国第一历史档案馆藏，胶片 129。
5. 刘潞、刘月芳：《清代宫中出现西方文化的原因探讨》，载于：清代宫史研究会 编. 清代宫史探微. 北京：紫禁城出版社，1991：199–212。

三友轩定制家具

玉粹轩通景画

Designing with such tacts, space contrast and Immortals' Level, one can achieve in composing an interior of high complicacy, and moreover, the procedure of designing would also be very much complicated and call for creative imagination of spaces and the media such as drawings and models that help thinking and representing thinking. As recorded in archives from Qing court[1]:

乾隆三十九年四月 初四 日

奴才李质颖谨奏为奏闻事窃奴才于上年六七等月接奉内务府大臣英廉等寄信奉旨交办景福宫符望阁萃赏楼延趣楼倦勤斋五处装修并烫样五座画样一百二张等因到杨奴才随即遴派熟谙妥商选购料物挑雇工匠择吉开工上紧成造奴才不时亲身查视详慎督办今已告成奴才逐件细看包裹装船于四月初四日开行专差家人小心运送进京除备文并造具清册呈送工程处逐件点收听候奏请安装外敬将装修五分镶嵌式样雕镂花纹绘图贴说先行恭呈御览谨缮折具奏伏乞皇上圣鉴谨奏。

It is clearly stated that the court had models made, above referred as Tangyang, of five buildings in Ningshou Gong Precinct (four in Qianlong Garden) and there were also 102 drawings, together with the models sent to the south tohave the screenings especially made for the court. We can infer that Pattern Office in the court was assigned to design, whose task did not only covered layout of rooms but also decorative mofives and patterns, and after inspection of the chiefs, and even Emperor Qianlong himself, commands were convey to teams for constructing in the captial and in the south, to have the details integrated well into the general design.

Treasure regale firstly refers to the interior screenings and decorations. As the emperor of a large empire, Qianlong was lucky for his predecessors had brought the country into a united and well-organized status that allowed him to enjoy prosperity. Almost all studies on Qianlong Garden come to a conclusion that the most prosperous period in Qiang Dynasty provides Emperor Qianlong whose nature was elegant, delicate, passionate about art and of a systematizing-inclination, a plentiful capital to pursue his artistic goals, and when tracing the Manchu emperor's life, the influence of Han culture and especially that of fine art in the southern regions on the monarch can be obviously detected. It is reasonable to say that a flourishing empire at peace was the back drop on which the colorful photomontage of treasures was rendered, and Han culture was one of the oftenest used pigment.

Another distinctive feature of the garden is the tromp l'oeil paintings. Unique and outstanding as the paintings for building decoration are, tromp l'oeil works and some vestiges remain preserved only in the 4th courtyard. Evidence from the imperial household archives indicates that more pieces were commanded to paint by the department of paintings in the court than the extant ones.

Records of the extant murals include:

In the 41st year of Qianlong period (1776), the emperor commanded Wang Youxue to paint a scenographic mural in the ground floor chamber (养和精舍) of the Building of Cloud Light (云光楼). 乾隆四十一年 "十八日传旨宁寿宫转角楼明间西墙着王幼学等画线法画一张得时交造办处托贴。钦此"[2];

尽管康熙学习西方科技没有实质性地影响帝国的未来，但是乾隆对西方艺术的爱好却以文物遗存的形式一直保留到了今天。在一批西方传教士的帮助下，乾隆在长春园盖起了西洋楼景区，并且同他父亲一样爱上了西方的透视法通景画。以圆明园为例，我们可以发现历史文献中记载了多处建筑中曾有过通景画：

雍正四年正月，"四宜堂后穿堂内安隔断，隔断上面着郎世宁照样画人物画片，其马匹不必画……再着郎世宁按三间屋内的远近，照小样画一分……"[1]；

雍正五年八月，"万字房通景画壁前着郎世宁画西洋栏杆，或用布画或用绢画，或用绫画，尔等酌量画罢，不必起稿呈览"[2]；

雍正七年闰七月，"西峰秀色处含韵斋殿内陈设的棕竹边、漆背书格二架，上层着郎世宁画山水二幅，要相仿"[3]；

乾隆十三年八月十四日，"淡泊宁静东墙并南北两边墙，连棚顶共四面，俱着郎世宁起稿呈览"[4]；

乾隆二十一年十一月，"新建水法西洋楼各处棚顶、墙壁有应画处，俱著郎世宁起稿呈览"[5]；

乾隆三十年五月，郎世宁去世的前一年，尚有"玉玲珑馆新建殿五间，著郎世宁画西洋线法画"[6]的记载；

通景画在当时肯定要远远多于上述几条记载。今天宁寿宫花园的通景画之所以珍贵，不仅由于它们得以保存下来，更因为这些建筑中大型绘画作品是如此丰富、如此集中。早在花园建成之前，郎士宁便已辞世，我们可以通过档案记载判断，花园中通景画的作者主要是这位西方绘画大师的弟子们——王幼学便是其中的突出代表。

3.3 探索宁寿宫花园的设计灵感

前人的研究表明，宁寿宫花园反映出精细、微妙的规划设计，其匠心贯穿了布局、建筑设计、叠山、绿化和室内设计。我们还有这样的理解，中国历史上的规划设计事实上是历史缓慢演进的结果，而不能简单地解释成个人的创作行为。历史同样慷慨地将宁寿宫花园和先人设计宁寿宫花园的线索留到了今天，我们不禁要问：宁寿宫花园的设计灵感到底是什么？

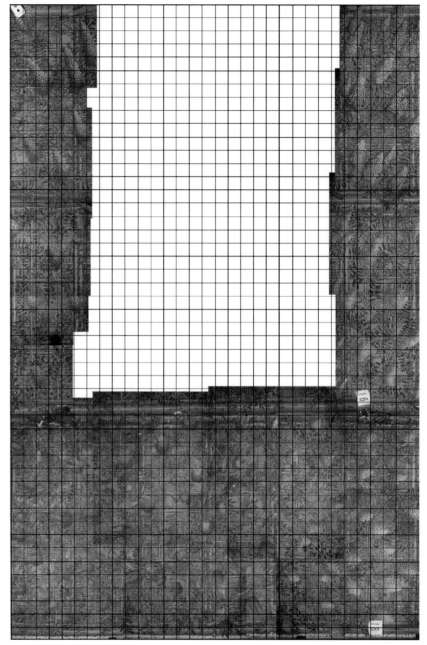

倦勤亭室内通景天顶画

1–6. 中国第一历史档案馆 编.《圆明园》(下)，上海：上海古籍出版社，1991 年。

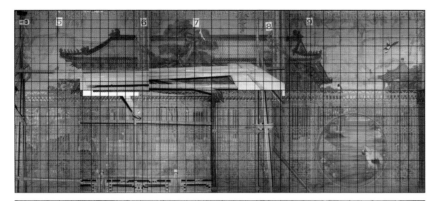

倦勤斋天顶画通景画

In the Pavilion of Jade Purity, Wang Youxue did not finish the painting the mural inside, and it was Yao Wenhan who had the assignment later (1775). 乾隆四十年三月"初十日接得员外郎六格押帖一件内开二月二十二日太监胡世杰传旨宁寿宫玉粹轩明间罩内西墙着王幼学等画线法画一张。钦此"[1];

乾隆四十年闰十月"十二日接得员外郎六格押帖内开十月二十一日首领董五经交宣纸一张传旨宁寿宫玉粹轩殿内明间罩内西墙通景画一张着姚文翰画。钦此"[2];

乾隆三十九年二月"二十日，接得郎中德魁等押帖一件，内开本月十一日太监胡世杰传旨，宁寿宫倦勤斋西三间内，四面墙、柱子、棚顶、坎墙俱着王幼学等照德日新殿内画法一样画。钦此"[3];

乾隆四十二年六月"十六日，接得郎中图明阿押帖一件，内开六月十三日太监常宁传旨，宁寿宫倦勤斋仙楼上北墙线法画一张，着如意馆用绢画。钦此"[4];

乾隆三十九年十月"二十二日，接得员外郎图明阿押帖一件内开十月初七日太监胡世杰传旨宁寿宫遂初堂正殿西墙着王幼学画线法通景绢画一幅。钦此"[5];

遂初堂艾启蒙乾隆三十九年二月"二十三日接得郎中德魁等押帖一件内开本月十三日太监胡世杰传旨宁寿宫遂初堂东配殿五间内着艾启蒙照玉玲珑馆林光澹碧殿内西洋景改正线法着王幼学等画。钦此"[6];

乾隆四十一年十八日，"传旨遂初堂明间后隔扇南墙用通景画一幅着方琮姚文瀚照奉三无私一样画。钦此"[7];

乾隆四十年十一月"十八日，接得员外郎图明阿押贴一件，内开十一月初三日太监胡世杰传旨，宁寿宫倦勤斋东进间北墙着王幼学等画线法画。钦此"[8]。

3.3.1 紫禁城与皇家离宫御苑

　　首先，了解乾隆皇帝的生活规律会为解答他如何设想宁寿宫花园有一些帮助。下文所列举的清代雍正至咸丰诸帝的驻跸记录颇具说服力——他们大致每年在紫禁城中居住三分之一的时间，在另三分之一的时间里住在圆明园，剩余的三分之一的时间则花在游历、秋狝、巡视盛京上[1]。因此，帝王们在圆明园的生活与紫禁城建筑的改造紧密地联系在了一起。

　　作为圆明园的创始者，雍正皇帝延续其父康熙驻畅春园的习惯，首开驻跸圆明园处理政务的定例。雍正皇帝在雍正三年八月二十七日（1725年）首次"*由神武门出西直门，幸圆明园驻跸*"，同年写下的《圆明园记》说他驻跸圆明园的主要目的是"*百务具举，宜宁神受福，少屏烦喧*"[2]。自此十年后雍正驾崩在圆明园，雍正皇帝平均每年驻园207天，且每一年驻园时间都超过在宫时间，一般只是在郊祀斋戒、视朝等大典时才回到紫禁城。不过雍正在圆明园也绝不闲适，而是"*朕在圆明园与宫中无异也，凡应办之事照常办理*"[3]（如图）。

　　右图是雍正皇帝在位各年在紫禁城和圆明园中的驻跸日期统计。

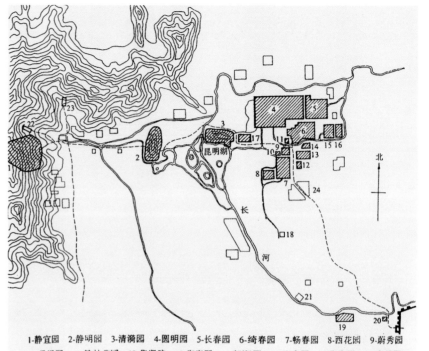

1-静宜园　2-静明园　3-清漪园　4-圆明园　5-长春园　6-绮春园　7-畅春园　8-西花园　9-蔚秀园　10-承泽园　11-翰林花园　12-集贤院　13-淑春园　14-朗润园　15-迎春园　16-熙春园　17-自得园　18-泉宗庙　19-乐善园　20-倚虹园　21-万寿寺　22-碧云寺　23-卧佛寺　24-海淀

清盛期北京西北郊皇家园林总平面图－引自《中国古典园林史》

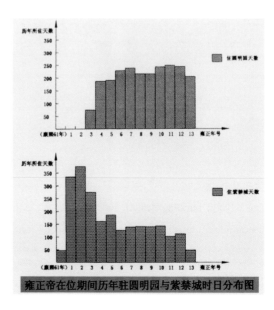

雍正帝在位期间历年驻圆明园与紫禁城时日分布图

Yongzheng period, 7th year, another again (1729), 雍正七年闰七月，"西峰秀色处含韵斋殿内陈设的棕竹边、漆背书格二架，上层着郎世宁画山水二幅，要相仿"[3];

Qianlong period, 13th year (1748), also Guseppe's work, 乾隆十三年八月十四日，"淡泊宁静东墙并南北两边墙，连棚顶共四面，俱着郎世宁起稿呈览"[4];

Qianlong period, 21st year (1756), the aged Italian painted a painting according to a so called western way in the complex of occidental buildings, 乾隆二十一年十一月，"新建水法西洋楼各处棚顶、墙壁有应画处，俱著郎世宁起稿呈览"[5];

Qianlong period, 30th year (1765), one year before the master passing away, 乾隆三十年五月玉玲珑馆新建殿五间，著郎世宁画西洋线法画[6]。

There were many more paintings though time had erased them. Today the perspective paintings, which are recently more popularly refered as tromp l'oeil paintings, in Qianlong Garden is not only surprising for its existence, but also for the richness, scale and density of their remaining in a single complex of buildings, even though the garden was built after Guiseppe Castiglione, and the murals were mostly painted by the master's students, among which Wang Youxue is seen as the most representative figure of the school of Castiglione.

3.3 Where does the afflatus come from

We know from earlier research that the planning of Qianlong Garden was delicate, subtly careful and ingenuous in its layout, building design, rockery, planting and interior design. We also know that examples of outstanding historic planning in China were refined over time rather than the result of a single creative individual. Time has left vestiges for us to trace, with the attendant question, where does the afflatus come from? Or, what were the resources of the design?

Qianlong organized a better and more productive painter's department (Ruyi Guan, 如意馆) than his predecessors. When speaking about Qianlong and his predecessors, we will not neglect that from the global view, the following generation of Qianlong was the inflexion point at which China's power and his position in the world development droped. Qianlong's personal interest, which was vividly reflected in the garden, played an important role in the history, and one interesting comment seeking for the foreshadowing factors should not be forgotten[9],

Cultural products substantial and spiritual that entered Imperial Court of China could be divided into three families, science and technology, art, and philosophy… The author found that the 3 families were introduced and influenced Chinese court in sequence and in accordance with the development of Qing Empire. In the prophase, western science and technology had greatest impact on the emperor; in the metaphase, it is art turn that enriched the most splendid imperial court with its exotic western flavour; in the anaphase at the fall of Qing dynasty, philosophical thoughts contributed to stimulate the ideas of the nation…

In summary, it was Qianlong's grandfather Kangxi who spent more energy in absorbing western science and technology, and Qianlong's favorite field was the exotic arts. When Lord Macartney and Sir George Staundon came to China as the first British embassies to China during Qianlong's reign, the gifts were altogether 19 kinds of over 590 pieces, among which there were a planetarium, a orrery, a map of celestial sphere, a map of the earth and a reflector. Qianlong did express enjoymnt on these but blamed brutality when he saw a high power cannon on a battleship model. In contrast, Kangxi invited western clergy men to his private garden house to teach him mathematics and geometry even during the hottest days and invited foreigners to make cannons for his armies.

Though his grandfather's example of learning from the west was not followed, the enthusiasm on foreign arts of Qianlong reserred until now by the ype of relics. He built the occidental building complex in Yuanming Yuan with the help of many western clergies, and he also had great enthusiasm in scenography like his father. At Yuanming Yuan for example, many records on mural painting in the halls of Yuanmingyuan can be read on yellow archive pages,

Yongzheng period, 4th year (1726), Guseppe Castiglione was asked to paint a wall painting according to perspective rules, 雍正四年正月，"四宜堂后穿堂内安隔断，隔断上面着郎世宁照样画人物画片，其马匹不必画……再着郎世宁按三间屋内的远近，照小样画一分……"[1];

Yongzheng period, 5th year (1727), Castiglione had another assignment, 雍正五年八月，"万字房通景画壁前着郎世宁画西洋栏杆，或用布画或用绢画，或用绫画，尔等酌量画罢，不必起稿呈览"[2];

乾隆皇帝使圆明园真正成为了"万园之园"，而他本人在园中的活动也很丰富。在雍正丧期满后，乾隆于乾隆三年正月十一日（1738年）首次以皇帝的身份驻跸圆明园，并且将这个习惯一直保持到嘉庆元年（1796年）他退位作了太上皇之后。最后在嘉庆三年十月十日（1798年）最后一次离开圆明园返回紫禁城，次年正月初三日崩于养心殿。在此六十一年间，乾隆每岁必幸圆明园，乾隆五年驻跸时日最多，为251天，乾隆四十五年最少，为10天。相比较而言，乾隆留宫的时间则较为平均。究其原因，大致是因为弘历其人，喜好巡幸，木兰秋狝时日增加，又有江南巡视，且其他园囿工程时兴，"看工乘凉"亦是消遣，于是才有了波动不定的活动记录。不过，乾隆皇帝在园中的活动范围因扩建和鼎新而更加广泛，四处游观，"帝王豫游之地无以逾此"[4]确实是他圆明园生活的写照。

右图是乾隆皇帝在位各年在紫禁城和圆明园中的驻跸日期统计。

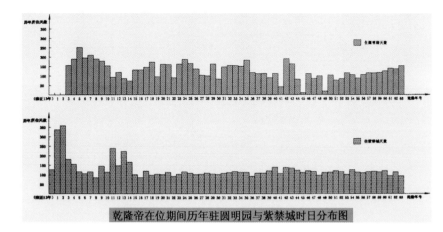

乾隆帝在位期间历年驻圆明园与紫禁城时日分布图

嘉庆皇帝是扩建绮春园的主角。颙琰在位期间，除嘉庆四、五两年在宫居丧，其余年份驻宫、驻园时间相对稳定，在园时间平均为162天，最多的是嘉庆十九年，247天，最少的是嘉庆元年，111天。嘉庆曾谕曰："我皇祖世宗宪皇帝勤求治理，整饬官联。自是以后，圆明园奏事文职衙门轮为九班，武职衙门轮为十班。我皇考纯皇帝遵行六十余年。朕嗣统二十年以来，亦恪遵不懈。诚以我朝家法，勤政为先，驻跸御园，与宫内办事，无一日稍闲"[5]。这里"御园"一语专指圆明园，足见嘉庆视圆明园之重。

右图是嘉庆皇帝在位各年在紫禁城和圆明园中的驻跸日期统计。

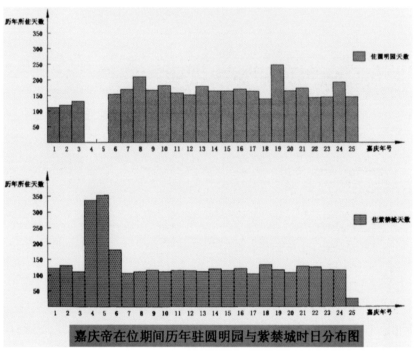

嘉庆帝在位期间历年驻圆明园与紫禁城时日分布图

1. 关于清代帝起居注的研究，以及驻跸圆明园的日程研究，参照贾珺：《清代离宫御苑朝寝空间研究》，博士学位论文，北京：清华大学建筑学院，2001年。下文相关文字与《清帝驻宫与驻园时间图表》内容亦然，不赘。
2. 雍正：《圆明园记》，载于：于敏中 等编：《日下旧闻考》，一三二二页。
3. 《大清世宗宪皇帝实录》，中国台湾：华文书局，1968年。
4. 乾隆：《圆明园后记》。载于：清于敏中 等：《日下旧闻考》，一三二三页。《大清太宗睿皇帝实录》，四五七九页，中国台湾：华文书局，1968年。
5. 《大清太宗睿皇帝实录》，四五七九页，中国台湾：华文书局，1968年。

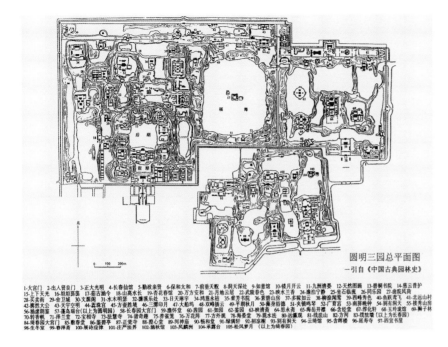

圆明三园总平面图
—引自《中国古典园林史》

1-大宫门 2-出入贤良门 3-正大光明 4-长春仙馆 5-勤政亲贤 6-保和太和 7-前垂天贶 8-洞天深处 9-如意馆 10-楼月开云 11-九洲清晏 12-天然图画 13-碧桐书院 14-慈云普护 15-上下天光 16-坦坦荡荡 17-茹古涵今 18-山高水长 19-杏花春馆 20-万方安和 21-地云远 22-武陵春色 23-映水兰香 24-濂溪乐处 25-坐石临流 26-同乐园 27-曲院风荷 28-买卖街 29-会卫城 30-文源阁 31-水木明瑟 32-濂溪乐处 33-廓然大公 34-西峰秀色 35-四宜书屋 36-紫碧山房 37-多稼轩 38-鱼跃鸢飞 39-四得角色 40-鱼跃鸢飞 41-北远山村 42-君教大公 43-天宇空明 44-慈雲宮 45-方壶胜境 46-三潭印月 47-大船坞 48-雷峰夕照 49-平湖秋月 50-接秀山房 51-接秀山房 52-别有洞天 53-接秀山房 54-别有洞天 55-接秀山房 56-福海坐落 57-蓬岛瑶台(以上为圆明园) 58-长春园大门 59-澹怀堂 60-茜园 61-如园 62-鉴园 63-映清斋 64-思永斋 65-海岳开襟 66-含经堂 67-淳化轩 68-玉玲珑馆 69-狮子林 70-转春桥 71-泽兰堂 72-宝相寺 73-法慧寺 74-谐奇趣 75-养雀笼 76-万花阵 77-方外观 78-海晏堂 79-观水法 80-远瀛观 81-线法山 82-方河 83-线法墙(以上为长春园) 84-绮春园大门 85-敷春堂 86-鉴碧亭 87-正觉寺 88-蔚心堂 89-河神庙 90-敷和室 91-绿满轩 92-招凉榭 93-别有洞天 94-云漪馆 95-含晖楼 96-延寿寺 97-四宜书屋 98-生冬室 99-展诗应律 100-展诗应律 101-庄严法界 102-凝秋馆 103-含晖麟图 104-承露台 105-松风萝月(以上为绮春园)

北
0   100   200m

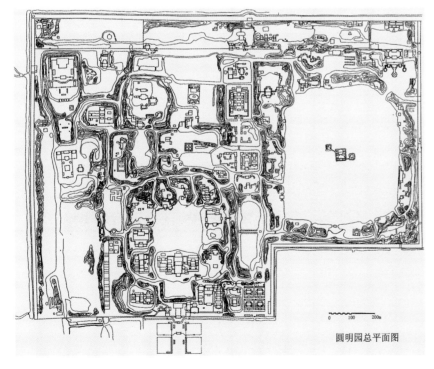

圆明园总平面图
0   100   200m

3.3.1 The Forbidden City and Para-palaces

The first question arises from the statistics of where the Qing emperors' resided. The following records show that Qing emperors almost set a rule to spend 1/3 of the year in the Forbidden City, 1/3 in the Summer Palace of Yuanmingyuan, and the remaining 1/3 in the Summer Palace in Chengde, except for the falling era of the empire after the foreign invasions.[1]

Record 1, residence of Emperor Yongzheng in the Forbidden City and in Yuanming Yuan. As the founder of Yuanming Yuan, Emperor Yongzheng followed his father's expample of residing and dealing with affairs of the state in the gardens in summer. He started his routine and that of his followers to reside in Yuanming Yuan in 1725, leaving the Forbidden City through the west gate. He also wrote a paragraph in his *Note on Yuanming Yuan* that his garden life was to allow for tranquility and more concentration on work by being away from disturbing[2]. From 1725 to his death 10 years later, Emperor Yongzheng spent 207 days a year on average in Yuanming Yuan. This is far more than his time in the Forbidden City which he most likely used for grand ceremonies, fasting and sacrificial activities. His comments on garden life were frank and accurate, that the working days differed little from those in the Forbidden City and affairs of state were never neglected[3].

Record 2, residence of Emperor Qianlong in the Forbidden City and in Yuanming Yuan. It is Emperor Qianlong who really built Yuanming Yuan into the Garden of A Hundred Gardens. He held many activities in Yuanming Yuan. After mourning his father, Qianlong began his regular pattern of residence in Yuanming Yuan from 1738 and kept it as a routine until shortly before his death while acting as the super-sovereign during the reign of his son, Emperor Jiaqing in 1798. In the 61 years of his reign, Qianlong stayed in Yuanming Yuan every year, with his longest stays for 251 days in 1740, and his shortest in 1780 for 10 days. In contrast to the flexibility of his stays in Yuanming Yuan, his days in the Forbidden City quite regular to which it can be attributed his nature love for travelling. He made frequent hunting tours to the north, inspections to the southern provinces and viewing the construction of his gardens every now and then. Though his travels covered vast places, he did not stint his eulogies to Yuanming Yuan, and deemed it the most preferred residence.

Record 3, residence of Emperor Jiaqing in the Forbidden City and in Yuanming Yuan. Emperor Jiaqing played a chief role in expanding the garden of Qichun Yuan which constitute the Grand-Yuanming Yuan with two other gardens. During the reign of Jiaqing, he stayed in the Forbidden City for the fourth and fifth year mourning for his father, and then arranged his days in palaces and garden quite regualarly. His longest stay in Yuanming Yuan was in 1814, 247 days, and the minimum was in 1796, 111 days, for an average of 162 days a year. As Jiaqing annouced in his edict, he and his ministers kept the tradition of dealing with government affairs while at Yuanming Yuan as if still working in the Forbidden City. Like his predecessors, it is significant that he also used "the Imperial Garden" to refer to Yuanming Yuan.

从起居注的记载来看，道光驻跸圆明园的时间最长。当时离宫御园处于萎缩的过程中，圆明园的功能便愈加显现出来。道光皇帝从即位的第三年（1823年）正月十二日首次驻园起，到他在道光三十年（1850年）正月十四日在圆明园驾崩止期间，停止了木兰秋狝，也很少外出巡幸，平均每年生活在圆明园的时间多达260天，最多的一年即道光二十九年（1849年），竟然达到355天。反观道光在紫禁城的时间只平均不足91天。

右图是道光皇帝在位各年在紫禁城和圆明园中的驻跸日期统计。

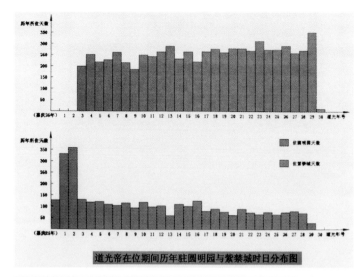

五代帝王中，咸丰皇帝的寿命和在位时间都是最短的，但他对圆明园中各殿宇的改造却由于样式房雷氏图档的流传而最为清晰。咸丰在道光三十年正月（1850年）即位，"恭移大行皇帝梓宫安奉正大光明殿……自是日始，上居飞云轩苫次"，即在圆明园居丧，至九月十八日方将梓宫引发回紫禁城。咸丰二年四月二十二日正式驻跸圆明园办理政务，后于三、四年停止驻园并于五年恢复。到咸丰十年，战事紧迫，咸丰仓皇北狩，未能再回御园。咸丰对圆明园守成小修，略加改造，便在此期间。总体来看，咸丰在驻园的七年中平均每年逗留217天，其活动范围并不广泛，多集中在九州清晏、勤政亲贤景区和绮春园的含辉楼一带（如图）。

右图是咸丰皇帝在位各年在紫禁城和圆明园中的驻跸日期统计。

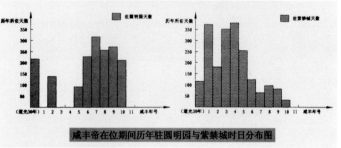

道光帝在位期间历年驻圆明园与紫禁城时日分布图

咸丰帝在位期间历年驻圆明园与紫禁城时日分布图

通过上述史实整理我们可以看出，圆明园曾经作为清代中期和中后期政治统治的核心，其历史重要性绝对不在紫禁城之下，完全可以称之为"清代第一离宫"。

康熙皇帝马鞭一指，营建了热河行宫[1]；雍正把在京园林的重心移到了圆明园；乾隆对这两处都深有感情——他六岁时曾第一次来到承德，十二岁时从百余名皇孙中被选出陪伴祖父[2]。但是对于乾隆自己来说，他最喜爱的还是圆明园中他父亲和他着手挑选的颇具江南风格的宫室园囿。

从上述分析可知，乾隆皇帝在为他归政后擘画宁寿宫花园的时候，心里不可避免地联想起圆明园和热河的宫室建筑。如果他将一些喜至之所移植到宁寿宫花园的话，我们一点也不会感到意外。他确实这样做了。

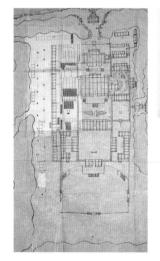

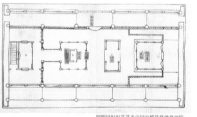

圆明园坦坦荡荡平面图内槛装修地盘画样

样式房图样中与宁寿宫花园有关图样选录

资料来源：中国国家图书馆

太簇始和图 [清]丁观鹏

Recors 4, residence of Emperor Daoguang in the Forbidden City and in Yuanming Yuan. Though the building and even the maintaining imperial gardens was in decline, Daoguang was the Qing emperor who stayed the longest in Yuanming Yuan. From the third year of his reign until his death in Yuanming Yuan, Daoguang stopped the tradition of hunting in the north, and seldom went on inspection tours, but averaged spend 260 days a year in Yuanming Yuan and in 1849 he set a record of 355 days. On the other hand, his average stay in the Forbidden City per year was 91 days.

Record 5, residence of Emperor Xianfeng in the Forbidden City and in Yuanming Yuan. Xianfeng lived and reigned the shortest period among the five emperors who used Yuanming Yuan as an imperial residence, but this did not prevent him from rebuilding or renovating many scenes in the garden, and he left behind the richest and most full historic records such as architectural representations and archives. Xianfeng escorted his father's coffin back to the Palace from Yuanming Yuan and formally resided there later. He also broke the tradition of living and reigning in garden for two years, and then resumed. His last year of reign was deeply affected by the battle against the Anglo-Francais Army which drove him out of the capital until he reached Chengde Xanadu hundreds kilometers away. Reconstructions and renovations took place during his stay there. On average Xianfeng spent in Yuanming Yuan for 217 nights over the seven years, and he seldom visted many other sites besides Jiuzhou Qingyan, Qinzheng Qinxian and Hanhuilou.

Beside Yuanmingyuan, the other frequent resort used by all Qing Emperors after Kangxi was Rehe Xanadu (热河行宫), i.e. the Summer Palace in Chengde (承德), approximately 250km northeast from Beijing. Rehe had played an important role in the activities of the north area where the founder of the empire originated from and where the Manchu emperors continued the tradition of autumn hunting[1]. For Qianlong, Rehe must have reminded him of his dear grandfather, Emperor Kangxi. Qianlong first came to Rehe when he was six years old, and when he was twelve he was fortunate to be the only one selected by Kangxi from over 100 grandsons to accompany him and listened to the Great Edification[2].

From the above discussions, it is quite understandable why Emperor Qianlong should have imitated some his favourite scenery from Yuanmin Yuan and Rehe Xanadu in the courtyard that would serve in retirement.

3.3.2 A History of Construction of Imperial Gardens and the Origin of the Qianlong Garden Design

The important constructional activities and relative events in the imperial gardens in the years before and during Qianlong's reign are outlined below.

In 1707, Kangxi the 46th year, construction of Rehe Xanadu commenced.

In1709, Kangxi the 48th year, Yuanming Yuan was bestowed on the prince Yongzheng by Emperor Kangxi[3].

3.3.2 离宫的兴建与宁寿宫花园的设计母本

将先于宁寿宫花园建设的皇家离宫御苑——尤其是圆明园——的营造大事整理出来，对于理解乾隆花园规划设计会有很大的帮助。

1707年，康熙四十六年，营建承德避暑山庄。

1709年，康熙四十八年，康熙将圆明园赐予皇四子胤禛[3]。

1722年，康熙六十一年，弘历作为皇孙奉康熙皇帝游历至圆明园牡丹台（四十景之镂月开云，主殿系无油饰彩画的楠木殿），后至热河行宫[4]。

1725年，雍正二年，雍正皇帝开始扩建圆明园，并作《圆明园记》[5]。

1735年，乾隆元年，改造紫禁城中乾隆皇帝的潜邸乾清宫西二所为重华宫；1739年，乾隆四年，将乾清宫西四五所改建为建福宫花园。

1738年，悬圆明园全图于圆明园九州清晏清晖阁壁上。

1744年，圆明园四十景图完成。

1747年，长春园三十二景区匾额制作完成，说明至此时为止，包括含经堂等长春园多处主要景观已经建成。

自1747年至1759年，长春园西洋楼景区建设完成。

1770年，改造长春园含经堂，"三友轩"之名首见于文献。

1770年，乾隆降旨设计宁寿宫花园，并估算耗费。

1772年，圆明园中仿苏州狮子林营造园中园狮子林。

将宁寿宫花园的各个院落布局与更早营建的清代皇家园囿的精彩局部进行对比，可以发现，其间确实存在诸多联系——其共同的背景是，乾隆皇帝追求江南园林中诸般美妙，将其升华后在自己的花园和宫室中大加运用。迄今，我们仍可以发现宁寿宫花园中以下布局和建筑曾经在其他皇家园囿中出现：

首先是宁寿宫花园的第四进院落。这个院落可以说几乎是紫禁城内建福宫花园西部的翻版；而建福宫花园的西部则由于面积的局限，在东距宁寿宫花园数十米宁寿宫后中路北端得到了重复。

再有，宁寿宫花园的第三进院落与长春园含经堂东花园的第二进院落几乎完全相同。根据现有资料推断，含经堂东花园的改造完成时间与宁寿宫花园始建的时间相比仅早数年，可以设想，当时乾隆皇帝一定认为自己已经找到了一种将中路的休憩空间与西花园联系起来一起设计的好方式，而且他还热衷于在这个花园的院子里堆砌大量的叠石——这个灵感主要来源于苏州园林狮子林，虽然在其他院落里乾隆同样使用了大量的叠石，但无疑地，在宁寿宫花园的这个院落中，山石绝对是占据了主导地位的。

圆明三园长春园含经堂遗址

1. 袁森坡：《清代口外行宫的由来和承德避暑山庄的发展过程》，《清史论丛·第二辑》，北京：中华书局，1980年。弘历：《永佑寺瞻礼神御纪事（丙戌）》诗序。载于 和珅：《热河志》，卷七十七。
2. 弘历：《永佑寺瞻礼神御纪事（丙戌）》诗序。载于 和珅：《热河志》，卷七十七。
3. 《日下旧闻考》，卷八十。
4. 《东华续录》。
5. 《日下旧闻考》，卷八十。

紫禁城建福宫花园遗址与复原工程

In 1722, Kangxi the 61st year, Qianlong accompanied Kangxi to Peony Platform in Yuanming Yuan, a complex with a hall of plain nan wood structure without painted finishes, and then to Rehe Xanadu[4].

In 1725, the second year of Yongzheng period, Emperor Yongzheng began to enlarge and improve Yuanming Yuan, and wrote Note on Yuanming Yuan (圆明园记)[5].

In 1735, the first year of Qianlong's reign, the second courtyard in the west row for princes, which had been the Emperor's former residence in the Forbidden City, were ordered rebuilt into a palace. It was the beginning of Qianlong's renovation efforts in the city. In the following year 1739, Qianlong commanded Jianfu Gong Garden be built in the fourth and fifth courtyards in the row for princes in the Forbidden City.

In 1738, the Great Map of Yuanming Yuan was finished and hung on the wall of Qinghui Ge (清晖阁, the Building of Clear Sunshine, in Yuanmingyuan).

In 1744, 40 scenes of Yuanming Yuan were painted.

In 1747, 32 plaques were made for the scenes in Changchun Yuan (forming the great Yuanming Yuan with Yuanming Yuan and Qichun Yuan), indicating the completion of the major sites including Hanjing Tang (含经堂, the Hall of Cherishing Sutras).

From 1747 to 1759, occidental buildings were constructed in Changchun Yuan.

In 1770, Hanjing Tang (含经堂) in Yuanmingyuan was renovated and the name of the Pacilion of Three Frienda located there first appeared in the archives.

In 1770, Qianlong Garden was ordered designed and estimated in cost.

In 1772, Shizi Lin (狮子林, the Lion Forest) imitating a garden of the same name in Suzhou, which was famous for rockery works was designed and constructed.

After comparing the layout of the Qianlong Garden with earlier imperial gardens, it becomes clear that the Emperor sought inspiration for Yuanming Yuan Gardens in south China and other exotic resorts, and then distilled the best from Yuanming Yuan for the retirement garden in the Forbidden City . The most eloquent similarities are found when comparing the courtyards in Qianlong Garden to sites in Yuanming Yuan.

The fourth courtyard of Qianlong Garden is almost a complete replica of the Jianfu Garden in the west part of the Forbidden City, differing only in the east part because of spatial limitations.

In addition, the third courtyard of Qianlong Garden copied quite precisely the second courtyard in the west rout of the complex of Hanjing Tang in Changchun Yuan in which renovation were likely completed very close in time to the start of Qianlong Garden, indicating that Qianlong might have been thinking about an ideal rear part of the palatial complex together with a west side garden. Together with the building of the rockery garden of Lion Forest in Yuanmin Yuan, there must have been some inspirations of the rockery and caves in the third courtyard derived from that of the Lion Forest, as well as those in the other yards.

宁寿宫花园的第二进院落布局平实，与无普通四合院无异，在此毋庸赘言。

笔者尚未发现宁寿宫花园的第一进院落的布局在其他皇家园囿中有雷同或相近者。然而院落中禊赏亭曲水流觞的主题却是中国园林所钟爱的。乾隆皇帝曾经在圆明园坐石临流景区中建兰亭一座，取王羲之禊赏踏青古意。但圆明园中兰亭做法与宁寿宫花园禊赏亭建筑形式、结构形式均不同，仅仅用典一致而已。迩来有学者研究蒨园委宛藏与宁寿宫花园第一进院之抑斋、矩亭、撷芳亭群组间的关系(端木泓，2005)，所言尚欠严谨。

3.4 关于重要历史人物的研究

3.4.1 乾隆和他的继任者们

究竟都有哪些人在营造宁寿宫花园的时候扮演着重要的角色呢？

无疑地，我们首先应当从乾隆皇帝开始，他不仅是花园的使用者，而且是花园的主创者。乾隆，在位达六十年，又作为太上皇训政三年。因为得到康熙的宠爱而确立在皇权争夺中的地位，他许愿如执政六十年，便将归政，传位给他的儿子。他确实得到了上天的眷顾，实现了这个愿望。身为太上皇期间，乾隆曾就整个宁寿宫在他死后的使用降旨，令此宫院长期作为太上皇宫使用，不可改作庙宇或改变布局[1]："宁寿宫乃朕称太上皇后颐养意地，在禁垣之左。日后尤不应照雍和宫之改为佛宇。其后之净室、佛楼，今有之，亦不必废也。其宫殿，永当依今之制，不可更改。若我大清亿万斯年，我子孙仰膺天眷，亦能如朕之享图日久，寿届期颐，则宁寿宫仍作太上皇之居。此旨著缮录两份，一交上书房，一交内阁存记。"于是，其后虽再无太上皇，宁寿宫在嘉庆、道光、咸丰、同治各朝也仅作为庆典、戏剧表演、宴会场所，均无大变化。直到光绪十三年（1887），光绪皇帝才奉慈禧太后在此小住，光绪皇帝驻跸养性殿，慈禧太后住乐寿堂；光绪末年，慈禧太后又将乐寿堂西暖阁作为自己的寝宫；宣统元年（1909），慈禧太后的葬礼在宁寿宫前朝部分的皇极殿举行。可见乾隆皇帝的旨意对于他的后世子孙们确实具有相当的约束力，这也是宁寿宫花园得以保留至今的重要历史原因。

乾隆皇帝同样对花园的设计倾注极高的热忱。从建成结果来看，如果我们要合理地回答为什么宁寿宫花园集成了那么多既有的院落模式，我们就不能不说，是乾隆皇帝选择了花园布局的模式，推敲了建筑和装饰主题，是他将这些决策下达给规划设计者们，而不是简单地审查设计人员提交的图纸和模型、赞赏或批判建筑师的种种创意，也是他关注并视察各个工程阶段，写有"步辇看工亦趁凉"的诗句[2]。正如帝王们所标榜的，乾隆皇帝勤于政务，同样也勤于对内府工程造作审查和监督。我们通过阅读清宫造办处活计档等历史档案，完全可以推想乾隆皇帝当时每天要在处理国家大事之外花去多少精力琢磨每一项装饰装修工程的各种细节。

除了乾隆皇帝，其后各朝清帝也在宁寿宫花园中留下了自己的印记。我们可以罗列一下：嘉庆皇帝曾多次来到宁寿宫并在花园中休息，花园建筑室内现存的御笔贴落主要出自于他的手笔；道光、咸丰、同治三朝帝王与宁寿宫花园关系并不密切；光绪时期，由于慈禧太后居住，宁寿宫又一度重新变成了太后宫，此时内务府为花园建筑室内的陈设宝物重新做了详细的统计，编辑成册。也正是因为乾隆后代在宁寿宫花园中的活动，一些现存状况与乾隆时期的历史文献记载有所出入，这种出入既为我们留下了推测宁寿宫原貌的想象空间，又在讲述着历史变迁过程中偶然和必然的故事[3]。

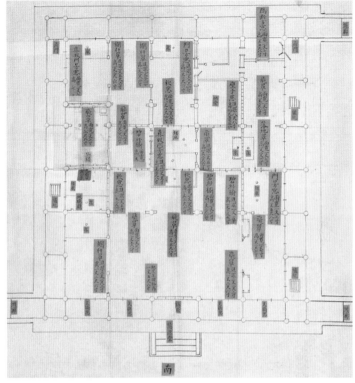

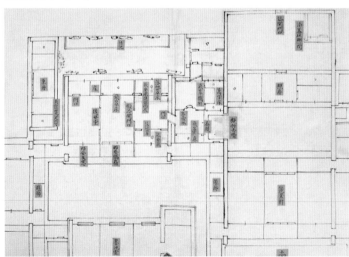

1.《大清高宗纯皇帝实录》，乾隆五十九年。北京：中华书局，1985年。
2. 转引自：章乃炜：《清宫述闻》，843页。
3. 以抑斋为例，乾隆时档案记载"抑斋续添进深板墙一槽，楠木落地罩床罩三槽"，而现状并未见所言各槽内檐装修，盖为后世拆除。

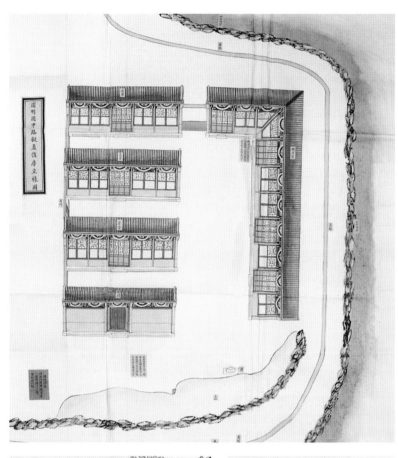

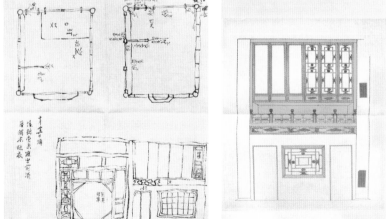

样式房立样举例 资料来源：故宫博物院

The second courtyard of Qianlong Garden is much more plain than the rear two, and lacks evidence of an original motif.

As for the first courtyard, a similar plan from an earlier garden has not come to light, however the motif of the Floating Cup Pavilion was so popular a theme in Chinese gardens that a related pavilion named Lan Ting (兰亭, the Orchid Pavilion) in Zuoshi Linliu(坐石临流, Sitting on the Rocks Facing the Stream) scenic site was built in Yuanming Yuan, which bears the same literary quotation as the Floating Cup Pavilion but is of a different layout and structural style. A recent article, *New Evidence Regarding Yuanming Yuan: A Study of the Qianyuan in Changchun Yuan*, attempts to establish the relationship between Weiwancang in Qianyuan and the small complex in the southeast corner of the first courtyard of Qianlong Garden, but some of the evidence is verifiable as imprecise.

3.4 Key Personages in the History of Qianlong Garden

3.4.1 Qianlong and His Successors

Who is responsible for the building of Qianlong Garden?

No doubt we must start from Emperor Qianlong, after whom the garden is named. He reigned as emperor for 60 years, and another three years as the Emperor Father. Emperor Qianlong was cherished by his grandfather Emperor Kangxi, which was a basis for his ascending throne years later, and this bond of affection also led him to make a vow that if the Heaven blessed him to be on the throne for sixty years, he would hand over his crown to his son. He did as he vowed. It is also remarkable that Emperor Qianlong issued an imperial edict that Ningshou Gong precinct be used as a palace for super sovereigns retired after him, rather than be changed into a Buddhist Monastery, and that no other changes to the settings should be carried out[1]. By these means the precinct survived through the reigns of emperors Jiaqing (嘉庆), Daoguang (道光), Xianfeng (咸丰) and Tongzhi (同治) who used this area for ceremonies, theatrical activities and feasts. In the 13th year of Guangxu (光绪) period (1887), emperor Guangxu escorted Empress Dowager Cixi (慈禧太后), known as the queen regent, to live in the precinct, Guangxu in Yangxing Dian (养性殿) and Cixi in Leshou Tang (乐寿堂), for a short time before moving back to her own palaces according to the imperial customs. But in the last years of Guangxu's reign, Cixi used again the west warm chamber inside Leshou Tang as her residential space, and in the first year of Xuantong (宣统) period (1909) the obsequial ritual for her was held in Huangji Dian (皇极殿) in the front area of the precinct. This reveals how the influence of Qianlong, the strongest emperor of Qing Dynasty, was effective in the succeeding centuries.

3.4.2 将作大匠与大匠

与勒诺特禾因设计法国园林而名声斐然不同，我们在乾隆史料中寻觅不到一点关于建筑师、造园家的线索——尽管当时必然存在至少是类似的角色在技术层面执行设计任务。幸运的是，这些史料中仍然经常出现一些当时人的名字——一些大臣的名字，他们或者是奏折的撰写人，或者是销算的负责人，或者仅仅是传令人。那么，臣工们在规划、设计、施工过程中的作用到底是什么样的呢？

海望是一个笔者必须首先提及的名字。《清史稿》中有海望传[1]，记载有他的谥号"勤恪"。在宁寿宫花园的设计母本之一建福宫花园的史料中反映，海望是整个工程的负责人。虽然他死于1755年，没有参与宁寿宫花园的设计，但是朱家溍先生的研究表明："海望，乌雅氏，满洲正黄旗人……雍正元年擢内务府主事，升员外郎……除管理造办处事务之外，有时还为各'作'设计作画……到雍正十年，他已升任内大臣，还时时作画"[2]。加之档案中所反映的海望屡屡介入宫廷不同规模的营造事务和内檐装修事务，我们可以发现确如朱老所言"如果写今天的工艺美术史，海望应该是一位名家"[3]。兹简要列举两则代表性史料如下：

"乾隆元年正月初九日（如意馆）内大臣海望奉上谕：将画画人冷枚传来照慈宁宫画画人赏给钱粮，令伊将圆明园殿宇处所照画过热河图样，每处画图一张，绘总画一张。钦此……"[4]；

"乾隆元年三月初十日（舆图房）……委署司库八十、柏唐阿赫申、七十九来说，内大臣海望交勤政殿地盘样一张、同乐园地盘样一张、长春仙馆地盘样一张，着照样做烫胎合牌房样。记此。于本月二十八日，委署司库八十将做得合牌烫胎房样三件持去。讫。"[5]

因此我们仍然可以判断，他的工作成果和工作方法已经深深影响了清中期的建筑设计和工程管理。

在宁寿宫工程奏折和奏销档中，列于奏报大臣之首的名字是福隆安。福隆安（？-1784），出自乾隆的孝贤纯皇后所在的富察氏家族，是乾隆朝著名的大臣傅恒之子，自己也"尚高宗女和嘉公主，授和硕额驸、御前侍卫"[6]，谥号"勤恪"。除了署名，档案中并无福隆安如何擘画管理宁寿宫花园的记载，留给我们很大推测的空间。福隆安负责了宁寿宫修建前期几乎所有最重要的奏报，而且历史资料表明，他当时是如此的忙碌：乾隆三十四年（1768年）第一次奏报宁寿宫花园设计的经费估算的奏折中，福隆安没有参与，取而代之的是内务府大臣三和，究其原因，是福隆安之父傅恒于当年从缅甸的战争前线返回京师，不久辞世，福隆安须居家守孝；《清史稿》载，乾隆三十六年，"用兵金川，总兵宋元俊劾四川总督桂林，命福隆安往谳。福隆安直桂林，抵元俊罪"，此番出差虽仅仅评议诉讼，用时不久，但从侧面说明福隆安更有繁忙的军务在身，直到后来在乾隆四十一年"复授兵部尚书，仍领工部"。工、军事务一并承担的福隆安在宁寿宫建设前期工作中具有不可替代的位置。

样式房烫样举例　资料来源：故宫博物院

1.《清史稿》，列传七十八。
2. 朱家溍，《雍正年的家具制造考》，《故宫博物院院刊》，1985 年 3 期。
3. 朱家溍，《研究清代宫史的一点体会》。载于：《故宫退食录》，373 页。北京：北京出版社，1999 年。
4. 中国第一历史档案馆 编：《圆明园》（下），1243 页《活计档》。
5. 中国第一历史档案馆 编：《圆明园》（下），1244 页《活计档》。
6.《清史稿》，列传八十八。

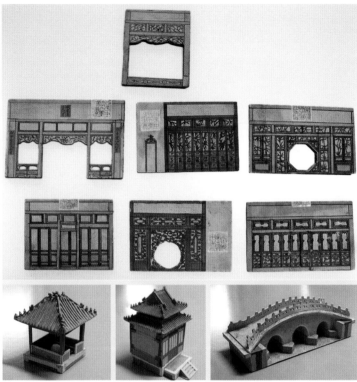

Concerning construction of the garden, it was Emperor Qianlong who originated the motifs, imposed them upon the executors, and controlled all the construction and decoration phases[2]. It was expected for emperors to proclaim themselves as most diligent individuals; certainly some were, and it will be very clear that Emperor Qianlong was particularly studious if one reades through imperial activity records and household archives.

Texts reveal abundant discussions of Qianlong's influence on all aspects of the garden, but it also should be remembered that many of Qianlong's successors are also left their marks in it. For instance it is Emperor Jiaqing who wrote most of the extant paintings or calligraphies mounted directly on walls, and it was during Emperor Guangxu's reign when Empress Dowager Cixi resided in Ningshou Gong precinct and when most of the Archives for Imperial Household Collection and Displaying were composed. Besides, it is reasonable to infer that some differences between the original records in Qianlong period and present status can be attributed to changes made by the later emperors[3].

3.4.2 Master and Master of Directing Masters

In contrast to Le Notre's fame as a designer of French gardens, there is not a name recorded in Qing archives that identifies who contributed chiefly to the design and building management, while there are many ministers' and lower officials' names which appear in memorial to the throne. What were the roles of these identified administration?

The author is quite confident to place the name Haiwang (海望, died in 1755) as the first key personage. He had played an important role in building Jianfu Gong Garden (建福宫花园) and was most influential before the construction of the Qianlong Garden. In The Drafted History of Qing Dynasty (清史稿,), one can read his biography [1].

Haiwang, form the clan of Wuya of Yellow Banner. He served the court as 内务府主事(chief director in Imperial Household Department) in Yongzheng period, and then he also served state affairs of higher grade till his death in the 20th year of Qianlong period. The late top expert in Qing history and handicraft, Mr. Zhu Jiajin had evaluated Haiwang as an skilled designer and drawer apart from a high rank official, "除管理造办处事务之外，有时还为各'作'设计作画……到雍正十年，他已升任内大臣，还时时作画"[2,3]. In imperial archives abundant paragraphs recoding Haiwang's work can be found, most of which were concerning design works for the royal. For example,

"乾隆元年正月初九日（如意馆）内大臣海望奉上谕：将画画人冷枚传来照慈宁宫画画人赏给钱粮，令伊将圆明园殿宇处所照画过热河图样，每处画图一张，绘总画一张。钦此……"[4], Haiwang was in charge of conveying Qianlong's words to the executive people.

"乾隆元年三月初十日（舆图房）……委署司库八十、柏唐阿赫申、七十九来说，内大臣海望交勤政殿地盘样一张、同乐园地盘样一张、长春仙馆地盘样一张，着照样做烫胎合牌房样。记此。于本月二十八日，委署司库八十将做得合牌烫胎样三件持去。记。"[5], Haiwang also acted as a designer and drew plans of buildings.

另外，奏折中署名的大臣还包括和珅、三和、德保、四格、刘浩等。在这些熟悉工部、户部事务的大臣中，和珅（？-1799）可以说是继福隆安之后又一代表型人物。作为历史上著名的污吏，和珅得到了乾隆的宠信但在嘉庆朝遭到了严惩。《清史稿》记载，和珅"字致齐，钮祜禄氏，满洲正红旗人。少贫无藉，为文生员……擢户部尚书、议政大臣。及复命，面陈云南盐务、钱法、边事，多称上意，并允行。授御前大臣兼都统。赐婚其子丰绅殷德为和孝公主额驸，待年行婚行。又授领侍卫内大臣，充四库全书馆正总裁，兼理藩院尚书事，宠任冠朝列矣"，可见他不仅如多数历史学者所言善于揣摩乾隆皇帝的心思，更在盐务、钱法、边事等方面确实有些见地。将他任命为户部大臣或许恰恰利用了他理财方面的长处。有趣的是在和珅覆灭之际，嘉庆皇帝罗列的他罪状中有"所钞家产，楠木房屋僭侈逾制，仿照宁寿宫制度，园寓点缀与圆明园蓬岛、瑶台无异，大罪十三"[1]，所说的宁寿宫制度既包括建筑规格也包括内檐格局，这与和珅对宁寿宫工程——尤其是内檐装修工程的了解是密不可分的。

再有，考虑到宁寿宫工程之外，当时内务府造办处等机构中还有不少有艺术修养又有管理才干的大臣，如我们今天所熟知的年希尧、唐英、沈喻等。以管窥豹，我们不难得出清中期内务府的中、高品级大臣之中有高水平的、广泛的设计参与。

或者将这些管理匠师们的大臣用古法称作"将作大匠"更能准确描述他们的工作性质。而这些"将作大匠"手下，尚有下层职掌官员——包括催督机构、厂库、技术部门、营造施工部门的头领。从品秩上看，各司、织造等处司库、园囿苑丞、库掌、委署主事等多六品衔食七八品原俸，广储司、武备院、御船处司匠、广储司、造办处、御船处催长系八品官，副职多领九品，此外，营造司、造办处司库、司匠，以及各个园囿的催长等尚为无品级的官员。这些下层职掌本身就是管理着真正为宫廷营造事务劳作的"大匠"，在他们的机构中是遍及风水、设计、制作加工各个门类的专业人员。

从设计专业的大匠说起。皇家和官方营造业的设计师——从行业性质和工作任务细节上讲，并非现代意义上的建筑师，其工作范围一方面涵盖规划设计工作，另一方面还需要完成制图任务。我们参照其他部门对"画样人"的档案记载，可以约略看出"画样"的工作和行业特点。据乾隆三年十一月三十日的奏销档记载，

> 造办处"……请于民匠内访其技艺精巧之画样人挑选一名，盔头立粉巾罩纱帽带花儿画等匠招募八名……奉旨匠人等准其添设，不必另立图记，着监造官员等亦归并养心殿造办处，即用造办处图记"[2]，

又，乾隆七年五月二十五日"画样人卢鉴、姚文瀚奉命帮助郎士宁画咸福宫藤萝架"。可以看出，此处画样人与画、做实物的工匠是不同的行当。而乾隆旨意中关于不设图记一句背后似乎有"以往匠人均单立图记"之意。营造业画样人，权责尤重，均非造办处画样人可比，然而笔者所见样式房遗图上既不见个人图记，又无一印有司院、工程处图记，样式房隶属颇难确定。我们只好大致推测，负责建筑设计，制作烫样、绘制图样的匠人可能隶属内务府管辖的一些部门：(1)内务府堂；(2)内务府营造司；(3)各个工程处，宁寿宫工程可能也单独设有工程处；(4)独立机构，

西方建筑师笔下的中国建筑 资料来源：《外国造园艺术》

The name Fulong'an (福隆安, ？—1784) appeared most frequently and prominently in the reports to the throne about construction affairs of Qianglong Garden.6 Fulong'an, whose father was one of the most important ministers at that time Fuheng (傅恒), and who married Qianlong's daughter, came from a famous Fucha clan (富察氏) and had long served for the royal family and in government office1. There was no record of Fulong'an's contributions to construction works, but as the primary household manager, his name was too often placed in the first position in memorials to be ignored. He also wrote the most important report to the throne on the work plan and budget estimation before the construction of Qianlong Garden, but his place was then taken by Sanhe (三和), since his father died in 1768 and then he was then entrusted with frequent errands outside the capital such as once in 1770 to Jinchuan in west China to mediate a dispute between local leaders.

As chiefs of the Imperial Household Department, the names of Heshen, Sanhe, Debao, Sige, Liu Hao etal, also appeared in the reports to Qinalong. While Heshen (和珅, ？—1799), gained infamy as one of the most famous corrupt ministers in the History of China and was then punished to death by Qianlong's successor, he contributed remarkably to Ningshou Gong Precinct. The Drafted History of Qing Dynasty (清史稿) records Heshen's parentage and life, from clan of Niugulu of red banner, to whom the special power of conjecturing Qianlong's mind was attributed. More important was his capacity gaining merit that must have played an important role in building Qianlong Garden. It is also interesting to note that when Heshen was indicted after Qianlong's passing away, the 13th charge was, "Having built his residence with Nan wood, and following the layout of Ningshou Gong; having decorated his gardens the same as the Immortals' Island in Yuanmingyuan"[1]. The author believes that the so called layout of Ningshou Gong not only refers to the courtyard layout, but also the interior spaces which survive in view today. The information vividly illustrates how deeply Heshen was involved in the building of Ningshou Gong Precinct.

There are other names worth mention as auxiliary contributions to the construction of the Qianlong Garden, such as Sanhe, Debao, Sige, Liu Gao. In a wider field of porcelain and other object making we have the names as Nian Xiyao (年希尧), Tang Ying(唐英) and Shen Yu (沈喻). It can be discerned from the the numerous achievements of the middle of Qing Dynasty that the involvement of high status officials in construction and handiworks was active and at the highest level.

It might be more accurate to define the above names as the master of directing masters. There were departments of lower rank under their control, serving various needs of the court, and in the departments there also were masters in various fields serving in the court: designers, hand workers, and geomantic experts.

随工而徙，服务各个工程处。著名的清宫样式雷世家所出的建筑模型、图纸、文档虽多，但几乎没有清代中期的。雷家之盛应在清道光之后。因而，我们不能过于大胆地推测雷家参与了宁寿宫花园的工程，但是从档案中记载的烫样、画样来看，当时必然有大量的专门从事设计的人员参与工作，实现乾隆的设计意图和大臣们具体的指令。

对于宁寿宫花园这样具有精美内檐装修的工程项目而言，必然有造办处的参与，供役造办处的南方匠人受到宫廷的特殊照顾，也必然参与其中[3]，史料中更是明确记载，多数最精美的内檐装修是交付两淮盐政办理的（详见下文）。总体来讲，涉及内檐装修工程的施工人员和部门的组成也比较复杂，既包括营造工种"南木作"，又有内务府造办处的各个相关匠作，甚至涉及如意馆的画师。前者如乾隆七年九月初二日《海望等奏安佑宫接迎门扣致祭祠公神请旨折》[4]提及的参加祭祀的工匠头领中便包括"南木匠　雷德、刘德珍"；次者如"木作"制作一般的室内床张等件[5]，"装修处"（后被合并）制作内檐装修[6]，"油木作"制作与装修构件[7]，其他各作配合装修制作[8]；后者如郎士宁等人绘制室内壁画[9]。这样，皇帝以各作之所长为目的，使得各个匠作的独特的装饰特点和技法便得以自然地融入到内檐装修的制作过程之中。

1.《清史稿》，列传。

2. 内务府全宗，奏销档，乾隆三年十一月三十日，卷65，册200。

3. 吴兆清：《清代造办处的机构和匠役》，《明清档案与历史研究论文选》（上），北京：国际文化出版社，1994年，第438页。

4. 中国第一历史档案馆编，《圆明园》（上），49页，《清单》。

5. 中国第一历史档案馆编，《圆明园》（下），1237页，《活计档》："雍正十二年五月初九日（木作）……据圆明园来帖内称，司库常保来说，太监沧洲传旨：着将安宁居东暖阁北面方床改做楠木床口。钦此。于本日司库常保带领匠役进内，将床口改讫。"

6. 中国第一历史档案馆编。《圆明园》（下）.1261页。《活计档》："乾隆三年九月十九日（装修处）……接得圆明园来帖内开，九月十六日，为七月二十二日员外郎常保将菱荷深处装修纸样七张交太监毛团、胡世杰、高玉呈览。奉旨：进深方窗不用，其二间房后檐方窗亦不用，再墙上格子照西峰秀色挂镜格子样做。钦此。"

7. 中国第一历史档案馆编。《圆明园》（下）。1559页。《活计档》："乾隆四十六年二月二十一日（油木作）……催长大达色、金江来说，太监鄂鲁里传旨：水法殿十一间楼下添做玻璃心紫檀木边匾式横披一面，先查玻璃画木边样，由报发往呈览。钦此。于二月二十八日，催长大达色、金江为水法殿十一间楼下添做玻璃心紫檀木边匾一面画得纸样一张，并做紫檀木边画纸样三张，由报发往呈览……"

8. 如珐琅作还曾经负责补画斑竹装修。中国第一历史档案馆编。《圆明园》（下）。1431页。《活计档》："乾隆二十九年三月十七日（匣裱作）……催长四德、笔帖式五德来说，太监胡世杰传旨：泽兰堂东近间现安文竹槅扇二槽，将不齐全处黏补，着珐琅作补画斑竹色。钦此。"

9. 中国第一历史档案馆编.《圆明园》（下）。1363页。《活计档》："乾隆二十一年十一月十四日（如意馆）……接得员外郎郎正培押帖一件内开，本月十三日郎正培奉旨：新建水法西洋楼各处棚顶、墙壁有应画处，俱著郎世宁起稿呈览。钦此。"

The designers that worked for the imperial family and the officials that supervised constructions were not exactly architects in present sense. They worked as planners and draughtsmen who had wide range of knowledge of craftsmanship, but their product did not grow into a highly specified industry. Historic documents do not make clear distinctions between a designer and a craftsmen with drawing skill, but only used the term Huayuang Ren (Painter, 画样人) to call them all. In the archives of imperial household cost report in 1738, Handiwork Department reported recruiting a draughtsman of high skill into the court as well as eight artisans of painting skills to make armets for the court. It reads, "……请于民匠内访其技艺精巧之画样人挑选一名，盔头立粉巾髯纱帽带花儿画等匠招募八名……奉旨匠人等准其添设，不必另立图记，着监造官员等亦归并养心殿造办处，即用造办处图记" [3], A record in 1742 also called those who executed tromp l'oeil painting Huayang Ren, "画样人卢鉴、姚文瀚奉命帮助郎士宁画咸福宫藤萝架". There is no doubt that designers and draughtsmen belong to an other trade than painters even in the time of Qianlong, and the vague indication only indicates that the trade of designing was not a solely independent job. Yet designers and draughtsmen in the builidng industry did have crucial responsibilities, therefore the department managing them must have a strict organization and regulations. Unfortunately the archives did not clearly record the name of the department and the relevant levels within it. Based on extant materials, the author would like to infer that the building-control department of the Qing court was not rigid, but organized and changed with differenct construction assignments. The designers' organization, the Pattern Office, would belong to any of the following administrative departments, (1) the Chief Imperial Household Department, (2) the Constructrion Bureau of the Chief Department, (3) temporarily established construction department for a specific construction task, as for the Ningshou Gong, (4) an independent Pattern Office that served works wherever these were happening. The Yangshi-Lei family left few drawings from the mid-Qing dynasty, though it had collected abundant materials while serving prominently in the court. It would be too bold to infer that the Leis' participated in building the Qianlong Garden, but there must have been some one who prepared the architectural drawings for the work, and even made models for it called Tang Yang (烫样, Model made by ironing).

Top craftsmen from construction units and departments for handiworks such as furniture and decorations were inevitably in need for such a delicate building complex. Although their names are yet to be found, it was the opinion that craftsmen from the south who were more creative and productive, and were respected in the court [1]. The branches of various kinds of handiworks that served regularly in Handiwork Department included, Nanmu Zuo [2] (fine carpentry), Muzuo [3] (carpentry), Zhuangxiu Chu [4] (interior works), Youmu Zuo [5,6] (wood finishes), and Ruyi Guan [7] (painters' studio).

3.4.3 关于李质颖

乾隆三十八、九年的几则简短的奏折揭示了两淮盐政李质颖对宁寿宫内檐装修工程的贡献。其中一则写道：

[两淮盐政]李质颖奏请陛见并交卸盐政印务事　乾隆三十八年十月六日

　　李质颖　恭请陛见
　　奏
　　奴才李质颖谨奏，为仰恳圣恩事。窃奴才前蒙皇上豢养望成擢用盐政。前岁在京仰遇，格外荣恩，垂慈教育，至厚至周，刻骨铭心，难酬万一。自叩辞回任今已二年，感激日深，孺恋倍切。伏查六七等月接奉内务府大臣寄信，奉旨交办景福宫、符望阁、萃赏楼、延趣楼、倦勤斋等五处装修。奴才已将镶嵌式样雕镂花纹，悉筹酌分别预备杂料，加工选定，晓事商人，遵照发来尺寸详慎监造。今已办有六七成，约计明岁三四月可以告竣。至监务一切应办事件，奴才俱以办理全完。现在正值闲暇之时，仰恳天恩俯准，奴才于十月二十八日将盐政印信照例暂交运使廷抡护理。奴才即束装起身，趋赴阙廷，瞻仰天颜，跪聆圣训。奴才犬马恋主之忱，得以少伸，感沐高厚恩遇于无次矣。为此恭折奏恳伏乞皇上恩允谨奏。
　　乾隆三十八年十月十八日，奉硃批不必来，钦此。

　　这则奏折很容易让人联想到《红楼梦》的作者曹雪芹家族的故事。康熙四十三、四年间，曹雪芹的爷爷曹寅任江宁织造，他与苏州织造李煦一道，为康熙南巡进献家具文玩等物，准备船只行宫。至康熙五十年，更主持办理了修造畅春园西花园房屋、挖河等项工程[1]。李质颖执掌的是两淮盐政，不是织造[2]，但为报答皇家"豢养望成"，所做的贡献颇有类似——他承办了宁寿宫中景福宫、符望阁、萃赏楼、延趣楼、倦勤斋等五处装修，其中景福宫以外的四处在宁寿宫花园。随后又承办了阅是楼东梢间方窗等项造作[3]。如此，我们可以解释为什么宁寿宫花园中符望阁、萃赏楼、延趣楼、倦勤斋四座建筑具有尤其精美的内檐装修，这些装修具有罕见的玉片、瓷片、驼骨、玻璃画、竹黄、竹丝装饰，并施用了南方擅长的漆器工艺。

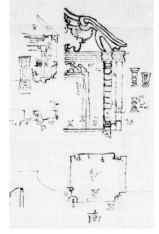
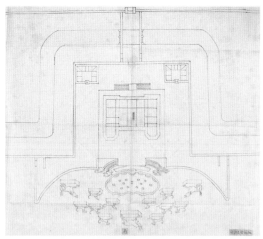
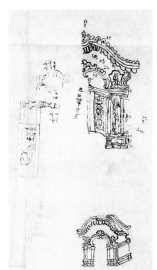
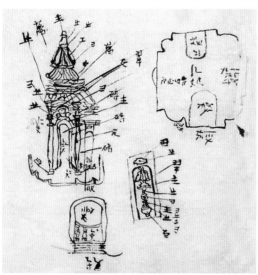

样式房图样中的西洋建筑　资料来源：中国国家图书馆 故宫博物院

1. 苏州织造李煦同样在此间扮演重要的角色。参见：故宫博物院明清档案部，《关于江宁织造曹家档案史料》，中华书局，1975 年 3 月。
2. 两淮盐政，负责淮河东南、西南流域的盐务；织造，则分江宁、苏州、扬州三处，并兼驻江南地方特务机构的功能。
3. 《宫中档乾隆朝奏折》，台北故宫博物院印行，第三十四辑，第 752 页。

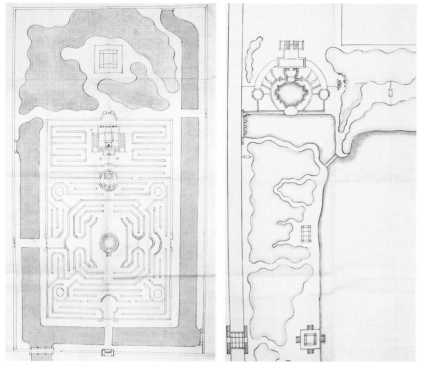

样式房图样中的西洋建筑　资料来源：中国国家图书馆

FIGURE 12. (Chambers, Designs of Chinese Buildings, plate 9.)　　FIGURE 31. A Little Chinese House. mann, Ideenmagazin, vol. 3, no. 31, pla　　FIGURE 75. Santeny, near Paris. (Krafft,

西方建筑师笔下的中国建筑　资料来源：《外国造园艺术》

3.4.3 Li Zhiying's Contribution

Brief references reveal an important name, Li Zhiying, Local Minister for Salt Industry Affairs, not only for his contribution to the interior handiworks of the Qianlong Garden, but also for his position as a south China minister. This reflects bothorigin and manner by which the interiors were furnished and decorated. One of the paragraphs records,

[两淮盐政]李质颖奏请陛见并交卸盐政印务事　乾隆三十八年十月六日

李质颖　恭请陛见

奏

奴才李质颖谨奏，为仰恳圣恩事。窃奴才前蒙皇上豢养望成擢用盐政。前岁在京仰遇，格外荣恩，垂慈教育，至厚至周，刻骨铭心，难酬万一。自叩辞回任今已二年，感激日深，孺恋倍切。伏查六七等月接奉内务府大臣寄信，奉旨交办景福宫、符望阁、萃赏楼、延趣楼、倦勤斋等五处装修。奴才已将镶嵌式样雕镂花纹，悉筹酌分别预备集料，加工选定，晓事商人，遵照发来尺寸详慎监造。今已办有六七成，约计明岁三四月可以告竣。至监务一切应办事件，奴才俱以办理全完。现在正值闲暇之时，仰恳天恩俯准，奴才于十月二十八日将盐政印信照例暂交运使延抢护理。奴才即束装起身，趋赴阙廷，瞻仰天颜，跪聆圣训。奴才犬马恋主之忱，得以少伸，感沐高厚恩遇于无次矣。为此恭折奏恳伏乞皇上恩允谨奏。

乾隆三十八年十月十八日，奉硃批不必来，钦此。

The record reminds one of the stories of the author of The Red Mansion, Cao Xueqin's family, whose ancestors prepared luxurious residential complexes for Emperor Kangxi's (Qianlong's grandfather) inspection to the Jiangnan region and for the emperor's west garden in the suburb of Beijing[8]. Li Zhiying was assigned Minister for Salt Industry in the Liang-Huai region[9]. Just before he was dismissed for an unknown reason, he demonstrated his loyalty by his hearty devotions to managing local producers and craftsmen in Jiangnan making the interior decorations in five buildings in Ningshougong, four in Qianlong Garden, including the Building of Wish Fulfilment, the Building of Gathered Enjoyment, the Building of Extended Delight, and the Lodge of Retirement. Later he also had a square window made in Yueshi Lou (in the east route of Ningshou Gong precinct)[10]. This record helps to explore the reason why the interior furnishing in the above four buildings are extraordinarily delicate and exuberant with precious inlay works of jade, porcelain, camel bone, painted glass and bamboo-inner-skin, the finest marquetry of bamboo and ebony thread, and elegant lacquer works all of which prevailed as decorative materials in the southern region.

威廉·钱伯斯（William Chambers）将中国广东地区的乡土建筑形式绘图解说，连同一些中国版画和绘画带回了欧洲，还有后来勒胡氏（Georges-Louis Le Rouge）出版刊行的中国园林资料，将中国文化带到了欧洲。与欧洲认识中国的方式不同，中国宫廷没有充分发扬西归者的所得，而是直接从旅居中国的那些受过良好教育的西方传教士那里获得相对更加直观而纯正的建筑文化。

郎士宁，这位来自意大利的传教士，作为画师长期服务于中国宫廷直至去世。他不但创作了大量宫廷绘画作品，而且培养出了很多著名的中国画师。王幼学(生卒不详)便是郎士宁的众多弟子中出色的一个，他既掌握了明暗面关系的表现技法，更领会了"线法"透视原理。他的这些本领在宁寿宫花园倦勤斋室内戏台墙壁上裱糊的通景画和天顶画上最为充分地施展了出来[1]。除了郎士宁以外，清宫著名洋画家还可以列举法国的王致诚（Jean Denis Attiret）和蒋友仁（P. Michel Benoit）、波希米亚的艾启蒙（Ignatius Sickeltart）等。

历史研究者曾就清代宫中出现西方文化展开探讨[2]，并指出"清朝的鼎盛时期，西方文化中的艺术对清宫影响最大"。大量的事例也表明，清代乾隆时期对西方建筑艺术的借鉴达到了高潮。最为典型就是在圆明三园中的圆明园和长春园中出现的西洋式建筑和建筑语汇。

首先就是长春园兴建的西洋楼景区。它的建筑设计有多个西方教士的参与，包括蒋友仁、郎世宁、王致诚、艾启蒙、汤执中等[3]。方豪先生认为，圆明园西洋楼遗迹所反映出的"若干门窗之形状，颇使人一望而知为仿波洛米尼"，"其他部分多类十六世纪末之热那亚王宫"，"壁间花饰，亦有纯然抄袭十八世纪法国之雕刻术者"，"所有岩石形、贝壳形、花叶形之雕饰及壁炉、方形柱等，则又极似路易十四时代之作风"，"圆明园西洋建筑之图式固极自由，而不宥于一式"[4]。长春园花园的平面设计则有郎世宁（1688—1766）的参与[5]，档案记载："乾隆二十一年四月十一日，如意馆，接得员外郎郎正培押帖一件，内开，本月初七日太监胡世杰传旨：长春园谐奇趣东边，著郎世宁起西洋式花园地盘样稿呈览，准时交圆明园工程处成造。钦此。于本日，郎世宁起得西洋式花园式小稿一张呈览，奉旨：照样准造，其应用西洋画处著如意馆画通景画。钦此"。西洋楼室内的陈设也属于比较典型的西方样式。罗马教廷传信部档案处藏有一则葡萄牙使臣纪实，有这样的记载："……后来富公爷带钦差去看西洋房子，很美很好的。照罗玛（罗马）样子盖的。内里陈设都是西洋来的，或照西洋样子做的"[6]。而关于内檐装修样式和工艺做法的记载尚属稀少和间接。

再有，一个有趣的现象是，在清代宫廷中的中国传统式样的建筑室内空间里，利用透视技法绘制通景画、天顶画的做法十分盛行（如图：故宫倦勤斋戏台室内效果）。如乾隆十三年八月十四日，"淡泊宁静东墙并南北两边墙，连棚顶共四面，俱着郎世宁起稿呈览"[7]；又如乾隆二十一年十一月，"新建水法西洋楼各处棚顶、墙壁有应画处，俱著郎世宁起稿呈览"[8]；再如乾隆三十年五月，郎世宁去世的前一年，尚有"玉玲珑馆新建殿五间，著郎世宁画西洋线法画"[9]的记载。如果说设计西式建筑是画作传教士的"分外工作"的话，室内设计中通景画、天顶画的设计和绘制

安德烈·波佐作品 圣依格那提欧的崇拜

1. 内务府活计档，如意馆，胶片127：乾隆三十九年二月"二十日，接得郎中德魁等押帖一件，内开本月十一日太监胡世杰传旨，宁寿宫倦勤斋西三间内，四面墙、柱子、棚顶、坎墙俱着王幼学等照德日新殿内画法一样画，钦此。"
2. 载于：清代宫史研究会 编，《清代宫史探微》，北京：紫禁城出版社，1991.199-212 页。
3. 童寯，《北京长春园西洋建筑》，《圆明园——历史、现状、论争》，北京：北京出版社，1999 年，264-285 页。
4. 方豪，《中西交通史》，岳麓出版社，1987。
5. 中国第一历史档案馆 编，《圆明园》（下），上海：上海古籍出版社，1991.1359 页。
6. 转引自：方豪，《中西交通史》，944-945 页
7. 中国第一历史档案馆 编，《圆明园》（下），1320 页。
8. 中国第一历史档案馆 编，《圆明园》（下），1363 页。
9. 中国第一历史档案馆 编，《圆明园》（下），1442 页。

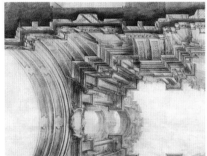

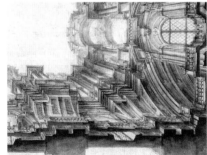

安德烈·波佐作品 圣依格那提欧的崇拜穹顶画面结构设计

3.4.4 Western Technical and Artistic Influence

William Chambers (1723—1796) brought back to Europe drafts and paintings on Canton vernacular architecture and some prints of Chinese painting, which were also published by Georges-Louis Le Rouge (1712—?). Unlike the way Europeans knew China, the Chinese way of peering into western culture was quite direct for there were important well-educated figures from the occident living and working in this eastern empire.

The Italian Guiseppe Castiglione (1688—1766), known as 郎士宁 in China, served in the court as an imperial court painter until his death. As part of his tremendous contribution to Qing Court Painting, the master had also trained many outstanding students. Wang Youxue (?—?) is among them, and it is explicitly recorded in Imperial Household Archive that he was the one who painted the trompe l'oeil murals in the Lodge of Retirement.

Other materials of the foreign catholic clergies who had served the Qing court and gained a reputation include Jean Denis Attiret and P. Michel Benoit from France and Ignatius Sickeltart form Bohemia.

First mention should be made of the site of Occidental Buildings in Changchun Yuan, for which many western clergies were invited, including Benoit, Castiglione, Attiret, Sickeltart, etc.[3] Mr. FANG Hao pointed out in his *History of Transportation Between China and the West* that many details, such as windows, metopes, fireplaces and columns, were western but from different stylistic origins such as Bolomini or Louis XIV[4]. It is acknowledged that Guiseppe Castiglione was summoned to design the plan for western garden[5]. The archive reads, "乾隆二十一年四月十一日，如意馆，接得员外郎郎正培押帖一件，内开，本月初七日太监胡世杰传旨：长春园谐奇趣东边，著郎世宁起西洋式花园地盘样稿呈览，准时交圆明园工程处成造。钦此。于本日，郎世宁起得西洋式花园式小稿一张呈览，奉旨：照样准造，其应用西洋画处著如意馆画通景画。钦此". Records of a Portugal emissary whose notes are now preserved in Vatican[6], indicates that the interiors of the occidental buildings were also occidental in style, though direct reards of the patterns and materials are extremely rare, except for some rough architectural drawings of later period.

Another amazing phenomenon is that many traditional structures in Qing court, had perspective paintings applied on walls and ceilings. The Lodge of Retirement in Qianlong Garden is one prominent surviving example, while they were abundantly used elsewehere. In 1748, "淡泊宁静东墙并南北两边墙，连棚顶共四面，俱著郎世宁起稿呈览"[7], and in 1756, "新建水法西洋楼各处棚顶、墙壁有应画处，俱著郎世宁起稿呈览"[8], and the year before Guiseppe Castiglione passed away, "玉玲珑馆新建殿五间，著郎世宁画西洋线法画"[9]. If we deem architectural design was a kind of job that quite beyond the clergies of painting skills, we definitely would agree that mural painting is their stunt in this oriental country that had also rehearsed in their previous endeavour of erecting folk churches. Mr. Nie Chongzheng from the Palace Museum had given attention to events that help to explain this. In 1688, the year that Guiseppe Castiglione was born, Andrea Pozzo (1642 ~ 1709), an Italian painter, started his masterpiece in the quarters of Sant Ignazio in Rome, Apotheoso di Ignazio. The mural is a representative work based on perspective techniques in which the composition is legible when viewed from only one position in the room (a motif can also be seen from his Illusionistic Architecture for the Vault of San Ignazio, collected in National Gallery of Art in Washington DC). Pozzo also made vault frescos in his hometown,

工作便是他们的特长。他们这种特长的发挥还建立在西方的艺术根源以及西洋做法早些时候在中国的"预热"的基础上。聂崇正先生曾经着重强调过如下史料记载：(1)在郎世宁出生的那一年，一位意大利画家安德烈·波佐（Andrea Pozzo，1642-1709）开始在罗马依格那提欧教堂绘制天顶画《圣依格那提欧的崇拜》，在1700年最终完成，"在这个作品里，他（指波佐）使用了不可思议的透视法，使壁画延续了教堂的实体，造成实际上并不存在的上层楼，惟妙惟肖的幻象。但这种真实感只存在于大厅中一个特定的视点，离开了视点，整个假的结构就好像要崩溃垮下来一样"[1]；(2)波佐也曾在郎世宁的家乡创作过教堂的装饰画，并著有《画家和建筑师的透视学》一书，"该书1698年（康熙三十七年）在罗马发行后，仅一两年就被送到了中国"[2]；(3)康熙时紫禁城外的天主教堂内，也存在天顶画，也对西方艺术走入宫廷起到了前导的作用。所以，我们说，作为文化传播者的郎世宁等西方传教士运用绘画手段创作室内空间的视觉幻觉效果的做法，是一个顺理成章的历史现象，是其发挥技艺的主要舞台。

汇总以上现象，可见在清代中期，宫廷中所吸收的西方建筑文化特点不仅包括建筑外形、水法、植物修剪等园林做法，还包括了室内壁画、天顶画的形式，以及楼梯、宝座、内檐装饰装修等室内语汇的形式和装饰做法。

至于这些西方大师们究竟给中国绘画艺术和建筑装饰绘画施加了多少影响，我们须得全面考察当时一个时代的艺术发展背景。这里有一则小故事从相反的角度说明中国传统绘画和装裱技术是怎样和原本是西方的壁画技法悄然结合的：清内务府造办处各作成做活计清档记载，郎世宁主持绘制工作时，"（乾隆七年六月初二日）建福宫敬胜斋西四间内，照半亩园糊绢，著郎士宁画藤萝"，系先糊绢，再绘制，工作方法与西方绘制壁画相似；而根据现场情况和历史档案的记载来看，当郎世宁的学生王幼学主持绘制倦勤斋通景画的时候，则是将绘制好的通景画裱糊在室内壁屉、顶屉之上[3]。"西法中化"的过程约略可辨。

3.5 宁寿宫花园历史大事记

对于宁寿宫花园的历史演变，我们应当注意到今引以为据的清宫历史档案为数众多，内容繁杂，间杂重复，需要梳理脉络；而乾隆的不时莅临和他偶尔闪现出的新灵感，以及后世帝后的使用和调整，又无疑给梳理工作增加了难度。下文将划分建筑营造、园林设施和内檐装饰装修三大项目类型，循着时间线索将宁寿宫花园的重大事件罗列出来，希望为研究者下一步的深入工作提供清晰一些的线索。由于嘉庆及其后诸帝对宁寿宫花园的改造资料不足，仅有园中少数现存文物可作线索，暂无法厘清。

1.《大英视觉艺术百科全书》.南宁：台湾大英百科股份有限公司、广西出版总社、广西美术出版社，1994年
2. 苏立文 著.莫小也 译.《明清时期中国人对西方艺术的反应》.《东西交流论坛》.上海：上海文艺出版社，1998年
3. 内务府活计档，胶片138：乾隆四十四年"如意馆，十一月初二日接得郎中保成押帖内开"

and his influential treatise *Prospettiva de'pittori a architetti*, [2] vols., Rome 1693—1700 (London 1707; Augsburg 1708—1711), which gave instructions for the painting of architectural perspectives, for stage set designs, ephemeral church decorations as well as practical advice to the designer and painter of quadrature, arrived in China only one or two years after the publication. Before their use in court, there had already been vault frescos painted in the churches built during Kangxi period in the capital. Castiglione is not only representative as a painter of western genre and perspective designs, but also as a figure who pioneered the merging of European and Chinese methods of composition and rendering.

From the above discussion, we can see that mid-Qing court absorbed various factors from western architecture, including building, water devices, plant trimming, and interior design including mural paintings.

The story of how a western master influenced Chinese paintings calls for broader research into the background and era, while the story how Castiglione's work became a vernacular style can be clearly depicted. It is explicitly written in the archive that when painters were working in Jingsheng Zhai (敬胜斋) and perhaps in the previous work in Banmuyuan (半亩园, the Chamber of Half-Acre Garden), the command was "*the Section of the Painters, mount on the wall silks; then Lang Shining (Guiseppe Castiglione), paint wisteria on it*", but when the Lodge of Retirement (倦勤斋) was decorated, it became "*the Section of the Painters bring in the painting by Wang Youxue and mount the work on the wall*"[3]. One can almost visually imagine Castiglione were facing up and fagging at raising his paintbrush rendering the highlight of a blossom, while Wang Youxue and his colleagues were debating by what means they could mount the painted works without disturbing the contents and sequence.

3.5 Memorabilia of Qianlong Garden

However numerous and out-of-order, the Qing court archives reflect that the garden was built in a ready to change mode in response to the unexpected visits of Qianlong with his aflutter afflatuses. Yet there are still clear vestiges of when and how the structures were built, when and how the gardens were composed, and when and how the interiors were decorated. Compilation and analyses of the important constructional events of the garden would benefit not only studies in general aspects, but also affect a deep understanding of what desires for the complex lay in Qianlong's heart. The researchers have not yet found enough historic material to identify the changes and construction events after the Qianlong period, therefore there more work remains to be done for comparing limited old documentations with relics and vestiges in the Garden itself.

3.5.1 建筑和构筑物

年份	历史记载	涉及建筑及要点	资料出处
1770	乾隆三十五年十一月二十六日，奴才三和英廉四格谨奏，奴才等遵旨修理宁寿宫工程，现今通盘查估，刘浩旧料抵对清楚新料始无浮糜…… 乾隆三十七年十一月……内奴才等遵旨修建宁寿宫殿宇房座，节次烫样呈览，荷蒙圣明指示，钦遵办理	所有宁寿宫建筑 另参见乾隆三十八年工程将行告竣关于销算耗羡的奏销档	奏销档胶片 94 奏销档胶片 99 第 315 册
1771	乾隆三十六年正月二十九日，臣福隆安三和英廉刘浩四格谨奏为奏请银两事臣等遵旨修理宁寿宫工程 所有今岁需修后面殿座并院内堆做山石以及砌拆北面大墙等工现在抵对旧料详细估计一时难得确数业经奏请先向广储司支领银两五万两在案……	拆修旧有建筑（原宁寿宫等）； 院内叠石假山工程； 重砌北大墙	奏销档胶片 95
	乾隆三十六年十一月二十六日，臣福隆安三和英廉刘浩四格谨奏为奏闻事臣等恭办宁寿宫中路后所殿宇工程应用大件杞梁自二丈八尺至四丈不等…现今四川省解运到通州……	宁寿宫后部中路养性殿等建筑	奏销档胶片 97
1772	乾隆三十七年十一月……奴才福隆安三和英廉刘浩四格谨奏，为奏闻估需工料钱粮数目事……请先修建后路殿座，各归各款二层……西边三友轩三间……西路，衍祺门三间，抑斋二间，矩亭一座，撷芳亭一座，重檐三出憩赏亭一座，古华轩三间，旭辉楼三间，前檐遂初堂五间，西边延趣楼三间，耸秀亭一座，萃赏楼五间，转角楼仿玉壶冰六间，重檐符望阁二十五间，后檐倦勤斋九间，西边玉粹轩三间，叠落楼竹香馆三间……西路符望阁前山上补建亭座、改堆山石……	宁寿宫后路各座殿宇，包括花园中各座建筑 "符望阁前山上补建亭座、改堆山石"等语值得注意，或为宁寿宫花园后院与建福宫不同所在	奏销档胶片 99 第 315 册
1773	乾隆三十八年十月（金玉作）二十一日接得笔帖式海寿持来堂抄一件内开宁寿宫工程处奏内开各殿外檐窗扇应用玻璃交造办处预备俱于临期安设等因来随回明额附福大人英金总管珠观准行记此	宁寿宫各座建筑门窗安装玻璃	内务府档胶片 127
	乾隆三十八年十一月十九日臣福隆安英廉刘浩四格谨奏…今后路工程已将告成……	整体工程即将完竣的报告	奏销档胶片 101
1774	乾隆三十九年（金玉作）十一月初七日……太监胡世杰传旨，新建宁寿宫各殿内，所有应安玻璃窗户，并镶墙玻璃镜等，俱着画样呈览，查库贮现有的玻璃对尺寸安用，如有不足者开写尺寸清单，奏明粤海关要……	设计并绘制建筑玻璃窗、镜子图样； 下令从广东海关进玻璃材料	内务府活计档胶片 129，（胶片 130 为关于倦勤斋档案）
1775	乾隆四十年五月二十四日臣福隆安英廉刘浩四格谨奏，为奏闻需估钱粮数目事恭查修建宁寿宫工程，先经臣等第次奏明，后三路殿座原续估需工料银七十六万五千八百八两二钱三分四厘……今据该管工监督等呈报，所有原续估外，第次遵奉御旨……乐寿堂西山外添做景点楼一座……符望阁南院内改墁冰纹石地面……养性门前添做暗沟一道……	涉及花园所有建筑； 如亭，颐和轩西符望阁东，为演戏之所； 符望南院落地面改墁； 花园以南添排水沟	奏销档胶片 105
1777	乾隆四十二年七月初二日臣福隆安英廉和绅刘浩谨奏为奏闻续需钱粮数目事……拆改抑斋一座计二间，添后廊进深四尺，挪盖矩亭一座，游廊五间，改盖游廊二间，添盖承廊一间……成堆山洞，添建仙台一座，罩门券三座，扒头券一座，如意券龛一座，安砌青白石角柱平水券脸过梁压面，汉白玉石栏板柱子，花斑石台面，细砖发券成砌台幇等项……墙外东北二面洩水暗沟一道，通长一百六十五丈二尺，口宽二尺，均深三尺二寸，沟幇下截并棚盖，俱豆渣石，背底背后及上截沟幇，俱灰砌城砖……	改造抑斋； 改造游廊和矩亭； 加建承露台、山洞； 宁寿宫东墙外添修排水沟（距花园较远）	奏销档胶片 108
1778	乾隆四十三年七月（记事录）二十二日，笔帖式苏楞额持来汉字知会一件，内开宁寿宫工程处为知会事……今本工已办造得匾工精清汉字一百八十一个，大小宝二十九个，相应移送贵处镀金，完日送工以便成锭可也……	制作宁寿宫各座建筑匾额铜字	内务府活计档胶片 134
1779	乾隆四十四年三月初一日奴才福隆安、英廉、和珅谨奏为请旨事……今查宁寿宫前后路殿宇房屋共计一千一百八十三间并成堆各处山石俱已如式敬谨成修完竣，至原估外节奉御旨添改一切活计……统俟将来工竣时按照做过活计详细查核一并奏销	工程基本完竣；添改工程即将完成	奏销档胶片 109
1817	嘉庆二十二年七月……古华轩敞厅三间揭瓦，延趣楼三间粘修，上檐石天桥遵旨拆去，补安琉璃挂檐……倦勤斋殿九间揭瓦，西山有碍游廊三间拆盖以及油漆彩画添补琉璃料件等项工程如式修理完竣。于嘉庆二十二年六月初六日恭折奏请钦派大臣查验收工	后期重要的改造工程。其中尤以拆除延趣楼的石桥对园林格局影响为大	奏案 05-0592-097

新阁谭瑢
故宫博物院宁寿宫花园历史研究与文物保护规划

Year	Event & Record	Building Involved	Provenance
1777	Minor rebuilding and infrastructure supplementary works, 乾隆四十二年七月初二日臣福隆安英廉和绅刘浩诸逢奏为奏闻续需钱粮数目事……拆改抑斋一座计二间，添后廊进深四尺，挪盖矩亭一座，游廊五间，改盖游廊二间，添盖游廊一间……成堆山洞，添建仙台一座，罩门券三座，扒头券一座，如意券龛一座，安砌青白石角柱平水券脸于梁庄面，汉白玉石栏板柱子，花斑石台面，细砖发券成砌台帮等项……墙外东北二面洩水暗沟一道，通长一百六十五丈二尺，口宽二尺，均深三尺二寸，沟帮下截并棚盖，俱豆渣石，背底背后及上截沟帮，俱灰砌城砖……	Chamber of Self Constraint; Corridors; Dew platform and the vaulted cell under it; An underground drain line	AIHE Film 108
1778	On making tablets for buildings, 乾隆四十三年七月（记事录）二十二日，笔帖式苏楞额持来汉字知会一件，内开宁寿宫工程处为知会事……今本工已办造得匾工铜清汉字一百八十一个，大小宝二十九个，相应移送贵处镀金，完日送工以便成锭可也……	Making copper Han and Manchu characters for the tablets of all buildings	AIHH Film 134
1779	Construction cost report after the completion of major building works, 乾隆四十四年三月初一日奴才福隆安、英廉、和珅谨奏为请旨事……今查宁寿宫前后路殿宇房屋共计一千一百八十三间并成堆各处山石俱已如式敬谨成修完竣，至原估续估之外节奉御旨添改一切活计……统俟将来工竣时按照做过活计详细查核一并奏销……	Completion of all major construction works	AIHE Film 109
1817	Repairs and reconstructions in Jiaqing's reign, 嘉庆二十二年七月……古华轩敞厅三间揭瓦，延趣楼三间粘修，上檐石天桥遵旨拆去，补安琉璃挂檐……倦勤斋殿九间揭瓦，西山有碴游廊三间拆盖以及油漆彩画添补琉璃料件等项工程如式修理完竣。于嘉庆二十二年六月初六日恭折奏请钦派大臣查验收工	Guhua Xuan, Yanqu Lou and Juanqin Zhai, among which the removal of the bridge over the upper floor of Yanqu Lou is the most substantial to the function and lauout of the Qianlong Garden	Report to the Throne 05-0592-097

3.5.1 Buildings and Structures

Year	Event & Record	Building Involved	Provenance
1770	Design and estimation of cost for the entire construction work of Ningshou Gong Precinct, 乾隆三十五年十一月二十六日……奴才等遵旨修理宁寿宫工程，现今通盘查估，务将旧料抵对清楚新料始无浮糜……乾隆三十七年十一月……内奴才等遵旨修建宁寿宫殿宇房座，节次烫样呈览……	All buildings in Ningshou Gong precinct; See also 1772 report	Archive on Imperial Household Expenditure (IHEA) IHEA Film 99; Vol. 315
1771	Estimation of cost, 乾隆三十六年正月二十九日，臣……谨奏为奏请银两事臣等遵旨修理宁寿宫工程所有今岁拆修后面殿座并院内堆做山石以及砌拆北面大墙等工现在抵对旧料详细估计一时难得确数业经奏请先向广储司支领银两五万两在案……	Removing old buildings; Rockery works; Rebuilding north wall	AIHE Film 95
1771	Material preparation, 乾隆三十六年十一月二十六日，臣……谨奏为奏办事臣等恭办宁寿宫中路后所殿宇工程应用大件杞梁自二丈八尺至四丈不等……现今四川省解运到通州……	Buildings along the rear middle route	AIHE Film 97
1772	Construction sequence and cost control, 乾隆三十七年十一月……奴才……谨奏……请先修建后路殿座，各归各款……二层……西边三友轩三间……西路，衍祺门三间，抑斋二间，矩亭一座，撷芳亭一座，重檐三出递赏亭六间，古华轩三间，旭辉亭三间，前檐遂初堂五间，西边延趣楼三间，耸秀亭一座，萃赏楼五间，转角楼仿玉壶冰六间，重檐符望阁二十五间，后檐倦勤斋九间，西边玉萃轩三间，叠落楼竹香馆三间……西路符望阁前山上补建亭座、改堆山石……	All garden buildings, and grouping of the buildings	AIHE Film 99; Vol. 315
1773	Mounting glass on windows, 乾隆三十八年十月（金玉作）二十一日接得笔帖式海寿持来堂抄一件内开宁寿宫工程处拆奏内开各殿外檐窗扇应用玻璃交造办处预备俱于临期安设等因前来随回明额附福大人英金总管珠观准行记此	Mounting glass on windows wherever necessary	AIHE Film 127
1773	Garden reaching completion, 乾隆三十八年十一月十九日臣……谨奏……今后路工程已将告成……	Reaching completion of buildings in rear part, including garden buildings	AIHE Film 101
1774	Supplementing wanted glass from Canton customs, 乾隆三十九年（金玉作）十一月初七日……太监胡世杰传旨，新建宁寿宫各殿内，所有应安玻璃窗户，并镶墙玻璃镜等，俱着画样呈览，查库贮现有的玻璃对尺寸安用，如有不足者开写尺寸清单，奏明粤海关等……	Draw pattern designs for all glass works on windows and mirrors; Ask for wanted glass from Canton customs	Archives on Imperial Household Handiworks (AIHH) Film 129, (130 For Juanqin Zhai)
1775	Supplementary constructions, 乾隆四十年五月二十四日臣福隆安英廉刘浩四格谨奏为奏闻需估钱粮数目事恭查修建宁寿宫工程，先经估等第次奏明，后三路殿座原续估需工料银七十六万五千八百八十二两二钱三分四厘……今据该管工监督等呈报，所有原续估外，第次遵奉御旨……乐寿堂西山外添做景点楼一座……符望阁南院内改墁冰纹石地面……养性门前添做暗沟一道……	All garden buildings; Ru Ting (an adjacent outside building); The Building of Wish and Reality in Accordance (changing pavement); Construction of an underground drain line	AIHE Film 105

3.5.2 园林设施

年份	历史记载	涉及园林设施及要点	资料出处
1772	乾隆三十七年六月初八日，奴才三和英廉刘浩四格谨奏为奏闻估需工料银两数目事……宁寿宫拆运三百七十七块其所拆分位补堆青山石并地基创槽下柏木地丁旧城砖掐当山洞石壁背后巩打灰黄土起创土山等项所用黄太湖石青山石及丁铁油灰杂料并山子匠扛夫工价运价预难确估……遵照烫样堆做………	叠石，中留山洞、通道等	奏销档胶片
1773	乾隆三十八年四月(铸炉处)二十一日宁寿宫各院安设水缸	庭院安设铜缸	内务府活计档胶片 127
	乾隆三十八年七月(铸炉处)二十九日宁寿宫后路各殿座前陈设周围添安铜栏杆	庭院陈设石座添加栏杆	内务府活计档胶片 127
	乾隆三十八年十二月初四日奴才英廉刘浩金辉谨奏为奏销工料银两铜斤事遵旨成造宁寿宫后所各殿宇院内安设烧古铜缸二十八件……	奏报庭院铜缸所耗材料	奏销档胶片
1777	乾隆四十二年七月初二日臣福隆安、英廉、和绅、刘浩谨奏、为奏闻续需钱粮数目事……各座柏木刻字镶条二副，字画镶条二十二副，并院内梅花罩五座，铜海杉木盖五十二个，各院内添安石座二十分……禊赏亭南边加堆太湖山石……	匾额及刻字；花卉保护罩；庭院陈设石座；一进院添加叠石	奏销档胶片 108
1780	乾隆四十五年十月(金玉作)于十月二十九日……太监厄鲁里传旨倦勤斋阶前东西两稍间阶前前石座一对着挪在符望阁东门阶前对东边游廊阶前石座安设其位分著将西门外拆下石座一对安设交铸炉处照符望阁阶前铜瓶配铸一对安设再倦勤斋垂带两边石座上珐琅铜瓶一对着撤去交造办处查石英二块安设……	调整四进院陈设及石座位置等	内务府活计档胶片 139

3.5.2 Garden Features

Year	Event & Record	Garden Features Involved	Provenance
1772	Cost estimation for the rockery works, 乾隆三十七年六月初八日，奴才三和英廉刘浩四格谨奏为奏闻估需工料银两数目事……宁寿宫拆运三百七十七块其所拆分位补堆青山石并地基创槽下柏木地丁旧城砖挡当山洞石壁背后巩打灰黄土起创土山等项所用黄太湖石青山石及丁铁油灰杂料并山子匠扛夫工价运价预难确估……遵照烫样堆做……	Rockery	AIHE Film
1773	Placing in all courtyards in Ningshou Gong copper vats, 乾隆三十八年四月 (铸炉处) 二十一日宁寿宫各院安设水缸	Placing copper vats in courtyards	AIHH Film 127
1773	Adding copper balustrades on pedestals for displaying, 乾隆三十八年七月 (铸炉处) 二十九日宁寿宫后路各殿座前陈设周围添安铜栏杆	Pedestals for displaying	AIHH Film 127
1773	Cost estimation for copper vats, 乾隆三十八年十二月初四日奴才英廉刘浩金辉谨奏为奏销工料银两铜斤事遵旨成造宁寿宫后所各殿宇院内安设烧古铜缸二十八件……	Cost report for copper vats	AIHE Film
1777	Cost estimation for courtyard furnishings, such as 乾隆四十二年七月初二日臣福隆安、英廉、和绅、刘浩谨奏、为奏闻续需钱粮数目事……各座柏木刻字镶条二副，字画镶条二十二副，并院内梅花罩五座，铜海杉木盖五十二个，各院内添安石座二十分……禊赏亭南边加堆太湖山石……	Wood tablets of calligraphy works; Frameworks for flowers and trees; Stone pedestals; Rockery south to Floating Cup Pavilion	AIHE Film 108

3.5.3 内檐装修

年份	历史记载	涉及内檐装修及要点	资料出处
1773	乾隆三十八年十月六日李质颖恭请陛见……伏查六七等月接奉内务府大臣寄信，奉旨交办景福宫、符望阁、萃赏楼、延趣楼、倦勤斋五处装修。奴才已将镶嵌式样雕镂花纹，悉筹酌的分别预备集料，加工选定，晓事商人，遵照发来尺寸详慎监造。今已办有六七成，约计明岁三四月可以告竣……	两淮盐政承办宁寿宫五座建筑之内檐装修	《乾隆朝汉文录副奏折》档号0133-091 缩微号009-1937-1938
自1774	（略）参见：1.2.3节；附件3	倦勤斋、玉粹轩、云光楼、遂初堂等处	内务府活计档胶片127,128,129,132,133
1774	乾隆三十九年（做钟处）正月二十三日催长福明持来押帖内开本月二十一日太监胡世杰传旨着延春阁现设大墙表样式成做大墙表一分得时在宁寿宫符望阁陈设钦此……	符望阁内墙面安装钟表	内务府活计档胶片128
1774	乾隆三十九年（行文）十二月十六日，员外郎四德、库掌五德、笔帖式福庆来说，太监胡世杰传旨，著福隆安、英廉将宁寿宫殿宇内有欧化、迎手、靠背、坐褥之处，查明数目，量准尺寸，开写清单分发三处织造、盐政、钞关等处成做，算伊贡利呈进，钦此……	定做宁寿宫各座殿宇室内铺垫	内务府活计档胶片128
1774	乾隆三十九年（记事录）十一月二十二日……福、英、刘、四谨奏恭查宁寿宫后路各殿宇楼座室内里装修均系遵旨发交两淮盐政李质颖办造送工现在俱已敬谨安装齐全惟是京师风土高燥与南方润湿情形不同各项装修俱系硬木镶嵌成做值冬令间有离缝走错在所嵌花结漆地等项俱微有爆裂脱落之处奴才等详细查看其硬木漆地活计有离缝走错者即令该工监督楦缝找补收拾完整其玉铜花结有脱落者亦交造办处随时修整务取妥固外惟花结内有磁片一项虽迸裂只有三小块但在京一时难于置办……	由两淮盐政承办宁寿宫中符望阁等五座建筑之装修由于气候不合破坏及修补事	内务府活计档胶片128
1774	（略）参见附件3	降旨造办宁寿宫中所有建筑室内毡毯等项铺垫	内务府活计档胶片129,130
自1775	乾隆四十年三月（如意馆）初十日，接得员外郎六格押贴，内开三月初三日首领董五经交宣纸三十七张。传旨，将宣纸交如意馆，着黄念、杨大章、顾全、贾全等画……	降旨绘制宁寿宫各座建筑室内贴落画	内务府活计档胶片129
自1775	（略）参见附件3	宁寿宫各座建筑室内添设家具	内务府活计档胶片130
1775	乾隆四十年五月二十四日臣福隆安、英廉、刘浩、四格谨奏，为闻需估钱粮数目事恭查修建宁寿宫工程……古华轩、碧螺梅花亭内里添安楠柏木天花……养性殿、乐寿堂、三友轩、颐和轩、景祺阁、阅是楼、符望阁、延趣楼、抑斋、遂初堂东配殿添配硬木装修等项……	古华轩添安楠木雕刻天花；碧螺亭添安楠木雕刻天花；养性殿、乐寿堂、三友轩、颐和轩、景祺阁、阅是楼、符望阁、延趣楼、抑斋、遂初堂东配殿添配硬木装修。可见在两淮盐政承办之外尚须内务府造办处之工	奏销档胶片105

年份	历史记载	涉及内檐装修及要点	资料出处
1776	乾隆四十一年（灯裁作）二月初六日……太监胡世杰传旨，宁寿宫中一路应挂之神画样呈览，准时发往苏州成做……倦勤斋……堆门神照数交苏州成做，画门神照数交造办处画……	发交苏州、造办处承办门神等	内务府活计档胶片131，旨意底档编号
1776	乾隆四十一年十二月二十日总管内务府谨奏，为奏闻报销用过缎纱布正事……宁寿宫新添养性殿，乐寿堂、颐和轩、景福宫、遂初堂、倦勤斋等座，应行安设帐幔、大褥、迎手、靠背、坐褥等项共计……	宁寿宫各座建筑室内铺垫等项报销事宜	奏销档胶片
1777	乾隆四十二年七月初二日臣福隆安、英廉、和珅、刘浩谨奏，为奏闻续需钱粮数目事……遂初堂，紫檀木三镶门口一座，东配殿插屏一座，西配殿松木柜十四座，木厢一个，冕柜一座。萃赏楼，楠木佛座七分。转角楼，花梨木包镶佛座一分。倦勤斋，木门口二座……	宁寿宫各座殿宇添置室内装饰、陈设座等	奏销档胶片108
1779	乾隆四十四年如意馆十一月初二日……倦勤斋通景画已得九成未完者一成本月可以完工但贴落画片计需二十余日方能完毕今拟请将已画得通景棚顶画片今伊兰泰赵士恒带学手佰唐阿等敬谨持往倦勤斋先期如式贴落其现画未完风窗药栏门一座已画得均有五六成未完者四五成着王儒学黄明询陈玺带学手佰唐阿等如期画庶可无惧接续贴落其贴落画片需用脚手架子向由工程处搭做奏明照例交工程处预备妥协即前往贴落……	倦勤斋通景画最后的绘制与贴裱	内务府活计档胶片138
自1784	（略）参见附件3	宁寿宫各座建筑室内贴落画和对联等项	内务府活计档胶片
1792	乾隆五十八年记事录 八月初八日……倦勤斋内西四间画藤萝顶棚饰墙油饰脱落呈报总理档房转行该处修理等因来相应移咨营造司即速修理等因前来倦勤斋殿内西四间画藤萝顶棚板墙油饰俱脱落今本司拟将后檐添做杉木壁子系本司成做其揭画片裱糊地仗咨行	倦勤斋内藤萝天画顶脱落；倦勤斋内板墙油饰（画？）脱落；修补上述二项事宜（拟添杉木壁子）	内务府活计档胶片
1792	乾隆五十八年八月日奉金大人、总管话谕如意馆应画倦勤斋内藤萝顶棚，著于本月二十五日之内即行完竣，断不可悞，特谕	倦勤斋内天顶画（笔者判断为上层看戏宝座顶棚部分及脱落部分）的绘制、修理与贴裱	内务府堂谕堂交第一包乾隆15-60年

Year	Event & Record	Interior Furnishings	Provenance
1776	Command supplementary decorations to be made, 乾隆四十一年（灯裁作）二月初六日……太监胡世杰传旨，宁寿宫中一路应挂之神画样呈览，准时发往苏州成作……倦勤斋……堆门神照数交苏州成做，画门神照数交造办处画……	Spirit figures on door leafs	AIHH Film 131, Archive on Imperial Edict
1776	Cost report for textile works, 乾隆四十一年十二月二十日总管内务府谨奏，为奏闻报销用过缎纱布疋事……宁寿宫新建养性殿，乐寿堂、颐和轩、景福宫、遂初堂、倦勤斋等座，应行安设帐幔、大褥、迎手、靠背、坐褥等项活计……	All buildings in Ningshou Gong	AIHH Film 106
1777	Cost report for furniture pieces and door frames, 乾隆四十二年七月初二日臣福隆安、英廉、和珅、刘浩谨奏，为奏闻续需钱粮数目事……遂初堂，紫檀木三镶门口一座，东配殿插屏一座，西配殿松木柜十四座，木厢一个，龛柜一座。萃赏楼，楠木佛座七分。转角楼，花梨木包镶佛座一分。倦勤斋，木门口二座……	All buildings in Qianlong Garden	AIHE Film 108
1779	Mounting Tromp l'oeil onto the walls in the Lodge of Retirement, 乾隆四十四年如意馆十一月初二日……倦勤斋通景画已得九成未完者一成本月可以完工但贴落画片计需二十余日方能完毕今拟请将已画得通景棚顶画片今令伊兰泰赵士恒带学千佰唐阿等敬谨持往倦勤斋先期如式贴落其现画未完风窗栏门一座已画得均有五六成未完者四五成者王儒学黄明询陈玺带学千佰唐阿等如期赴画庶可无悮接续贴落其贴落画片需用脚手架子向由工程处搭做奏明照例交工程处预备妥协即前往贴落……	Tromp l'oeil in the Lodge of Retirement	AIHH Film 138
From 1784	Interior decorative paintings and tablets		AIHH Film
1792	Repair wisteria ceiling tromp l'oeil in the Lodge of Retirement, 乾隆五十八年记事录八月初八日……倦勤斋殿内西间画藤萝顶棚板墙油饰脱落呈报总理档房转行该处修理等因前来相应移咨营造司即速修理等因前来查倦勤斋殿内西间画藤萝顶棚板墙油饰俱脱落今本司泥将后檐添做杉木壁子系本司成做其揭画片裱糊地仗咨行	The Lodge of Retirement	AIHH Film 152
1792	Command wisteria ceiling tromp l'oeil work be finished soon, 乾隆五十八年八月日奉金大人，总管话谕如意馆应画倦勤斋内画藤萝顶棚，著务于本月二十五日之内即行完捷，断不可悮，特谕	The Lodge of Retirement	Archive on Household Dept. Commands Package 1: Qianlong Year 15-60

3.5.3 Interior Furnishings

Year	Event & Record	Interior Furnishings Involved	Provenance
1773	Ordering interior screens to be managed by Li Zhiying and to be made in south China, 乾隆三十八年十月六日李质颖恭请陛见……伏查六七等月接奉内务府大臣寄信，奉旨交办景福宫、符望楼、萃赏楼、延趣楼、倦勤斋五处装修。奴才已将镶嵌样雕镂花纹，悉筹酌分别预备集料，加工选定，晓事商人，遵照来尺寸详慎监造。今已办有六七成，约计明岁三四月可以告竣……	Interior screenings and decorations for Fuwang Ge, Cuishang Lou, Yanqu Lou and Juanqin Zhai in the Ningshou Gong Garden, and Jingfu Gong in the neighbourhood courtyard.	Memorial Ectypes in Mandarin: 0133-091; Film 009-1937-1938
From 1774	Orders painters' studio to paint the interior trompl'oeil, see Chapter 3	Tromp l'oeil paintings in the Lodge of Retirement and other buildings	AIHH Film 127, 128, 129, 132, 133
1774	Making a wall-clock, 乾隆三十九年（做钟处）正月二十三日催长福明持来押帖内开本月二十一日太监胡世杰传旨着延春阁现设大墙表样式成做大墙表一分得时在宁寿符望阁陈设钦此……	The Building of Wish and Reality in Accordance	AIHH Film 128
1774	Calculating and ordering textile works for buildings in entire Ningshou Gong, 乾隆三十九年（行文）十二月十六日，员外郎四德、库掌五德、笔帖式福庆来说，太监胡世杰传旨，著福隆安、英廉将宁寿宫殿宇内有欧化、迎手、靠背、坐褥之处，查明数目，量准尺寸，开写清单分发三处织造、盐政、钞关等处成做，算伊贡内呈进，钦此……	All buildings in Ningshou Gong	AIHH Film 128
1774	Repairing interior screens made in south China, which was damaged because of change of humidity, 乾隆三十九年（记事录）十一月二十二日……福、英、刘、四谨奏恭查宁寿宫后路各殿宇楼座内里装修均系遵旨发交两淮盐政李质颖办造送工现在俱已敬谨安装齐全惟是京师风土高燥与南方润湿情形不同各项装修俱系硬木镶嵌成做现值冬令间有离缝走错并所嵌花结漆地等项微有爆裂脱落之处奴才等详细查看其硬木漆地活计有离缝走错者即令该工监督楦缝找补收拾完整其玉铜花结有脱落者亦交造办处随时修整务取妥固外惟花结内有磁片一项虽迸裂只有三小块但在京一时难于置办……	Decoration came from the south	AIHH Film 128
From 1775	Command felts and curtains to be made.	All garden buildings	AIHH Film 129, 130
From 1775	Tie'lou to be painted for interior wall decoration, 乾隆四十年三月（如意馆）初十日，接得员外郎六格押贴，内开三月初三日首领董五经交宣纸三十七张。传旨，将宣纸交如意馆，着黄念、杨大章、顾全、贾全等画……	All garden buildings	AIHH Film 129
From 1775	Begin to add pieces of furniture in buildings		AIHH Film 130
1775	Installing and making interior ceilings and screens, 乾隆四十年五月二十四日臣福隆安、英廉、刘浩、四格谨奏，为闻需估钱粮数目事恭查修建宁寿宫工程……古华轩、碧螺梅花亭内里添安楠柏木大花……养性殿、乐寿堂、三友轩、颐和轩、景祺阁、阅是楼、符望阁、延趣楼、抑斋、遂初堂东配殿西配殿添配硬木装修等项……	Nan-wood-carving ceiling in the Pavilion of Ancient Flower; Nan-wood-carving ceiling in the Pavilion of Jade Conch; Adding screens in the Building of Wish and Reality in Accordance, the Building of Extended Delight, the Chamber of Self Constraint, east Hall of the Hall of Original Wish Fulfillment and etc	AIHE Film 105

第四章
宁寿宫花园及其内容的独特价值

4.1 宁寿宫花园与紫禁城

　　紫禁城中现存格局完整的花园共计四座：内廷后中路的御花园、太后太妃生活区的慈宁宫花园、乾清宫以西的建福宫花园和宁寿宫区的宁寿宫花园（俗称乾隆花园）。前两座花园始建于明代，经历了多次历史改造，始终是紫禁城中重要的组成部分。园林是中国宫殿建筑群中不可缺少的部分，对于帝王自己和那些上代帝王的遗孀——尤其是当时皇帝的生母而言，园林更是他们喜至之所，因此园林中又往往专设太后太妃们所用的宗教、游观空间。此二者确是"皇家"的花园。四座花园中的后两座都是在乾隆皇帝的决定下修建的，只是修建目的各有不同。由于乾西二所所在区域曾经是乾隆青年时代居住的地方，整个乾西五所便在乾隆登基后得到了改造，西四五所被改为了建福宫花园。而后，乾隆皇帝又决定为自己归政后的生活建造一座太上皇宫，宁寿宫花园理所当然地被规划成为年迈的乾隆专用的花园。这一早一晚两座乾隆的花园也确实具有相似的基因。此二者至少在乾隆时期主要属于乾隆个人。

　　具体而言，宁寿宫花园具有浓厚的乾隆个人色彩，反映乾隆的精神世界；他所在的宁寿宫一区也是唯一现存的太上皇宫，宁寿宫所贯彻的指导思想也都是出于乾隆皇帝本人。也正因如此，宁寿宫花园恰当地被俗称为乾隆花园。说到乾隆归政的原因，历史记载是非常明确的，无庸赘言；但说到乾隆对他归政后生活的设想，则反映在宁寿宫整体布局之中。

　　首先可以说乾隆得到他继任者的绝对尊重，即使在训政期间也在帝国中拥有绝对权威。正如许多学者所指出的，整个宁寿宫因而被规划为紫禁城核心区的缩影。在此有必要重新强调一下到底宁寿宫中各座主要建筑是如何与紫禁城核心建筑进行规划呼应的。如果要进行建筑的一一对照的话，乾隆皇帝是将整个太上皇宫与皇帝的后宫作为并列骈置的同等规格来设计的。这一点尤其体现在宁寿宫前半部：皇极殿仿乾清宫、宁寿宫仿坤宁宫；宁寿宫后部的第一座殿宇养性殿则仿照雍正以来皇帝的正寝养心殿，只不过又将原来养心殿相对于紫禁城偏西的位置在宁寿宫中调整至中轴线上——这种布局上的变化实际上反映出乾隆对于宫殿规制的理解——"以大清门至午门间区域为外朝，以自午门、经太和门至乾清门区域为治朝，以乾清内区域为燕朝"[1]，所得到的结果也与古代宫殿制度形成比较恰当的吻合。至于宁寿宫后部花园的各座建筑，如符望阁仿延春阁、景福宫仿静怡轩、梵华楼和佛日楼仿慧曜楼和吉云楼、倦勤斋仿敬胜斋等，则可以归结为下一点。

　　其次，乾隆在宁寿宫花园中"填满"了他所钟爱的花园的片段、建筑和室内装修装饰，在这一点上，乾隆无疑表现出了比较强烈的怀旧情绪，换言之，或许是期冀在归政后仍然在同以前一样的生活空间中，过着同以前一样的没有羁绊的生活。无论是对建福宫花园的追仿，还是照搬长春园含经堂的做法都是这种情绪或者说是期望的直接反映。

4.2 宁寿宫花园与乾隆时期的花园

　　总体而言，中国古典园林与西方古代造园相比，在建筑与园艺相结合方面，更为综合，园林的功能属性更加复杂。具体而言，中国历史上曾经出现过不同的园林类型，也有不同的角度区分各种园林，诸如可以按照皇家园林和文人园林来区分，也可以根据地域的风格将园林归为南方和北方。谈及宁寿宫花园，我们还可以引用《园冶》中的一个说法，造园"三分在匠人，七分在主人"[2]。乾隆这位众多园林的真正主人，他所起到的七分作用到底在哪里呢？理解乾隆头脑中"园林"的真正含义，发现乾隆在宁寿宫花园里到底实现了多少他的"园林"的概念，是全面理解宁寿宫花园历史价值的基础，也是确立保护宁寿宫花园基本策略的基础。

4.2.1 乾隆时期兴建的皇家御苑及其共性

　　在此须系统地回顾一下乾隆这位风度优雅的皇帝的"造园观"。

　　第一，乾隆是非常喜好汉族文化的—尤其是传统汉语文学。他总是在他的诗文中—以及他的园林中—"填充"大量的典故，以至于使他所作的御制诗文有些晦涩艰深。特别是在造园方面，品题固然非典不用，造园母题也动辄追访一些著名的江南园林—其中一些是他南巡行程中亲眼所见的。在乾隆二十九岁那年（公元1738年），刚刚登上皇帝宝座四年，他开始着手营造第一座自己的园林—建福宫；时至1751年，乾隆四十二岁那年，他开始了第一次江南之行，直到此时，他才真正有机会切身感受江南园林的风韵。

1. 刘畅：《清代宫廷内檐装修设计问题研究》，[博士学位论文]，北京：清华大学建筑学院，2002年。
2. 计成：《园冶》，卷一。

乾隆遗珍
故宫博物院宁寿宫花园历史研究与文物保护规划

4.1 Qianlong Garden in the Forbidden City

There are four gardens remained integral inside the Forbidden City, i.e. the Imperial Garden in the rear middle part of the city, the Ci'ning Gong Garden in the west for the retired imperial concubines, the Jianfu Gong Garden in the northwest, and Qianlong Garden (Ningshou Gong Garden) in the northeast. The first two gardens were originally built in Ming Dynasty and had functioned as the spaces for leisure of the large imperial family. It is understandable the family should have at lease one garden inside the Forbidden City, and one dedicated for the empress dowagers of the late emperor, titled Taihou or Taifei, who were very honored but lived in tediousness. The other two gardens were both built by Emperor Qianlong who is responsible for many reconstructions in the Forbidden city for various reasons. The birth of Jianfu Gong Garden attributes to the history that Qianlong spent his youthhood there; after reigining the country for decades, Qianlong planned and then built Ningshou Gong Garden for retirement bearing genesis and mimesis of Jianfu Gong Garden.

From another aspect, Qianlong Garden is rendered with a color of emperors' private and mental world, for Ningshou Gong Garden is one part of the most attractive Ningshou Gong precinct which is the only extant building complex for the supper sovereign. The title of supper sovereign (太上皇, Taishang Huang) is given to the father emperor who abdicated and handed the crown to his son for some reason. The reason of Qianlong's abdication is discussed in previous text. Though Qianlong did not mention literally what kind of live he anticipated after abdication, the layout of the precinct and garden devices can reveal his thought to certain extent.

Firstly, Qianlong must have planned that the supper sovereign should be very respected by his successor and worshiped by the people for the fact that the ceremonious halls were sublimely designed, Though there might be some kind of worry of Qianlong about his absolute authority in the court after dismounting the throne.. Being a Forbidden City in the Forbidden City, as described by many scholars, Ningshou Gong precinct follows a similar series of buildings with that of the main axis of the Forbidden City.

Secondly, Qianlong put his favorite segments of gardens, building structures and interior settings into the precinct, revealing the monarch's deep nostalgia for the unfetter life before retirement.

It is reasonable to conclude that Qianlong Garden was not a normal garden functioned generally for the imperial family, nor an ordinary private garden of an emperor, quite the contrary, it was and is an unmatchable condensation of the most influential emperor in the far east at that time and probably the richest individual in the world, moreover it reflects the belief, taste and the way how the condensation came into being that tells the most colorful backgroung story and the stories of the changing point of rise and fall of the empire.

4.2 Garden in Emperor Qianlong's Dictionary & Qianlong Garden in Qianlong's Gardens

In an overall view, Chinese gardens are more comprehensive in comparison with western garden for its coordination with buildings and structures, and a more multi-purposed function arrangement. To be specific, there have appeared in China's history many genres of gardening, e.g. the imperial versus the literati's, and the northern versus the southern. As a famous gardener in Ming dynasty Ji Cheng wrote in his influential book *Creating Garden (园冶)* [1] that 3/10 of gardenning rests with the gardener, while 7/10 rests with the owner. It is well accepted that Emperor Qianlong contributed significantly to the history of gardening[2], but yet what the ideal garden in Qianlong's thought should be further expatiated. Understanding what the word garden really stands for in Qianlong's dictionary and what peculiarity Qianlong had dissolved in Qianlong garden will definitely shed light on understanding historical values of the heritage and on establishing future conservation policies.

4.2.1 Qianlong's Gardens and Their Common Colors

By systematically and closely reviewing into all the gardens built by Qianlong, we can summarize the top interests of the elegant emperor as below.

Firstly Qianlong showed great passion to Mandarin Culture, which especially can be seen from that he was extremely zealous in using very rich idioms and quotations in his poems and verses. While in the gardens, his usual inditing impulsion came from a most famous literati garden that he had seen during his inspections to southern provinces. Before going to the south personally, Qianlong had his first garden built in the Forbidden City in 1738 when he was 29 years old and when he had reigned the country for 4 years. After the first inspection travel to southern provinces in 1751, Qianlong must had a more vivid experience of literati garden of mandarin culture.

Qianlong's Collector's
The Studies and Master Conservation Plan for Qianlong Garden

在通常意义上的汉族文化之外，乾隆对于汉族风格的室内设计是尤其偏爱的。这种偏爱是如此的强烈，以致于他早就将祖父的一些教诲当作了耳旁风——而祖父对乾隆的影响恰恰又是如此之深。从童年时代开始，弘历便得到了康熙皇帝的特殊宠爱[1]。正是康熙皇帝将大清帝国领上了稳定和繁荣的道路；也正是康熙皇帝给予了儿孙们一段"断不可做套房"（指汉式曲折隔断的室内布局）的训诫[2]。不过从乾隆的父亲雍正皇帝开始，已经没有人在装饰他们的宫室的时候真正想到这段祖宗的教诲了。亲身经历过康熙教导的乾隆，在这个方面极大地起到了为汉族式样室内设计推波助澜、甚至是领导潮流的作用。

与大多数中国传统的装饰主题一样，宁寿宫花园的装饰设计主要采用象征手法。室内的装饰设计大多采用松、竹、梅主题，以象征人的品质；装饰材料主要采用玉、珐琅、铜，而几不用金，表现出乾隆在象征气质与财富的材料之间的取舍。这种做法一直以来都是汉族传统文化所推崇的，尤其在文人阶层最为流行。

第二，从大量乾隆谕旨、诗文中我们都可以得出这样的结论——乾隆皇帝善于将事物体系化，以应乎天地之"道"。他曾经命章嘉呼图克图整理藏传佛教诸佛、菩萨的系统和造像规矩；而在建筑和园林设计中，他更加关注朝寝制度和等级制度。正是在乾隆在位期间，整理并定型了具有典型清代正统意志的紫禁城布局与主要殿宇的功能设置。为何宁寿宫花园的后部几乎全盘照搬建福宫花园呢？仅仅是因为乾隆在堆砌他所钟爱的园林片段吗？其中难道没有"朝夕"呼应，平衡紫禁城布局的想法吗？

第三，乾隆对于艺术的热爱同样涵盖西方舶来风格。众所周知，他在圆明三园的长春园北部建有著名的西洋景区；他在各处宫室室内所下令绘制的大量通景画则不甚被人了解。无论是建筑，还是室内装饰、喷泉设施，清宫西洋风格的完成都是在西方传教士的直接帮助，甚至直接参与施工的情况下，"纯正"地完成的，而非派遣工程技术人员远赴西洋了解学习。因此，乾隆的西洋式样是完全不同于西方同时期"点缀"和"创造"式的英、法中式园林的；他也仅仅将西洋式园林作为他"园林收藏"中的一个片段，从未全心投入西式园林的建设。

4.2.2 宁寿宫花园的独特之处

通过在上述大背景下的分析，可以看出，宁寿宫花园与紫禁城其他园林和其他皇家离宫园林不同的首先在于其凝聚了乾隆至为钟爱的造园艺术——在更广泛的意义上讲，也包括了装饰艺术和相关门类的艺术。

从建筑学的角度上看，宁寿宫花园的布局是在空间条件十分苛刻的条件下完成的，为此，乾隆也将一些在类似条件下曾经创造出来的园林片段组织了进来。这里，整体上最为突出特色反映在"组织片段"的方式方法。

进一步关注宁寿宫花园的园林设施和内檐装修，便不难看出，乾隆皇帝的两个苦心经营之处。

其一，乾隆降旨将一些重要殿宇的内檐装修和家具等装饰配饰在南方完成。南方工匠一向以精美细腻著称，南方工匠所偏爱的材料范围广泛，包括了竹、玉、珐琅、瓷器、玳瑁、铜器、漆器，及各种硬木镶嵌。这一切在当时的宫中也属稀有。有雍正皇帝的一段谕旨可资参考。他当时讲："朕看从前造办处所造的活计好的虽少，还是内廷恭造式样，近来虽其巧妙，大有外造之气。尔等再造时不要失去内廷恭造之势。"他没有亲身感受到江南格调，他的主要审美情趣也是基本排斥江南风格的。把康熙、雍正、乾隆三代帝王对于内檐装修的要求排比起来，这条从满洲传统风格逐步走向对新奇风格的追求的轨迹是多么明显，又是多么有趣！

其二，为了避免花园中有限的室内空间所带来的压抑感，乾隆有规模地引进了通景画手段。尽管宁寿宫花园不是唯一存在通景画的地方，但是这里的通景画的使用密度确实非比寻常，郎士宁这代画师的工作方法和成果也没有其他地方得到重复。如果将宫廷绘制通景画的频率绘制成图表，郎士宁时期无疑是一个创作高峰，而他的学生王幼学在宁寿宫花园中的创作实践无疑是又一个高峰。

4.3 宁寿宫花园建筑的内檐装修研究

清代中期宫室室内空间的人都会有这样的体会：走过养心殿暖阁、倦勤斋仙楼的时候，不禁会想，雍正、乾隆皇帝一定身材不高，因为他是如此热衷于营造变幻无穷、狭小私密的空间；走过乐寿堂门厅、颐和轩明间的时候，又不禁会想乾隆皇帝一定气魄很大，因为他同时还拥有那么高大弘敞、明亮轩昂的大堂（如图所示）。仅仅判断乾隆偏爱狭小空间是武断的。

如果归纳反映雍正乾隆时期宫室室内布局的样式房图样，如慎修思永[3]、

1. "上生而神灵，天挺其表，庭珠方广，隆准颀身，发音铿洪，举步岳重，规度恢远，巍然拔萃。自六龄就学，受书于庶吉士福敏，过目成诵，课必兼治，进业日勤，动契凤悟。泊康熙壬寅，年十二，祗谒圣祖于圆明园之镂月开云。见即惊爱，命宫中养育，抚视周挚，备荷饴顾恩慈，亲授书课，教牖有加……"。载于：《清实录·高宗实录（一）》，卷一，一三九页，北京：中华书局，1985年。
2. 《庭训格言》本文所据载于《望三益斋所刻书》卷六十一页五十七雍正刊本："训曰：朕从前曾往王大臣等花园游幸，观其盖造房屋率皆效法汉人，各样曲折隔断，谓之套房。彼时亦以为巧，曾于一两处效为之，久居即不如意，厥后不为矣。尔等俱各自有花园，断不可作套房，但以宽广宏敞居之适意为宜"。
3. 慎修思永，圆明园内。1757年首见于乾隆御制诗。张恩荫：《圆明园变迁史探微》，北京：北京体育学院出版社，1993。

From a view of an architect, layout of Qianlong Garden reflects the special way of arranging a garden in a space of tight restrictions. It will be sensible to say that Qianlong Garden is mainly a composition of the successful gardens segments in other garden complexes, and its achievement of creativity is chiefly reflected in the way of composing.

Further looking into details of garden features and interior features, one can see that Qianlong Garden are special for the following two points.

The emperor ordered interior screens and decorations made in the southern provinces where long traditional of the most exquisite craftsmanship on bamboo, jade, enamel, porcelain, conch, lacquer and copper macquetry and inlay works were active. This was not normal at that time, especially when taking into consideration that emperor Yongzheng had once stressed to Imperial Household Handi-workshop (内务府造办处), "Though esent handiworks are delicately made, exotic flavor is too strong for court crafts; imperial works be never short of imperial genre." How interesting it is when one recalls the episode of history that Yongzheng did not obey Kangxi's will that interior space should follow Manchu custom of simple decoration, and then Qianlong did not carry on his father, Emperor Yongzheng's favor for plain and stately taste but went in for southern décors let alone they were very and fragile for the north climate.

In order to avoid uncomfortable feeling of the limited space inside rooms, Qianlong adopted the art of perspective mural paintings. Though this method was not only used in Qianlong Garden, the level of density of the murals in Qianlong Garden and the working methodology of the generation after Castiglione cannot be found elsewhere. If a diagram of frequency of using perspective mural painting is drawn, Castiglione's works dispersing in various garden buildings must be one peak, and Wang Youxue's work concentrated in Qianlong Garden must be the other.

4.3 On Qianlong-style Interior Space

Those have wandered in the Lodge of Retirement must infer that Qianlong was not tall and had a delicate nature otherwise he would not have such cozy and "tiny" cells for reading, meditating and residing. But in other buildings for ceremonious purposes as Leshou Tang (乐寿堂, the Hall of Enjoying Longevity) one can also experience spacious interior of two storeys in a building of one level facade. It would be arbitrary to conclude that Qianlong only preferred small spaces.

Further than overall love for Han culture, Qianlong was fond of living in richly planned interior spaces which then was mainly known as Han style. This inclination was so strong that even his grandfather's word did not prevent him from doing this. From his childhood, Qianlong had been cherished by not only his parents but also his grandfather, Emperor Kangxi[3] who brought the empire into a stable and prosperous status, and who had always been keen on western science. Qianlong had been living with and learning directly from Kangxi for quite some time. More interestingly, though Qianlong showed his filial piety toward his grandfather, he did just like his father in disobeying the late Kangxi's will that living spaces be furnished according to Manchu tradition other than contain diverse interior spaces that beloved by Han literati[4].

As other Chinese traditional themes, the decorations in Qianlong garden did not exceed symbolism. Friends of Humanity being décors within daily reach, Qianlong made his rooms full of decorative patterns of bamboo, plum blossom and pine tree; jade standing for human quality and gold for wealth, Qianlong used more jade carvings, enamels than gold. All these motifs were of strong mandarin color and had rooted for tens of centuries in China.

Secondly Qianlong had shown in his many edicts that he was the one who had a well organized mind and wanted everything well organized according to the structure he deemed, substantially to what the Tao, rules of the Heaven and Earth, deems. He had ordered to comb out a system for Lamaist Spirits, which was done by Zhangjia Hutuketu (Living Buddha). In the field of building and gardening, Qianlong also wanted everything to have meaning and be right in the hierarchy system. It was during Qianlong's reign that ceremonial procedure was improved and functions of the Main Halls in the Forbidden City were set. Why Qianlong garden had a rear part quite the same as Jianfu Gong Garden? One cannot help but thinking that Qianlong wanted the Forbidden City to be built into a balancing way during his reign, and tht Qianlong must have been thinking to place the garden for his youthhood in the west and a similar garden for his retirement in the east.

Thirdly Qianlong's passion for art stimulated him seeking for exotic art and western way of decoration. Occidental yard in Changchun Yuan among the three gardens of Yuanming Yuan is well known, while interior perspective mural paintings in palaces are unfamiliar to outside. Whatever structure, interior, decoration or fountain devices, all facets of the occidental works were done with help of western clergies other than sending people abroad to learn, therefore Qianlong had built more authentic western buildings as a small input in his court "collection of garden" as merely interspersion in comparison to the Anglo-Chinese or Francais-Chinese gardens and buildings that had been constructed in Europe which is apparently quite far from their origins in China.

4.2.2 Qianlong Garden's Special Colors

The primary special color of Qianlong Garden lies in the fact that unlike other gardens built in summer palaces and the Forbidden City, as mentioned in the above paragraphs, it is the condensation of the Emperor's paramount loves for art.

春耦斋[1]、淳化轩[2]、乐寿堂[3]等，再将其特点与清代晚期的慎修思永、九州清宴[4]、畅和堂[5]等进行并置比较，那么很自然地，可以发现以下变化：

1. 雍乾时期的室内布局设计参考柱网平面，但并不拘泥于此，空间划分丰富；清代晚期则往往仅沿柱网轴线布置装修。

2. 建筑平面虽呈对称形式，雍乾时期的室内布局设计往往打破对称，相对强调使用功能和空间情趣；清代晚期则大多采用相对严格的对称布局。

3. 雍乾时期的室内空间尺度对比显著，小空间仅容床张，而大空间敞亮，几可容数十人聚会；清代晚期室内空间划分平均，缺乏戏剧性变化。

4. 雍乾时期大量在单层建筑中使用仙楼空间；清代晚期偏爱采用假仙楼。

如果说清代中期的室内设计较之清代晚期具有更高的复杂程度、更高的空间创造能力，应当是公允的；而乾隆皇帝在这高水平、高难度的室内设计过程中所起的作用，也应当得到公认，所谓三分在匠人，七分在主人。

"仙楼"称谓本身，来源于江南。李斗在《扬州画舫录》有所记载[6]。值得注意的是，《扬州画舫录》中有很长一段文字与《圆明园内工现行则例》之《硬木装修作则例》相雷同。可以肯定，这段文字是摘抄宫内则例的。乾隆皇帝在大量吸取江南风格和工艺之后，将地方做法提高、升华了，并使这种规范提高后的风格在更广的范围内流行开来，甚至重新影响了风格的诞生地。

4.4 南北方工艺的融合

如前文所述，两淮盐政李质颖为将江南工艺引入宁寿宫起到了非常关键的作用——而且是竭尽全力地将最为精美奢华的工艺进呈乾隆；同时宁寿宫其他建筑的内檐装修仍然是内务府造办处承办的，表现出相对朴实简约的风格。可以通过将同样存在于宁寿宫中的两种风格进行比较而得出它们的相对特点。兹简要整理如下：

1. 两淮盐政承办的内檐装修多采用珍稀木材"实做"或"包镶"，如紫檀、黄花梨、乌木、鸡翅木等；北京造办处所用多系楠、柏木，少量使用紫檀木雕刻花结作为点缀。

2. 两淮盐政承办的内檐装修采用多种镶嵌手法，涉及玉器、珐琅、瓷器、錾铜等工艺，并大量使用竹丝、竹黄等不甚适合北方气候的做法；北京造办处所做除绦环、群板云盘纹路之外，不使用镶嵌做法。

3. 两淮盐政承办的内檐装修多用夹纱绣片纹饰、技法均高于内务府所出。

还有一则历史上的小插曲应当补充，即在1774年，就是南方承办的带有竹丝、竹黄镶嵌的隔扇运抵北京后的一年，由于温度湿度的差异，不少竹质镶嵌做法便开裂破坏："惟是京师风土高燥与南方润湿情形不同，各项装修俱系硬木镶嵌成做，现值冬令，间有离缝走错，并所嵌花结漆地等项俱微有爆裂脱落之处。奴才等详细查看其硬木漆地计有离缝走错者，即令该工监督楦缝找补，收拾完整；其玉铜花结有脱落者，亦交造办处随时修整务取妥固；外惟花结内有磁片一项，虽迸裂只有三小块，但在京一时难于置办，奴才等愚见该盐政从前成造时或有余存亦未知，请交与李质颖坐京家人，寄信顺便照式寄送数块应用。是否允协伏候圣明训示遵行"[7]。

江南造作除了直接承办内檐装修工程之外，还派送大量匠人供役内务府造办处，是为"南匠"。研究表明，造办处中"南匠"比"旗匠"具有更高的地位，报酬也丰厚得多[8]。北方匠作在主持制作部分硬木装修之外，还主要负责有裱糊壁画、墙纸，安装隔扇等工作。但是这些现象并不意味着北方匠作在宁寿宫花园内檐装修保护工作中可以被忽略掉，恰恰相反，只有保护好这种历史上南北匠作并存的信息，才能更加完整地保存宁寿宫花园室内造作的历史信息。

1. 春耦斋，位于西苑内，始建于1757年。于敏中等《钦定日下旧闻考》北京：北京古籍出版社，1981年。
2. 淳化轩，位于长春园内。始建于1770年。乾隆：《淳化轩记》。
3. 这里的乐寿堂，位于宁寿宫内。
4. 九州清宴，位于圆明园。
5. 畅和堂，位于颐和园。
6. 清李斗《扬州画舫录》北京：中华书局，1991年。卷十七四二一页："大屋中施小屋。小屋上架小楼。谓之仙楼。江园工匠。有做小房子绝艺。"
7. 乾隆三十九年《记事录》。内务府活计档，胶片128。
8. 吴兆清：《清代造办处的机构和匠役》，《明清档案与历史研究论文选》（上）。

Qianlong Garden were exceedingly luxurious and become almost the synonym of delicacy of material and craftsmanship, while those made locally in Beijing were relatively plain and modest in nature and also with elegant essence. The differences are chiefly reflected in the following points:

1.Interior screening from the south were made of more precious iron wood, while those made in Beijing were usually cypress wood with some iron wood wherever decorative purpose calls for.

2.Decorations on screenings from the south used much more inlay works of jade, enamel, porcelain and copper engraving, and much more macquetries of bamboo thread and bamboo inner husk. Those made in the capital were rather plain and even without any inlay.

3.Textiles on screening from the south were of higher quality than that from Beijing, for the center of textile had for long time been in southern cities.

Another aspect should be stressed was that many decorations made in the south were made of bamboo thread and bamboo-inner husk, and on account of different humidity and temperature of the south and north some nature damages occurred in 1774, only a year after the works transported to the capital[2].

Apart from the works from the south, craftsmen from the south who served in the Handi-workshop were very respected and earned more than their Manchu apprentices[3]. By no means north craftsmanship can be neglected in today's preservation efforts. It is important to keep in mind that the full preservation and exhinition of them both would interpret more vividly the history. Besides, mounting techniques of wallpaper and Tie'luo, and working methods of installing screenings from the south into the structures, and the repairs were all done in the capital.

If more architectural drawings that reflect interior spaces built in Qianlong period are brought together for comparison, we can find examples such as Shenxiu Siyong (慎修思永, the Hall of Careful Self-cultivation and Eternity)[1], Chun'ou Zhai (春耦斋, the Hall of Spring Lotus Root)[2], Chunhua Xuan (淳化轩, the Pavilion of Chunhua Calligraphy)[3] and Leshou Tang (乐寿堂, the Hall of Enjoying Longevity)[4], and we can also find the plans of interiors designed in late Qing Dynasty of Shenxiu Siyong (慎修思永), Jiuzhouqingyan (九州清宴, the Hall of Peaceful Nine Continents)[5] and Changhe Tang (畅和堂, the Hall of Freeness and Harmony)[6]. Sizes of interior spaces in these examples bear common characteristics below which were quite the contrary to those of later period.

1. Interior spaces designed in Qianlong period were separated based on but not restricted to axial-grid of columns.

2. Plans of buildings being symmetrical, Qianlong had the interior spaces designed in a way which gave much particular considerations to functions and avoided strict symmetry.

3. Sizes of spaces form apparent contrast. There were tiny spaces containing nothing more than a sitting bed, and there were also large space that could hold a dancing ball.

4. Double-storeyed spaces, which was then called Xianlou (仙楼, *the storey* where the immortals live), were often used in inside single storey buildings.

If we say that skill of design of interior in Mid-Qing dynasty is much more sophisticated than that of later generation, there would be no much debate. If we say Emperor Qianlong had played the most significant role in the design procedure, as the saying goes, 3/10 of design rests with the designer, 7/10 with the owner, no body will deny.

From the name of Xianlou, one can tell that the interior double-storeyed space was invented and was prevailing in southern provinces, but from a later literati's book containing one chapter on interior design in south China, noticing that some important long paragraphs were merely excerpts from *The Exemplifications and Regulations for Interior Works in Yuanming Yuan*[1], and Qianlong's style of interior design influenced back the southern area by setting examples of space structure, and delicacy and luxury.

4.4 On Northern and Southern Craftsmanship

Knowing that Li Zhiying managed to make many important productions in south province for the interior furnishing of many buildings in Qianlong Garden, while other works were mainly done in the capital by the Handi-workshop of Imperial Household Department (内务府造办处), researchers can bring together the north-made works for comparative studies on craftsmanship traits between the two regions. One should also keep in mind that because of the involvement of Li Zhiying and his unusual servile attempts, southern handiworks in

调查、评估与诊断

5.1 构成要素的类型与编号系统

鉴于宁寿宫花园中现存文物种类繁多，数量较大，必须建立一套完整的类型划分和编号系统才能全面地、无遗漏地开展调查记录工作，为进一步勘察评估奠定基础。有了这个系统，调研者同时还应当注意各类文物遗存自身和之间的布局关系，这些关系问题实际上是日后研究揭示众多尚未厘清的疑问的钥匙。

此外，对于宁寿宫花园建筑室内外温湿度情况的调查及其对文物安全的影响尚未全面开展研究，计划结合倦勤斋的保护工作确立专项课题，再推广到整个花园。

本规划所建立的编号体系是建立在宁寿宫花园院落划分的基础上的，基础设施、建筑、室内遗存、园林设施也因其所在院落不同而逐一编码。

(1) 地下排水系统。宁寿宫花园的地下排水设施是宁寿宫整体系统，乃至是紫禁城总体系统的一部分。地下排水沟的编号是根据紫禁城内排水沟编号体系制定的。根据我们以前的研究，紫禁城地下排水沟编号应当按照从内金水河为排水终点的干沟、支沟体系确定，即直接排水入内金水河的沟定义为干沟，标记为M（Main）+0A（其中A代表从上游至下游的顺序号）；直接排水入干沟的沟定义为支沟，标记为Sub-I（并标明所在干沟号）+0A（其中A代表从上游至下游的顺序号）；直接排水入支沟的沟定义为次支沟，标记为Sub-II（标明所在支沟号）+0A（其中A代表从上游至下游的顺序号）；依次类推。这种编号方法从原则上是系统化的，改变了以往仅仅参照排水沟断面尺寸的标号方法及对紫禁城内排水沟的模糊描述。

(2) 地炕系统是宁寿宫花园中重要的基础设施。然而此系统并非相互联系形成整体，而是随建筑而设，随建筑中需要采暖的部位而设。因此地炕的编号是根据建筑标号而制定的，采用院落中建筑编号加之以地炕编号。

(3) 花园中的园林设施十分多样，包括假山叠石、庭院陈设和陈设座、小径、地面铺装和植物配置。由于种类和数量均较多，园林设施的编号主要根据某类设施所在院落的编号制定。植物编号则根据现有的两种编号体系——北京市古树编号和故宫博物院古树编号。

(4) 建筑编号采用如下方法：主要建筑物，X（建筑所在院落编号）+ Y（建筑序列号）；游廊，9（游廊标记号）+ Z（由南至北各游廊段的序列号）。

(5) 内檐装修，包括室内罩隔（含床张）、室内地平、楼梯、帖落（纸面、绢面、木版）、壁画（通景画、天顶画）、家具及其他。编号方法先根据所在建筑确定大项，再根据室内位置排成序列。

5.2 基础设施调查

基础设施调查目的在于回答以下问题：宁寿宫花园中的排水系统是如何设计的？建筑基础坚固程度如何？地下采暖设施是如何分布的？上述系统的现状情况如何？

5.2.1 排水系统

我们曾于1997年尝试系统整理紫禁城地下排水设施，该论文发表于《紫禁城学会论文集 第二辑》。论文提出以下阶段性论断。

(1) 必须建立一套完整、有序的编号体系，各沟的命名必须遵循从内金水河逐步向低级排水沟过渡的原则（如前文所述）；

(2) 一般来说，越是与内金水河联系直接的，即级别越高的排水沟，比低等级的排水沟具有越大的截面；

(3) 所有已勘察的排水沟沟底标高形成的坡度并不均匀，尤其是在接近上级排水沟处存在一段陡降坡度段；

(4) 一些排水沟为双向排水，沟的中间存在分水线。

如下页图所示，宁寿宫花园所在的紫禁城东北部，在宁寿宫东西两侧各有一条排水支沟，北侧有一条排水干沟，花园南门外单体建筑宁寿宫后有一条次支沟，另外有一条排水支沟贯穿花园而出，排入北侧干沟。

根据本次规划勘察过程中，揭取部分排水孔盖石后对隐蔽水沟的初步勘察，尽管尚未发现规律性的结论，但仍然可以作出下列判断。

(1) 急需针对排水沟隐蔽部位的沟底、沟壁和沟盖板的状况进行全面勘察；

(2) 花园中主排水沟，即贯穿花园的排水支沟，至今仍然发挥着作用，但存在显著的构造破坏，沟中同时存在大量树叶和泥土的淤积物，亟待清理。

5.1 Feature Types and Numbering System

To avoid confusion on account of the multiple and numerous varieties of relics in Qianlong Garden, the author first establishes a system of classification and numbering and uses it as the basis for investigation. Having the system of recording, one should also remember that maintaining the layout and relationship of all remaining features is extremely essential for it is the relation that links the disperse items, and many historic mysteries to reveal have closer relationship with the links among items other than with the items themselves.

Other research such as recording and analyzing the relative humidity and temperature of the interior and exterior spaces and their influences to historic relics have not yet been conducted in the master plan phase and are planned to be done based on specific pilot project in the Lodge of Retirement which will benefit the whole project of restoring Qianlong Garden.

Numbering system for all features in Qianlong Garden is mainly based on the number of the courtyard that consists of the Qianlong Garden, as listed below,

(1) Underground drainage in Qianlong Garden is a part of the integral system of Ningshou Gong precinct, and in a more general view, is a part of that of the Forbidden City. Numbering for the drainage lines follows the method for numbering that of the whole city. According to the author's precedent research, the drainage system in the Forbidden City should be numbered according to draining sequence to the Inner Gold River (内金水河), i.e. name the line directly drains rain and sewage water into the river M (Main) + 0A (serial number), name the line directly drains water into the main drains Sub-I + 0A (serial number), name the line directly drains water into the sub drains Sub-II + 0A (serial number) and so on. This method is believed better than previous ambiguous definitions which mainly recognize drains from their importance and section dimensions.

(2) Heating system as basic building facility in Qianlong Garden was not a built collaborative system but was separate heating units for indivudual building of residential purposes, therefore underground heating facilities are numbered after individual buildings and the courtyard serial numbers.

(3) For garden features in the courtyards, including rockeries, pedestals for displaying wares, lanes and paths, and plants, some are merely represented in site plans and numbered after the courtyards in which the features are located, since it is difficult to identify each item both briefly and exhausively. Among the garden features the plants have already two systems for numbering, i.e. that of Beijing Municipality, and that of the Palace Museum.

(4) Building and structures in Qianlong Garden are numbered according to the formula: for buildings, X (Number of Courtyard) + Y (Number of Building); for verandas, 9 + Z (Number of Veranda from South to North).

(5) Interior furnishings, i.e. screenings (with or without sitting beds), interior platforms, stairs, Tie'luo, murals, furniture, etc., are numbered in sequence in accordance with the building in which the furnishing is located.

5.2 Status Quo of Infrastructures

What kind of the drainage system was used in Qianlong Garden? What kind of foundation works was rammed for the buildings? What kind of heating devices were adopted in the buildings? And what are the safety conditions of the infrastructure settings? Above are the most essential questions to answer in infrastructure investigation.

5.2.1 Drainage System

The first endeavor to number drain lines was made by the author of this book in 1997 in an article contributed to a conference organized by the Society of the Forbidden City. Remarkable conclusions drawn in the article include,

(1) A numbering system should be established, and each drain line should be named after its location in the system according to how many steps the drain is to go to reach the final water receiver, the Inner Golden River, and a proposed sequence for the drains of the same level,

(2) It is easy to understand, drains of higher level, that are closer connected to the river, usually have a bigger section size than the lower level drains,

(3) Bottoms of the drains are not of one constant gradient, but at the end of each drain there is a steeper segment before the water mouth to the drain of the upper level,

(4) Some drains have two directions with a water falling demarcation somewhere within the span.

In the northeast part of the Forbidden City where Qianlong Garden is located, there are two lines of sub-drains passing at both east and west side of Ningshou Gong precinct, and a main-drain in the north, a Sub-II-drain in the south.

By opening some of the water inlet and detecting into the drains, though no systematical conclusion could be drawn, the author comes to the following points,

5.2.2 地炕系统

从现存的木制地炕烧火口盖板可以看出，宁寿宫花园的一些建筑中确实使用了地炕采暖系统。这些烧火口一般布置在建筑廊步或檐下；而排烟口或不单设或设于台明侧面。

应当注意到，不是所有宁寿宫花园中的建筑都设有地炕，不是所有建筑室内都是采暖空间，而是仅在为皇帝较长时间停留而备的寝宫、书房、佛堂等重要日常功能空间中才布置有地炕设施。

虽然在目前的规划阶段尚没有发掘考证地炕设施的可能，我们仍然可以参考一些相关的考古发现推断宁寿宫花园建筑中采暖设施的大致情况。我们以为，近年来发掘的圆明三园之长春园含经堂遗址的状况可以基本说明宁寿宫花园地下的样子。仔细考察含经堂建筑遗址发掘平面图，可以发现该处遗址上的地下采暖管线是由砖瓦结合砌筑的，有的只是一道从烧火口引向建筑中心部位的烟道，更多的则是曲折回转，或添设支沟，以便尽量为室内空间均匀供热。

多数宁寿宫花园中的地炕烧火口已被土壤封堵多年，仅少数基本保存完整。下表完整统计各座具有采暖设施的建筑、采暖设施位置，及其保存现状。

本规划认为对于宁寿宫花园建筑中的地下采暖设施的清理和保护已经迫在眉睫。

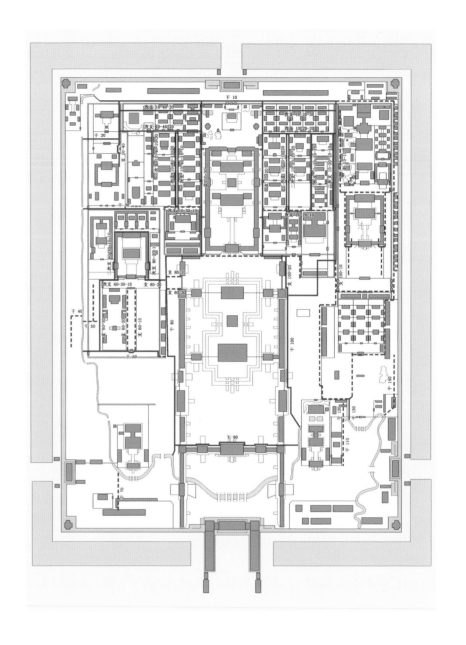

编号	位置	保存状况	地炕服务房间
101	第一进院，抑斋	砖砌体封堵	西间
201	第二进院，遂初堂	当代采暖管线占用	东进间
202	第二进院，遂初堂	当代采暖管线占用	西进间
301	第三进院，三友轩	基本完好	西次间
302	第三进院，三友轩	基本完好	东次间
303	第三进院，延趣楼	土壤填埋	南次间
304	第三进院，延趣楼	土壤填埋	北次间
401	第三进院，萃赏楼	土壤填埋	西进间
402	第三进院，萃赏楼	土壤填埋	东进间
403	第四进院，云光楼一层，养和精舍	土壤填埋	北次间
404	第四进院，玉粹轩	土壤填埋	南次间
405	第四进院，玉粹轩	土壤填埋	北次间
406	第四进院，倦勤斋	土壤填埋	东五间之西进间
407	第四进院，倦勤斋	土壤填埋	东五间之东进间

5.2.3 建筑基础稳定性评价

建筑基础埋于地下，必须借助物探方能考察其层叠状况，但是由于园中干扰因素较多，物探方法也受到了极大的限制。所幸规划小组并未发现建筑基础有不均匀沉降的现象，建筑墙体也没有显著的因地基沉降产生阶梯状裂缝。本规划认为，宁寿宫花园的建筑基础基本是稳定的。

乾隆花园文物保护规划

Master Conservation Plan for Qianlong Garden

清华大学文化遗产保护研究所
故宫博物院

Part II

现状勘察图
Drawings for Survey and Analysis

II-01 周边基本管线平面图
Basic Systems of Utilities

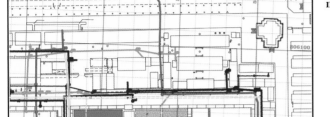

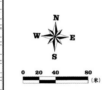

N
W E
S

0 20 40 80 (米)

■ 供水系统
■ 雨水管线
■ 污水系统
■ 电力系统
■ 消防管线
■ 避雷针引下线
■ 电信系统

紫禁城排水系统示意图
Underground Drainage System

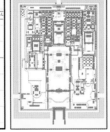

(1) Future investigation must be taken soon to expose the safety and function status of the drains, and attentions should be paid especially to the two sides, cover and bottom inside the drainage line,

(2) The main drain in the garden is still functioning, but there are obvious constructional damages and much sullage of mud and leafs of decades to be removed.

5.2.2 Underground Heating Distribution System

Underground heating system is applied in some of individual buildings, which can be detected from wooden covers of underground furnace entrance on the building platform in corridors and smoke outlets on plinths.

It is worth noticing that not all buildings in the garden have a set of heating facilities, but only those building that the emperor expected to stay longer, e.g. for reading or resting spaces or praying-meditating chambers.

Though it is impossible at present stage to excavate and research the heating system, we can still infer that the system might be based on previous constructions, which studies on other historic sites have shown. A recent excavation of a complex of ruins in Yuanming Yuan, Hanjing Tang site (含经堂) is representative. When taking a closer observation into the excavation plan of the site, one can clearly find that in some buildings there are lines of small tunnels built with bricks and tiles. Some of them are only straightforward tunnels from the furnace to the interior chamber; some are more complicated for there might have been more spaces inside the house to be heated so that they have branches to conduct heat.

Some furnace pits in Qianlong Garden have been long stuffed with earth, while there are still some remain well preserved.

Following table shows the furnace pits, heated rooms and the remaining status of the pits.

No.	Location	Remaining Status	Room Heated
101	Yi Zhai, the Chamber of Self-constraint, in the 1st courtyard	Blocked with bricks	West bay
201	Suichu Tang, the Hall of Fulfilling Original Wishes, in the 2nd courtyard	Occupied by heating line	East end bay
202	Suichu Tang, the Hall of Fulfilling Original Wishes, in the 2nd courtyard	Occupied by heating line	West end bay
301	Sanyou Xuan, the Pavilion of Three Friendship, in the 3rd courtyard	Sound	West side bay
302	Sanyou Xuan, the Pavilion of Three Friendship, in the 3rd courtyard	Sound	East side bay
303	Yanqu Lou, the Building of Extended Delight, in the 3rd courtyard	Earth filled	South side bay
304	Yanqu Lou, the Building of Extended Delight, in the 3rd courtyard	Earth filled	North side bay
401	Cuishang Luo, the Building of Collection and Appreciation, in the 3rd courtyard	Earth filled	West end bay
402	Cuishang Luo, the Building of Collection and Appreciation, in the 3rd courtyard	Earth filled	East end bay
403	Yanghe Jingshe, the Chamber of Reposing Harmony, at the ground floor of the Building of Cloud Light, in the 4th courtyard	Earth filled	North side bay
404	Yucui Xuan, the Pavilion of Jade purity, in the 4th courtyard	Earth filled	South side bay
405	Yucui Xuan, the Pavilion of Jade purity, in the 4th courtyard	Earth filled	North side bay
406	Juanqin Zhai, the Lodge of Retirement, in the 4th courtyard	Beyond this survey; Earth filled	West side bay of the east part
407	Juanqin Zhai, the Lodge of Retirement, in the 4th courtyard	Beyond this survey; Earth filled	East side bay of the east part

本规划引以为参考的是故宫博物院白丽娟女士针对紫禁城及周边地区建筑基础做法所做的研究。此项研究表明：

(1) 古代工匠对于具有不同承载能力的地基采用不同的方式进行基础处理。做法包括独立基础（柱子磉墩）、条形基础（一般墙体基础）、桩基础及桩基结合承台（砂地加固基础）等。

(2) 对于一些重要建筑及其临近场所的下层基础采用换土做法，逐层采用碎砖加黄土与灰土层相间使用形成具有弹性的基础做法。

(3) 对于广场和院落中的地面铺墁，紫禁城内的普遍做法是在面层砖下累砌两层垫层砖，其下施灰土夯实，再下施黄土夯实。

本规划认为，鉴于宁寿宫花园地表建筑墙体台基未见结构异常变化的现象，可以初步断定，宁寿宫花园建筑基础基本是稳定的。

5.3 园林设施调查

为避免子项目过多，本规划将宁寿宫花园中的植物配置单独列项调查，本园林设施一节以假山叠石为主，同时调查庭院地面铺装和室外陈设、陈设座的现状。

5.3.1 假山

宁寿宫花园四进院落中有三进院落建有大规模的假山叠石。这些假山不是仅仅作为观赏对象，而且作为园林地形、环境的一部分用来营造空间，模拟自然景观。

外部观察和三维激光扫描记录工作表明，花园中假山的保存状况基本完好，未见显著崩塌和结构性裂缝。但是同样存在诸多局部问题。这些问题包括：

(1) 一些山顶叠石松动走闪，有的失位坠落；

(2) 一些内部铸铁拉扯构件裸露在大气环境中；

(3) 大多数循山径而设的石栏杆望柱已遭折断，部分缺失，木寻杖已全部缺失；

(4) 在一多数假山脚下，泥土、落叶堆积厚重，致使局部湿度过高，影响叠石勾缝灰浆的保存状况。

抑斋地炕烧火口

遂初堂地炕烧火口

玉粹轩、萃赏楼地炕烧火口

倦勤斋地炕烧火口

新阁潭琼
故宫博物院宁寿宫花园历史研究与文物保护规划

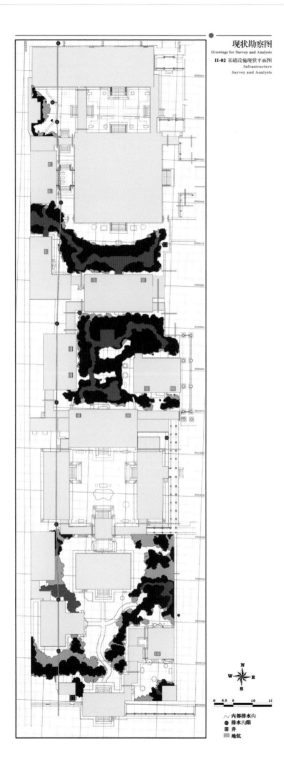

现状勘察图
Drawings for Survey and Analysis
II-02 基础设施现状平面图
Infrastructure
Survey and Analysis

5.2.3 Foundation Stability Evaluation

Hidden under the structures, foundation survey calls for high-tech measures to detect which is not yet available in this work. Fortunately, we have not yet found any uneven sedimentation of the foundations and obvious crack on the walls.

For reference, an article by Ms. Bai Lijuan from the Palace Museum has investigated into many representative foundation constructions in and around the Forbidden City. It was concluded in the article that,

(1) Workers in history applied different foundation constructions in sites of different load bearing capacities, including independent footing, strip foundation, pile-raft foundation and pile-cap.

(2) In the case of most important places, there would be layers of crushed bricks with clay in between layers of lime earth, which reinforce the foundation under structures.

(3) Under square, courtyard and path pavement, there are usually applied bedding bricks, mostly of two layers, then under the bricks, lime earth, and then rammed earth.

Superficially speaking at present master plan phase, foundations of the buildings in Qianlong Garden are well preserved, for no obvious structural crack on the wall found and no obvious sedimentation of the platform discerned visually.

5.3 Status Quo of Garden Features

As important members apart from the plants, rockery, exterior pedestal for displaying and other decorative devices like remaining posts for balustrade at two sides of stairs on rockeries should be included into the survey list.

5.3.1 Rockery

Among the four courtyards in Qianlong Garden, three have rockeries not only for displaying as an object but also as an element that takes a part in composing a natural scene.

Generally the rockeries remain well preserved, and there are not remarkable collapse nor visible serious cracks. The problems include:

(1) Some rocks on the top are loose and have fallen away from their original location.

(2) Some iron ties are exposed to the air and rain.

(3) Many of the stone posts for barriers are broken or lost.

(4) At foot of the piles of rocks, earth is thickly accumulated, which might lead to the rise of moisture that might be hazardous to aged lime joints.

兹将假山叠石安全状况和循山栏杆保存状况统计如下表。

编号	位置	落石	可辨栏杆数	完好栏杆	折断栏杆	缺失栏杆
101	第一进院东南角	0	0	0	0	0
102	第一进院东北角	2	9	8	1	?
103	第一进院西南角	0	0	0	0	0
104	第一进院西北角	0	0	0	0	0
301	第三进院	6	12	1	0（现存10根）	11
401	第四进院南部	7	26	1	0	25
402	第四进院竹香馆	2	0	0	0	0

5.3.2 庭院地面铺装

宁寿宫花园地面铺装做法比较复杂，如构成道路、建筑散水、院落铺墁等；铺装的材料做法包括普通的砖铺地、五色片石铺地、石子铺地等。近年来一些砖、石子铺墁得到了修复，而保护工作难度最大的还是五色石片铺地，因现阶段既无成熟的保护做法，也缺乏对现存采石渠道的调查。

花园中各院落地面铺墁主要存在的残损问题总结如下表。

院号	铺装材料	典型残损	残损评估	备注
I	砖	不均匀沉降；磨损；历史变更	30	
	石子（庭院地面）	局部残缺	30	近期破坏
	五色石板（道路、散水）	风化、剥落；磨损	40	
II	砖（庭院地面、散水）	不均匀沉降；磨损；历史变更	40	
	石子（装饰铺地）	局部残缺	40	近期破坏
III	砖（庭院地面、道路、附属建筑散水）	不均匀沉降；磨损；历史变更	30	
	石子（庭院地面）	局部残缺	40	多埋藏于地面淤积之下
	五色石片（道路、主要建筑散水）	不均匀沉降；磨损；历史变更	40	
IV	砖（庭院地面、道路、散水）	不均匀沉降；磨损；历史变更	40	存疑：是否经历史变更
	石子（庭院地面）	局部残缺	40	位于云光楼之前
	五色片石（庭院地面、道路、散水）	不均匀沉降；磨损；历史变更	30	主要集中在符望阁以南

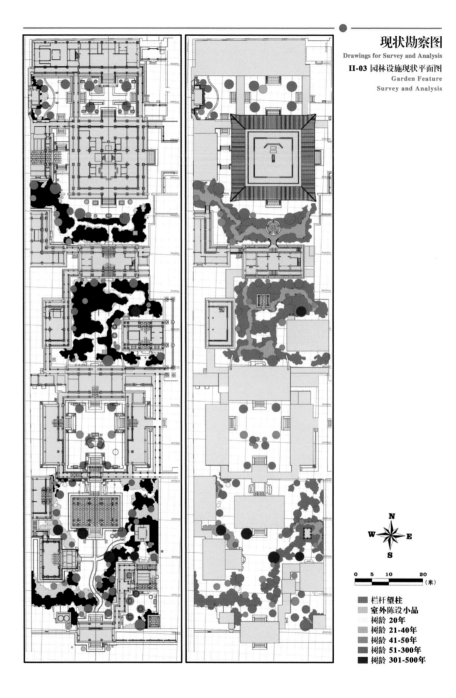

现状勘察图
Drawings for Survey and Analysis
II-03 园林设施现状平面图
Garden Feature
Survey and Analysis

N
W E
S

0 5 10 20（米）

■ 栏杆望柱
■ 室外陈设小品
树龄 20年
树龄 21-40年
树龄 41-50年
树龄 51-300年
树龄 301-500年

新阁潇玲

故宫博物院宁寿宫花园历史研究与文物保护规划

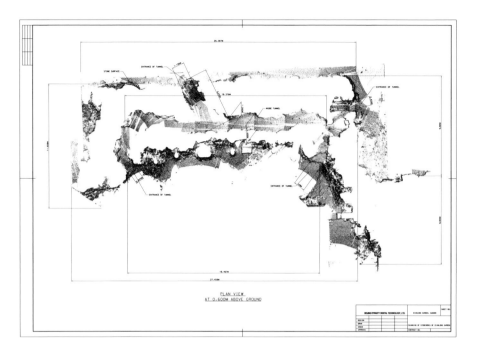

PLAN VIEW
AT 0.600M ABOVE GROUND

Fallen rocks and status of the stone posts are listed below.

ID.	Location	Fallen Rock	Discernable Post	Post in Good Condition	Broken Post	Missing Post
101	Southeast corner, 1st courtyard	0	0	0	0	0
102	Northeast side, 1st courtyard	2	9	8	1	?
103	Southwest corner, 1st courtyard	0	0	0	0	0
104	Northwest corner, 1st courtyard	0	0	0	0	0
301	3rd courtyard	6	12	1	0 (10 remaining)	11
401	South part, 4th courtyard	7	26	1	0	25
402	The Chamber of Bamboo Fragrance, 4th courtyard	2	0	0	0	0

5.3.2 Courtyard Pavement

Qianlong Garden has a rich variety of pavement as path, ground apron and as ground-fill-in, i.e., ordinary brick pavement, 5-color-slate pavement. Some scree and brick pavement had been restored in recent times, while leaving most of the 5-color-slate because of lacking of material.

Most representative damages occurred in the pavements can be summarized below.

Courtyard	Pavement Material	Representative Damage	Damage Value	Memo
I	Brick	Irregular sedimentation; Abrasion; Changes in history	30	
	Scree (Ground pavement)	Part losing	30	Recently restored
	5-Color-Slate(Path and Ground apron)	Efflorescence and exfoliation; Abrasion	40	
II	Brick(Ground pavement and Ground apron)	Irregular sediment; Abrasion; Changed in history	40	
	Scree (Decorative ground pavement)	Partly lost	40	Recently restored
III	Brick(Ground Pavement, Path and Ground apron of Auxiliary part)	Irregular sedimentation; Abrasion; Changed in history	30	
	Scree (Ground pavement)	Partly lost	40	Hidden under sullage
	5-Color-Slate(Path and Ground apron)	Irregular sedimentation; Efflorescence and exfoliation; Abrasion	40	
IV	Brick(Ground Pavement, Path and Ground apron)	Irregular sedimentation; Abrasion; Changed in history	40	Time of changes not clear
	Scree(Ground pavement)	Partly lost	40	In front of the Building of Cloud Light
	5-Color-Slate(Ground pavement, path and Ground apron)	Irregular sedimentation; Efflorescence and exfoliation; Abrasion	30	In front of the Building of Wish and Reality in Accordance

5.3.3 庭院陈设和陈设座

与文人花园和其他皇家园林不同，宁寿宫花园采用了一种极为奢侈的方式来展现财富和品位。在庭院中，极其丰富的陈设和陈设座便是这种做法的集中体现。至今保存有很多配有陈设座的庭院陈设，但是仍然有相当数量的陈设座或残缺不全，或倾倒弃置。据此推断，在乾隆时期，庭院陈设的密度是远高于今天所见的。

兹将勘察发现的所有陈设座及其上陈设整理如下表。

院号	陈设座编号	保存状况	陈设	保存状况
I	1001	良好	铜水缸	良好
	1002	良好	铜水缸	良好
	1003	良好	铜灯	失
	1004	良好	铜灯	失
	1005	良好	铜瓶	失
	1006	良好	铜瓶	失
	1007	良好	铜瓶	失
	1008	良好	铜瓶	失
	1009	良好	铜瓶	失
	1010	良好	铜瓶	失
	1011	良好	山石	良好
	1012	良好	山石	残缺
	1013	良好	山石	残缺
	1014	良好	山石	良好
	1015	良好	山石	良好
	1016	良好	铜瓶	失
	1017	良好	铜瓶	失
	1018	良好	铜瓶	失
	1019	良好	铜瓶	失
	1020	良好	铜灯	良好
	1021	良好	铜灯	良好
II	2001	良好	铜瓶	失
	2002	良好	铜瓶	失
	2003	良好	铜瓶	失
	2004	良好	铜瓶	失
	2005	良好	铜瓶	失
	2006	良好	铜瓶	失
	2007	良好	铜瓶	失
	2008	良好	铜瓶	失
	2009	残	铜瓶	失
	2010	良好	石	良好
	2011	良好	石	良好
	2012	良好	石	良好
	2013	良好	石	良好
	2014	良好		失
	2015	良好		失
	2016	良好	玉石	良好

第一进院地面铺墁做法举例

第二进院地面铺墁做法举例

第三进院地面铺墁做法举例

乾隆花园
故宫博物院宁寿宫花园历史研究与文物保护规划

第四进院地面铺墁做法举例

5.3.3 Displaying & Pedestal

Unlike most of literati's gardens and even most of other imperial gardens, Qianlong Garden had displayed in its history a strong sense of wealth and taste. There are still many pieces of courtyard displaying survived to present time, though many are lost and only leave their pedestals lying or standing, sepatated or damaged. The vestiges show that during Qianlong's time, the density of courtyard displaying must have been much higher than what we see today.

The survey and damage assessment is listed in the table below.

Courtyard	Pedestal ID	Pedestal Status	Displaying	Display Status
I	1001	Good	Copper Vat	Good
	1002	Good	Copper Vat	Good
	1003	Good	Copper Lamp	Missing
	1004	Good	Copper Lamp	Missing
	1005	Good	Copper Vase	Missing
	1006	Good	Copper Vase	Missing
	1007	Good	Copper Vase	Missing
	1008	Good	Copper Vase	Missing
	1009	Good	Copper Vase	Missing
	1010	Good	Copper Vase	Missing
	1011	Good	Ornamental Rock	Good
	1012	Good	Ornamental Rock	Damaged
	1013	Good	Ornamental Rock	Damaged
	1014	Good	Ornamental Rock	Good
	1015	Good	Ornamental Rock	Good
	1016	Good	Copper Vase	Missing
	1017	Good	Copper Vase	Missing
	1018	Good	Copper Vase	Missing
	1019	Good	Copper Vase	Missing
	1020	Good	Copper Lamp	Good
	1021	Good	Copper Lamp	Good
II	2001	Good	Copper Vase	Missing
	2002	Good	Copper Vase	Missing
	2003	Good	Copper Vase	Missing
	2004	Good	Copper Vase	Missing
	2005	Good	Copper Vase	Missing
	2006	Good	Copper Vase	Missing
	2007	Good	Copper Vase	Missing
	2008	Good	Copper Vase	Missing
	2009	Damaged	Copper Vase	Missing
	2010	Good	Ornamental Rock	Good
	2011	Good	Ornamental Rock	Good
	2012	Good	Ornamental Rock	Good
	2013	Good	Ornamental Rock	Good
	2014	Good		Missing
	2015	Good		Missing
	2016	Good	Jade	Good

院号	陈设座编号	保存状况	陈设	保存状况
III	3001	良好		失
	3002	良好		失
	3003	残		失
	3004	良好		失
	3005	良好		失
	3006	良好	石	良好
	3007	良好		失
	3008	良好	石	良好
	3009		石桌	缺腿二条
IV	4001	残		失
	4002	残		失
	4003	良好	铜瓶	良好
	4004	良好	铜瓶	良好
	4005	良好	石	良好
	4006	良好	石	良好
	4007	良好	石	良好
	4008	良好	铜缸	良好
	4009	良好	铜缸	良好
	4010	残		失
	4011	良好		失
	4012	良好		失
	4013	良好	玉马	失
	4014	良好	玉马	失
	4015	良好	铜缸	良好
	4016	良好	铜缸	良好
	4017	良好	铜缸	良好
	4018	良好	铜缸	良好
	4019	良好	石	良好
	4020	良好	石	良好
	4021	良好	石	良好
	4022	良好	石	良好
	4023	良好	铜瓶	良好
	4024	良好	铜瓶	良好
	4025	良好	铜瓶	良好
	4026	良好	铜瓶	良好
	4027		石桌	缺腿一条

衍祺门前陈设水缸　　　　古华轩前陈设石座

遂初堂周围陈设石座

耸秀亭前假山上陈设石座　　　　萃赏楼周围陈设石座

三友轩周围陈设石座

竹香馆前的景观石及其石座

云光楼周围散落陈设石座

符望阁周围陈设石座

遂玉粹轩旁陈设山石　　倦勤斋前陈设及其石座

Courtyard	Pedestal ID	Pedestal Status	Displaying	Display Status
III	3001	Good		Missing
	3002	Good		Missing
	3003	Damaged		Missing
	3004	Good		Missing
	3005	Good		Missing
	3006	Good	Ornamental Rock	Good
	3007	Good		Missing
	3008	Good	Ornamental Rock	Good
	3009		Stone Table	Two broken legs
IV	4001	Damaged		Missing
	4002	Damaged		Missing
	4003	Good	Copper Vase	Good
	4004	Good	Copper Vase	Good
	4005	Good	Ornamental Rock	Good
	4006	Good	Ornamental Rock	Good
	4007	Good	Ornamental Rock	Good
	4008	Good	Copper Vat	Good
	4009	Good	Copper Vat	Good
	4010	Damaged		Missing
	4011	Good		Missing
	4012	Good		Missing
	4013	Good	Jade Horse	Missing
	4014	Good	Jade Horse	Missing
	4015	Good	Copper Vat	Good
	4016	Good	Copper Vat	Good
	4017	Good	Copper Vat	Good
	4018	Good	Copper Vat	Good
	4019	Good	Ornamental Rock	Good
	4020	Good	Ornamental Rock	Good
	4021	Good	Ornamental Rock	Good
	4022	Good	Ornamental Rock	Good
	4023	Good	Copper Vase	Good
	4024	Good	Copper Vase	Good
	4025	Good	Copper Vase	Good
	4026	Good	Copper Vase	Good
	4027		Stone Table	1 Broken leg

5.4 绿化系统调查

宁寿宫花园中的植物可以分为乔木、竹丛、灌木和花卉。其中古乔木是最重要的历史遗存，并且一直以来作为国家和故宫的重要保护对象，植株和树种具有完整的记录和编号体系。

5.4.1 植物明细表

宁寿宫花园中共有主要植物93株/丛，其中古树53株，普通乔木/灌木（近50年内栽种者）40株/丛，竹不计在内。

北京地区编号	故宫博物院编号	树种	大约树龄	树干直径	所在院落	重要等级
B01104	B01-0312	侧柏	300	70	1	2
B01103	B01-0311	侧柏	300	60	1	2
B00884	B02-0203	桧柏	300	—	1	2
—	—	桧柏	50	—	1	3
B01102	B01-0310	侧柏	300	—	1	2
—	—	侧柏	50	—	1	3
B00883	B02-0202	桧柏	300	50	1	2
—	—	桧柏	50	—	1	3
B00882	B02-0201	桧柏	300	50	1	2
B01101	B01-0309	侧柏	300	60	1	2
B00881	B02-0200	桧柏	300	50	1	2
—	—	海棠	50	—	1	3
B01100	B01-0308	侧柏	300	60	1	2
—	—	丁香	50	—	1	3
—	—	桧柏	50	—	1	3
B00885	B02-0204	桧柏	300	80	1	2
B00886	B02-0205	桧柏	300	—	1	2
—	—	侧柏	50	—	1	3
—	—	榆叶梅	20	—	1	3
B00887	B02-0206	桧柏	300	50	1	2
—	—	侧柏	50	—	1	3
—	—	桧柏	50	—	1	3
—	—	太平花	20	—	1	3
A00172	A01-0173	侧柏	400	100	1	1
A00171	A01-0172	侧柏	400	70	1	1
B00771	B04-0001	油松	300	50	1	2
—	—	侧柏	50	—	1	3
—	—	海棠	50	—	1	3
B00880	B02-0199	桧柏	300	60	1	2
—	—	侧柏	50	—	1	3
B20334	B01-0342	侧柏	300	60	1	2
B01099	B01-0307	侧柏	300	60	1	2
B00879	B02-0198	桧柏	300	60	1	2
A00853	A09-0010	楸树	500	60	1	1

北京地区编号	故宫博物院编号	树种	大约树龄	树干直径	所在院落	重要等级
B00888	B02-0207	桧柏	300	60	1	2
B00889	B02-0208	桧柏	300	40	1	2
A00717	A09-0009	楸树	400	100	1	1
—	—	楸树	50	—	1	3
B01105	B01-0313	侧柏	300	—	1	2
—	—	太平花	20	—	1	3
—	—	太平花	20	—	1	3
B20324	B01-0341	侧柏	300	40	1	2
B00890	B02-0209	桧柏	300	70	1	2
—	—	榆叶梅	50	—	1	3
—	—	侧柏	50	—	1	3
—	—	桧柏	50	—	2	3
B00891	B02-0197	桧柏	300	60	2	2
B00874	B02-0192	桧柏	300	—	2	2
—	—	桧柏	50	—	2	3
B00878	B02-0196	桧柏	300	50	2	2
—	—	桧柏	50	—	2	3
—	—	桧柏	50	—	2	3
B00875	B02-0193	桧柏	300	60	2	2
—	—	丁香	50	—	2	3
B00877	B02-0195	桧柏	300	—	2	2
B00876	B02-0194	桧柏	300	—	2	2
-（残根）	-（残根）	香椿	300	—	3	2
—	—	侧柏	50	—	3	3
A00888	A02-0092	桧柏	400	—	3	1
—	—	油松	50	—	3	3
B01098	B01-0305	侧柏	300	—	3	2
—	—	丁香	50	—	3	3
B00873	B02-0180	桧柏	300	—	3	2
—	—	桧柏	50	—	3	3
B00869	B02-0189	桧柏	300	—	3	2
—	—	侧柏	50	—	3	3
B00870	B02-190	桧柏	300	—	3	2
—	—	侧柏	50	—	3	3
B00871	B02-0191	桧柏	300	—	3	2
—	—	侧柏	50	—	3	3
B01097	B01-0304	侧柏	300	—	3	2
B01095	B01-0303	侧柏	300	—	4	2
—	—	侧柏	50	—	4	3
B00868	B01-0187	侧柏	300	—	4	2
B01094	B01-0302	侧柏	300	—	4	2
—	—	侧柏	50	—	4	3
—	—	侧柏	50	—	4	3
—	—	丁香	50	—	4	3
—	—	侧柏	50	—	4	3
B89496	B01-0301	侧柏	300	—	4	2

Beijing ID	Museum ID	Species	App. Age	Trunk (cm)	Courtyard	Grade
B00888	B02-0207	Chinese Juniper	300	60	I	2
B00889	B02-0208	Chinese Juniper	300	40	I	2
A00717	A09-0009	Manchurian Catalpa	400	100	I	1
—	—	Manchurian Catalpa	50	—	I	3
B01105	B01-0313	Chinese Arborvitae	300	—	I	2
—	—	Beijing Mockorange	20	—	I	3
—	—	Beijing Mockorange	20	—	I	3
B20324	B01-0341	Chinese Arborvitae	300	40	I	2
B00890	B02-0209	Chinese Juniper	300	70	I	2
—	—	Flowering Akmond	50	—	I	3
—	—	Chinese Arborvitae	50	—	I	3
—	—	Chinese Juniper	50	—	II	3
B00891	B02-0197	Chinese Juniper	300	60	II	2
B00874	B02-0192	Chinese Juniper	300	—	II	2
—	—	Chinese Juniper	50	—	II	3
B00878	B02-0196	Chinese Juniper	300	50	II	2
—	—	Chinese Juniper	50	—	II	3
—	—	Chinese Juniper	50	—	II	3
B00875	B02-0193	Chinese Juniper	300	60	II	2
—	—	Clove,	50	—	II	3
B00877	B02-0195	Chinese Juniper	300	—	II	2
B00876	B02-0194	Chinese Juniper	300	—	II	2
- (Stub)	- (Stub)	Chinese Toona	300	—	III	2
—	—	Chinese Arborvitae	50	—	III	3
A00888	A02-0092	Chinese Juniper	400	—	III	1
—	—	Chinese Pine	50	—	III	3
B01098	B01-0305	Chinese Arborvitae	300	—	III	2
—	—	Clove	50	—	III	3
B00873	B02-0180	Chinese Juniper	300	—	III	2
—	—	Chinese Juniper	50	—	III	3
B00869	B02-0189	Chinese Juniper	300	—	III	2
—	—	Chinese Arborvitae	50	—	III	3
B00870	B02-190	Chinese Juniper	300	—	III	2
—	—	Chinese Arborvitae	50	—	III	3
B00871	B02-0191	Chinese Juniper	300	—	III	2
—	—	Chinese Arborvitae	50	—	III	3
B01097	B01-0304	Chinese Arborvitae	300	—	III	2
B01095	B01-0303	Chinese Arborvitae	300	—	IV	2
—	—	Chinese Arborvitae	50	—	IV	3
B00868	B01-0187	Chinese Arborvitae	300	—	IV	2
B01094	B01-0302	Chinese Arborvitae	300	—	IV	2
—	—	Chinese Arborvitae	50	—	IV	3
—	—	Chinese Arborvitae	50	—	IV	3
—	—	Clove	50	—	IV	3
—	—	Chinese Arborvitae	50	—	IV	3
B89496	B01-0301	Chinese Arborvitae	300	—	IV	2

5.4 Status Quo of Horticultural Items

Horticultural items in Qianlong Garden can be classified into four categories, i.e. tree, bamboo, shrub and flower, among which trees are also strictly identified according to the age and species.

5.4.1 List of Plants

There are 93 major plant items in the Qianlong Garden, among which 53 are ancient trees and 40 trees and shrubs are planted in the recent 50 years. Bamboo is not included in this statistic table.

Beijing ID	Museum ID	Species	App. Age	Trunk (cm)	Courtyard	Grade
B01104	B01-0312	Chinese Arborvitae	300	70	I	2
B01103	B01-0311	Chinese Arborvitae	300	60	I	2
B00884	B02-0203	Chinese Juniper	300	—	I	2
—	—	Chinese Juniper	50	—	I	3
B01102	B01-0310	Chinese Arborvitae	300	—	I	2
—	—	Chinese Arborvitae	50	—	I	3
B00883	B02-0202	Chinese Juniper	300	50	I	2
—	—	Chinese Juniper	50	—	I	3
B00882	B02-0201	Chinese Juniper	300	50	I	2
B01101	B01-0309	Chinese Arborvitae	300	60	I	2
B00881	B02-0200	Chinese Juniper	300	50	I	2
—	—	Chinese Crabapple	50	—	I	3
B01100	B01-0308	Chinese Arborvitae	300	60	I	2
—	—	Clove	50	—	I	3
—	—	Chinese Juniper	50	—	I	3
B00885	B02-0204	Chinese Juniper	300	80	I	2
B00886	B02-0205	Chinese Juniper	300	—	I	2
—	—	Chinese Arborvitae	50	—	I	3
—	—	Flowering Akmond	20	—	I	3
B00887	B02-0206	Chinese Juniper	300	50	I	2
—	—	Chinese Arborvitae	50	—	I	3
—	—	Chinese Juniper	50	—	I	3
—	—	Beijing Mockorange	20	—	I	3
A00172	A01-0173	Chinese Arborvitae	400	100	I	1
A00171	A01-0172	Chinese Arborvitae	400	70	I	1
B00771	B04-0001	Chinese Pine	300	50	I	2
—	—	Chinese Arborvitae	50	—	I	3
—	—	Chinese Crabapple	50	—	I	3
B00880	B02-0199	Chinese Juniper	300	60	I	2
—	—	Chinese Arborvitae	50	—	I	3
B20334	B01-0342	Chinese Arborvitae	300	60	I	2
B01099	B01-0307	Chinese Arborvitae	300	60	I	2
B00879	B02-0198	Chinese Juniper	300	60	I	2
A00853	A09-0010	Manchurian Catalpa	500	60	I	1

北京地区编号	故宫博物院编号	树种	大约树龄	树干直径	所在院落	重要等级
B00867	B02 — 0186	桧柏	300	—	4	2
B00863	B02 — 0182	桧柏	300	70	4	2
B00862	B02 — 0181	桧柏	300	60	4	2
B18555	B01 — 0353	侧柏	300	—	4	2
—	—	侧柏	50	—	4	3
B01093	B01 — 0299	侧柏	300	—	4	2
B00866	B02 — 0185	桧柏	300	—	4	2
B01092	B01 — 0300	侧柏	300	—	4	2
B00865	B02 — 0184	桧柏	300	50	4	2
—	—	黑枣	40	—	4	3
B00864	B02 — 0183	桧柏	300	50	4	2
B00861	B02 — 0180	桧柏	300	70	4	2

5.4.2 土壤样本检测报告

取样位置	树木编号	取样深度(cm)	有机质(g/kg)	全氮(g/kg)	速效磷(mg/kg)	速效钾(mg/kg)	pH	EC(ms/cm)
IV-07 竹香馆	B00865	0～20	71.06	2.140	3.25	120	7.87	0.210
		45～50	15.20	0.306	2.47	170	8.16	0.200
评估			高	中等	极低	高	碱性	非盐渍化土
IV-03 倦勤斋	B00863 B00864	0～20	46.24	1.612	3.41	180	7.63	0.285
评估			高	中等	极低	高	碱性	非盐渍化土
III-03 三友轩	B00868	0～20	58.58	1.822	4.18	190	7.49	0.200
评估			高	中等	极低	高	碱性	非盐渍化土
III-02 翠赏楼	B00873	0～20	45.33	1.051	5.25	120	7.33	0.500
评估			高	中等	低	高	中性	非盐渍化土
I-02 古华轩		0～20	27.35	0.935	3.34	180	7.24	0.210
评估			高	低	极低	高	中性	非盐渍化土
I-04 矩亭		0～20	35.90	1.416	2.96	230	7.75	0.185
评估			高	中等	极低	高	碱性	非盐渍化土

土壤一般化学性质

宁寿宫花园第一进院落庭院绿化小景

宁寿宫花园第二进院落庭院绿化小景

宁寿宫花园第三、四进院落庭院绿化小景

宁寿宫花园第四进院落庭院绿化小景

Beijing ID	Museum ID	Species	App. Age	Trunk (cm)	Courtyard	Grade
B00867	B02-0186	Chinese Juniper	300	—	IV	2
B00863	B02-0182	Chinese Juniper	300	70	IV	2
B00862	B02-0181	Chinese Juniper	300	60	IV	2
B18555	B01-0353	Chinese Arborvitae	300	—	IV	2
—	—	Chinese Arborvitae	50	—	IV	3
B01093	B01-0299	Chinese Arborvitae	300	—	IV	2
B00866	B02-0185	Chinese Juniper	300	—	IV	2
B01092	B01-0300	Chinese Arborvitae	300	—	IV	2
B00865	B02-0184	Chinese Juniper	300	50	IV	2
—	—	Dateplumb Persimmon	40	—	IV	3
B00864	B02-0183	Chinese Juniper	300	50	IV	2
B00861	B02-0180	Chinese Juniper	300	70	IV	2

5.4.2 Chemical and Physical Analyses of Soil Samples

Chemical Properties of Soil Samples

Site	Tree ID	Depth (cm)	Organic (g/kg)	Pan-N (g/kg)	APA (mg/kg)	Active K (mg/kg)	pH	EC (ms/cm)
IV-07	B00865	0 ~ 20	71.06	2.14	3.25	120	7.87	0.210
		45 ~ 50	15.20	0.306	2.47	170	8.16	0.200
Assessment			High	Medium	Too Low	High	Alkalescent	Non-salted
IV-03	B00863 B00864	0 ~ 20	46.24	1.612	3.41	180	7.63	0.285
Assessment			High	Medium	Too Low	High	Alkalescent	Non Saltaffected Soil
III-03	B00868	0 ~ 20	58.58	1.822	4.18	190	7.49	0.200
Assessment			High	Medium	Too Low	High	Alkalescent	Non Saltaffected Soil
III-02	B00873	0 ~ 20	45.33	1.051	5.25	120	7.33	0.500
Assessment			High	Medium	Low	High	Neutral	Non Saltaffected Soil
I-02		0 ~ 20	27.35	0.935	3.34	180	7.24	0.210
Assessment			High	Low	Too Low	High	Neutral	Non Saltaffected Soil
I-04		0 ~ 20	35.90	1.416	2.96	230	7.75	0.185
Assessment			High	Medium	Too Low	High	Alkalescent	Non Saltaffected Soil

土壤一般物理性质

院落	古树编号	采样深度(cm)	密度(g/cm³)	相对密度	总孔隙度(%)	田间持水量(%)	质地	黏粒(%)(<0.002mm)	渗透系数(mm/min)	湿度(%)
IV-07 竹香馆	B00865	0~20	2.55	1.20	50.9	22.5	砂黏壤	16	0.53	18.0
		45~50	2.60	1.45	44.2	21.0	砂壤	11	0.30	16.5
评估							适中			
IV-03 倦勤斋	B00863 B00864	0~20	2.56	1.24	51.5	23.4	砂黏壤	21	0.40	15.8
评估			适中	适中	适中	适中				适中
III-03 三友轩	B00868	0~20	2.59	1.13	56.4	26.2	砂黏壤	21	0.52	15.0
评估			适中	适中	适中	适中				适中
III-02 翠赏楼	B00873	0~20	2.58	0.69	73.3	47.0	砂黏壤	19	2.84	15.4
评估			适中	高	高	适中				良好
I-02 古华轩		0~20	2.61	1.22	53.2	22.3	砂黏壤	23	0.48	16.5
评估			适中	适中	适中	适中				适中
I-04 矩亭		0~20	2.64	1.14	56.8	29.1	砂黏壤	21	0.34	16.7
评估			适中	适中	适中	适中				适中

各院落土壤微量元素及重金属元素含量

院落	古树编号	层次(cm)	B(mg/kg)	Cu(mg/kg)	Zn(mg/kg)	Fe(g/kg)	Mn(mg/kg)	Pb(mg/kg)	Mo(mg/kg)	Cd(mg/kg)
IV-07 竹香馆	B00865	0~20	1.28	60.4	65.1	12.0	297	92.8	0.67	4.05
		45~50	3.47	156	146.0	14.0	360	219	1.49	3.86
IV-03 倦勤斋	B00863 B00864	0~20	2.54	236	187.0	14.1	381	180	2.60	4.59
III-03 三友轩	B00868	0~20	1.89	295	292.0	15.5	433	207	1.90	4.31
III-02 翠赏楼	B00868	0~20	2.25	183	107.0	14.1	336	263	2.98	3.85
II-02 古华轩		0~20	3.37	187	65.1	15.5	405	182	0.31	4.58
I-04 矩亭		0~20	2.52	128	114.0	16.8	425	179	2.18	4.50

古树土层动物区系调查报

取样地点	取样方法	样本数量	样本尺寸(cm)	深度(cm)	昆虫	昆虫密度
IV-07 竹香馆	挖土取样	1	90×50×55	0~15	谷婪步甲成虫3头，幼虫8头；福婆鳃金龟幼虫1头	26.6头/m² 92.3%
				16~30	谷婪步甲幼虫1头	2.2头/m² 7.7%
				31~55	无	
IV-03 倦勤斋	土钻取样	4	—	20	福婆鳃金龟幼虫1头	88.2头/m²
III-03 三友轩	挖土取样	1	30×30×5	5	福婆鳃金龟幼虫3头	33.3头/m²
III-02 翠赏楼	土钻取样	4	—	20	福婆鳃金龟幼虫1头	88.2头/m²
II-02 古华轩	土钻取样	4	—	20	福婆鳃金龟幼虫1头	88.2头/m²

5.4.3 土质和植物生长评价

(1) 所研究的各个院落中土壤有机质的含量均高，在15~71g/kg之间；土壤的氮素处于中等水平，在1~2g/kg之间；所有土壤均显示极低的土壤速效磷水平，多在5mg/kg以下，建议施用磷肥；土壤速效钾的含量高，在120mg/kg以上；土壤显碱性，应改良成中性或微酸性；土壤无盐渍化现象。

(2) 研究结果显示各个院落土壤的物理性质均适中，无不良土壤物理性质。土壤的比重在2.6左右；土壤的容重在1.2左右；土壤属砂黏壤，质地适中；土壤中含有20%的黏粒；土壤有23%~30%的田间持水量，土壤总孔隙度在55%左右；土壤有适中的渗透性。

(3) 土壤中有效硼充足，其含量在1.3~3.5mg/kg之间。土壤全铜的含量比世界平均水平（20mg/kg）多3至10倍，在60~300mg/kg之间。土壤全锌含量在65~292mg/kg之间，比世界平均水平（50mg/kg）多。我国土壤全锰量在42~3000mg/kg之间，各个院落土壤全锰量比我国平均水平（710mg/kg）要少。我国土壤中全铁的含量在35~70g/kg之间，各个院落土壤全铁的含量在12~15g/kg，比全国水平要低。我国土壤中全钼的含量在0.1~7.0mg/kg之间，各个院落土壤全钼的含量在0.3~2.98mg/kg之间。我国非污染土壤中铅的含量在3~198mg/kg之间，一些院落中土壤全铅的含量偏高。各个院落土壤中镉的含量在3.86~4.59mg/kg之间，大于土壤中镉污染的临界值（1mg/kg）。

(4) 需要指出的是由于本次土壤采样只采集了土壤0~20cm的表层土壤进行分析，所得结果不能反映深层土壤的情况，在应用本研究结果时请只作参考。

Insect in Soil Samples

Site	Sampling Method	Sample Number	Sample Size (cm)	Depth (cm)	Insect	Insect Density
IV-07	Digging	1	90×50×55	0-15	Harpalus calealus, Imago 3, Larva 8 Brahmina faldermann, Larva 1	26.6 insect/ m² 92.3%
				16-30	Harpalus calealus, Larva 1	2.2 insect/ m² 7.7%
				31-55	No	
IV-03	Drilling	4	-	20	Harpalus calealus, Larva 1	88.2 insect/ m²
III-03	Digging	1	30×30×5	5	Harpalus calealus, Larva 3	33.3 insect/ m²
III-02	Drilling	4	-	20	Harpalus calealus, Larva 1	88.2 insect/ m²
II-02	Drilling	4	-	20	Harpalus calealus, Larva 1	88.2 insect/ m²

5.4.3 Results of present status of soil and plants

(1) Samples taken from the courtyards are proved to have high organic contents, between 15-71 g/kg. Nitrogenous material is at medium level, between 1-2 g/kg. Phosphoric materials is showed extremely low in the reports, mainly below 5 mg/kg, which means applying phosphoric fertilizer will benefit the plants, while potassic material is high in the samples, mainly above 120 mg/kg. Some of the soil samples are alkalescent, which should be neutralized or turned into weak acid-ish. The soil samples are not salt affected.

(2) Analyses show that soil samples in the courtyards have moderate physical character, bearing no obvious negative threats. Propotions of the samples are around 2.6 g/cm³, and volume weights are around 1.2. Soil is mainly sand clay loam of moderate texture, containing 20% clay particles. Water retaining capacity of the soil is chiefly between 23% to 30%, and the porocity is around 55%, from which we can infer the soil has moderate penetrability.

(3) Active Boron is rich in the samples, with a content between 1.3 and 3.5mg/kg. Pan-Cuprum content, which is between 60-300 mg/kg, is 3 to 10 times higher than global average. Pan-Zincum in the soil is from 65 to 295 mg/kg, higher than the global average, which is 50 mg/kg. Pan-Manganese is between 297 and 433 mg/kg, and when taking into consideration China average Pan-Mn content in soil, which is from 42 to 3000 mg/kg, with an average value of 710 mg/kg, it can be regarded as lower than the country's average. Pan-Ferrum content in the courtyard soil is 12-15 g/kg, lower than the courty standard of 35-70 g/kg. Pan-Molybdenum content of the samples is within the country's average range, 0.3-2.98 mg/kg in 0.1-7.0 mg/kg. In China's non-polluted soil, Plumbum contents is between 3 and 198 mg/kg, while the sample tests prove that in Qianlong Garden soil Pb content is higher. Cadmium content, 3.86-4.59mg/kg, is also proved to be higher

Physical Properties of Soil Samples

Site	Tree ID	Depth (cm)	Propotion (g/cm³)	Volume Weight	Porocity	W-retaining Capacity(%)	Texture	Caly Particle(%) (<0.002mm)	Plastic Index	Moisture (%)
IV-07	B00865	0 ~ 20	2.55	1.20	50.9	22.5	Sandy clay loam	16	0.53	18.0
		45 ~ 50	2.60	1.45	44.2	21.0	Sandy loam	11	0.30	16.5
Assessment				M	M	M	M		M	
IV-03	B00863 B00864	0 ~ 20	2.56	1.24	51.5	23.4	Sandy clay loam	21	0.40	15.8
Assessment				M	M	M	M		M	
III-03	B00868	0 ~ 20	2.59	1.13	56.4	26.2	Sandy clay loam	21	0.52	15.0
Assessment				M	M	M	M		M	
III-02	B00873	0 ~ 20	2.58	0.69	73.3	47.0	Sandy clay loam	19	2.84	15.4
Assessment				M	H	H	M		Good	
I-02		0 ~ 20	2.61	1.22	53.2	22.3	Sandy clay loam	23	0.48	16.5
Assessment				M	M	M	M		M	
I-04		0 ~ 20	2.64	1.14	56.8	29.1	Sandy clay loam	21	0.34	16.7
Assessment				M	M	M	M		M	

Microelements and Heavy Metal Elements Content of Soil Samples

Site	Tree ID	Depth (cm)	B (mg/kg)	Cu (mg/kg)	Zn (mg/kg)	Fe (mg/kg)	Mn (mg/kg)	Pb (mg/kg)	Mo (mg/kg)	Cd (mg/kg)
IV-07	B00865	0-20	1.28	60.4	65.1	12.0	297	92.8	0.67	4.05
		45-50	3.47	156.0	146.0	14.0	360	219.0	1.49	3.86
IV-03	B00863 B00864	0-20	2.54	236.0	187.0	14.1	381	180.0	2.60	4.59
III-03	B00868	0-20	1.89	295.0	292.0	15.5	433	207.0	1.90	4.31
III-02	B00868	0-20	2.25	183.0	107.0	14.1	336	263.0	2.98	3.85
II-02		0-20	3.37	187.0	65.1	15.5	405	182.0	0.31	4.58
I-04		0-20	2.52	128.0	114.0	16.8	425	179.0	2.18	4.50

5.5 建筑普查

5.5.1 文物建筑结构残损评估标准

本规划认为，文物建筑的残损评估的关键在于建立对建筑各部分残损等级的评价和建筑整体残损"值"两个系统。在此应当强调，对文物建筑各部位的残损等级的累计评价只是"加和性"的统计，并不能完全反映文物建筑的整体状况，须结合各组成部位间空间位置关系及其他相关的"不可简单加和"的特征，综合形成对文物建筑整体残损情况的评价。因此，本规划制定以下对文物建筑残损等级的评价标准。

(1) 残损A级，0～20%的构件存在轻度表面残损，无构造变形；

(2) 残损B级，21%～40%的构件存在表面残损，无构造变形；

(3) 残损C级，41%～60%的构件存在显著残损，具有潜在形变等结构问题，或具有轻微结构问题；

(4) 残损D级，大于60%的构件存在严重残损，或存在较严重结构问题。

总体来说对于文物建筑各组成部分——构件组的残损等级确定为A到D四级，以反映构件组中1%～100%的构件的残损，并适当辅助以构件组整体变化的因素。进而，文物建筑的整体残损评估也使用同样的原则，辅助以整体结构形变的因素，为方便下文估算保护经费，以百分比表示整体建筑的残损率。

5.5.2 残损评估调查统计

宁寿宫花园文物建筑残损现状统计如下表。

宁寿宫花园庭院病虫害情况调查工作现场

建筑残损统计				
建筑编号	建筑名称	各部分残损等级	建筑残损评估	图纸编号
I-01	衍祺门	台明，A/B=A；室内地面，C；大木结构，A/C=B；墙体，B；木装修，A；油饰彩画，B；屋面，A	B, 25[1]	
I-02	古华轩	台明，A/C=B；室内地面 B；大木结构，A/C=B；墙体，无；木装修，无；油饰彩画，B；屋面，B	B, 27	

现状勘察图
Drawings for Survey and Analysis
II-04 建筑残损现状平面图
Building and Structure
Survey and Analysis

残损等级1
残损等级2
残损等级3
残损等级4
残损等级5

than soil Cd-pollution level of 1 mg/kg.

(4) It is important to point out that the soil samples are taken from the depth between 0-20 cm, so the result cannot fully show the soil character of deeper locations. Albeit, the reports are used here in the master plan as a basic reference to possible soil improvements.

5.5 Status Quo of Buildings and Structures

5.5.1 Damage Assessment

Damage grade and value are two basic systems for assessment for the building and structure. The author would like to stress that the damage assessment should be based on both plus-ible damages of components and the non-plus-ible damage such as deformation and distortion of the components and among them. Thus the determination of the damage grade also contains an overall judgement of the structure and the damage statistic of the components. The survey is made according to requirement for master plan and a series of damage survey principles as following.

(1) Grade A, for 0%-20% slight superficial damage, and structurally sound,

(2) Grade B, for 21%-40% superficial damage, and structurally sound,

(3) Grade C, for 41%-60% serious superficial damage, or facing obvious structural threat, or having slight structural failure, and

(4) Grade D, for above 60% superficial damage, or having structural failure.

In general the damage is divided into 4 grades from A to D, and each grade covers a damage value ranging respectively from 1-20, 21 to 40, 40 to 60, and >60. Then, the overall damage assessment of a building also follows the same principle and method, by both satistic record and judgement of strutural safety, resulting in percentage numbers, which to be further used in budget estimation.

5.5.2 Table of Damage Survey

Status quo of buildings and structures are listed in the flowing table,

Damage Survey of Buildings and Structures

No.	Building	Component Damage Grade	Damage Evaluation	Drawing Index
I-01	Yanqi Men Gate of Extended Felicity	Platform, A/B=A; Pavement inside the building, C; Structure, A/C=B; Wall, B; Window &door, A; Color Painting, B; Roof, A	B, 251	

建筑残损统计				
建筑编号	建筑名称	各部分残损等级	建筑残损评估	图纸编号
I-03	撷芳亭	台明，A/C=B； 室内地面，A； 大木结构，B/C=C； 墙体，A； 木装修，无； 油饰彩画，B/C=C； 屋面，B	B，30	
I-04	矩亭	台明，A； 室内地面，B； 大木结构，A/B=A； 墙体，A； 木装修，B； 油饰彩画，C； 屋面，A	B，22	
I-05	抑斋	台明，A/B=A； 室内地面，B； 大木结构，A； 墙体，A； 木装修，A； 油饰彩画，B； 屋面，C	B，21	
I-06	承露台	台明，B； 室内地面，B； 大木结构，A； 墙体，A； 木装修，A； 油饰彩画，无； 屋面，无	B，21	
I-07	井亭	台明，A/B=A； 室内地面，B； 大木结构，A/B=A； 墙体，B； 木装修，C； 油饰彩画，C； 屋面，B	B，34	
I-08	禊赏亭	台明，A； 室内地面，B； 大木结构，A/B=A； 墙体，B； 木装修，B； 油饰彩画，B； 屋面，B	A，20	

衍祺门建筑各部位残损状况

古华轩建筑各部位残损状况

赖阗馨琇

故宫博物院宁寿宫花园历史研究与文物保护规划

撷芳亭建筑各部位残损状况

矩亭建筑各部位残损状况

抑斋建筑各部位残损状况

承露台建筑各部位残损状况

Damage Survey of Buildings and Structures

No.	Building	Component Damage Grade	Damage Evaluation	Drawing Index
I-02	Guhua Xuan Pavilion of Ancient Flower	Platform, A/C=B; Pavement inside the building, B; Structure, A/C=B; Wall, No; Window &door, No; Color Painting, B; Roof, B	B, 27	
I-03	Xiefang Ting Pavilion of Embosoming Fragrance	Platform, A/C=B; Pavement inside the building, A; Structure, B/C=C; Wall, A; Window &door, No; Color Painting, B/C=C; Roof, B	B, 30	
I-04	Ju Ting Square Pavilion	Platform, A; Pavement inside the building, B; Structure, A/B=A; Wall, A; Window &door, B; Color Painting, C; Roof, A	B, 22	
I-05	Yi Zhai Chamber of Self Constraint	Platform, A/B=A; Pavement inside the building, B; Structure, A; Wall, A; Window &door, A; Color Painting, B; Roof, C	B, 21	
I-06	Chenglu Tai Dew Platform	Platform, B; Pavement inside the building, B; Structure, A; Wall, A; Window &door, A; Color Painting, No; Roof, No	B, 21	
I-07	Jing Ting Well Pavilion	Platform, A/B=A; Pavement inside the building, B; Structure, A/B=A; Wall, B; Window &door, C; Color Painting, C; Roof, B	B, 34	

建筑编号	建筑名称	各部分残损等级	建筑残损评估	图纸编号
I-09	旭辉庭	台明，A/B=A； 室内地面，B； 大木结构，A； 墙体，B； 木装修，B； 油饰彩画，B； 屋面，B	B，21	
II-01	垂花门	台明，A/C=B； 室内地面，A； 大木结构，A/C=B； 墙体，A； 木装修，B； 油饰彩画，B； 屋面，B	B，23	
II-02	遂初堂	台明，A/C=B； 室内地面，C； 大木结构，A/B=A； 墙体，A； 木装修，B； 油饰彩画，B/C=B； 屋面，B	B，28	
II-03	遂初堂东配殿	台明，A/B=A； 室内地面，B； 大木结构，A； 墙体，A； 木装修，A； 油饰彩画，A； 屋面，A	A，16	
II-04	遂初堂东配殿北耳房	台明，A； 室内地面，A； 大木结构，A/B=B； 墙体，A； 木装修，B； 油饰彩画，B/C=B； 屋面，A	B，21	
II-05	遂初堂东耳房	台明，A/B=B； 室内地面，B； 大木结构，A； 墙体，B； 木装修，B； 油饰彩画，C； 屋面，B	B，26	

井亭建筑各部位残损状况

旭辉庭建筑各部位残损状况

禊赏亭建筑各部位残损状况

遂初堂东配各部位残损状况

垂花门建筑各部位残损状况

遂初堂建筑各部位残损状况

Damage Survey of Buildings and Structures

No.	Building	Component Damage Grade	Damage Evaluation	Drawing Index
I-08	Xishang Ting Pavilion of Floating Cup	Platform, A; Pavement inside the building, B; Structure, A/B=A; Wall, A; Window &door, B; Color Painting, B; Roof, B	A, 20	
I-09	Xuhui Ting Pavilion of Morning Splendour	Platform, A/B=A; Pavement inside the building, B; Structure, A; Wall, B; Window &door, B; Color Painting, B; Roof, B	B, 21	
II-01	Chuihua Men Pendent-flora Gate	Platform, A/C=B; Pavement inside the building, A; Structure, A/C=B; Wall, A; Window &door, B; Color Painting, B; Roof, B	B, 23	
II-02	Suichu Tang Hall of Fulfilment of Original Wishes	Platform, A/C=B; Pavement inside the building, C; Structure, A/B=A; Wall, A; Window &door, B; Color Painting, B/C=B; Roof, B	B, 28	
II-03	East Side Hall of Suichu Tang	Platform, A/B=A; Pavement inside the building, B; Structure, A; Wall, A; Window &door, A; Color Painting, A; Roof, A	A, 16	
II-04	North Ear Room of East Side Hall of Suichu Tang	Platform, A; Pavement inside the building, A; Structure, A/B=B; Wall, A; Window &door, B; Color Painting, B/C=B; Roof, A	B, 21	

		建筑残损统计		
建筑编号	建筑名称	各部分残损等级	建筑残损评估	图纸编号
II-06	遂初堂西配殿	台明，A/B=B； 室内地面，B； 大木结构，A； 墙体，A； 木装修，B； 油饰彩画，A； 屋面，A	A，18	
II-07	遂初堂西耳房	台明，A； 室内地面，B； 大木结构，A； 墙体，A； 木装修，A； 油饰彩画，A； 屋面，A	A，14	
II-08	遂初堂西穿堂	台明，A/C=B； 室内地面，C； 大木结构，A； 墙体，B； 木装修，C； 油饰彩画，D； 屋面，A	B，39	
III-01	耸秀亭	台明，B/C=B； 室内地面，A； 大木结构，A/C=B； 墙体，无； 木装修，B； 油饰彩画，B； 屋面，B	B，25	
III-02	萃赏楼	台明，B/C=B； 室内地面，B； 大木结构，A； 墙体，A； 木装修，A； 油饰彩画，A； 屋面，A	B，21	
III-03	三友轩	台明，A/B=A； 室内地面，B； 大木结构，A/B=A； 墙体，A； 木装修，A； AV 油饰彩画，B； 屋面，A	A，19	

遂初堂西配各部位残损状况

遂初堂东配北耳房建筑各部位残损状况

遂初堂西穿堂残损状况

乾隆潜珍·故宫博物院宁寿宫花园历史研究与文物保护规划

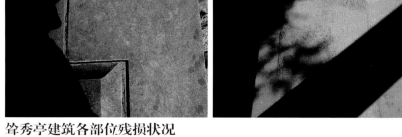

耸秀亭建筑各部位残损状况

Damage Survey of Buildings and Structures

No.	Building	Component Damage Grade	Damage Evaluation	Drawing Index
II-05	East Ear Room of Suichu Tang	Platform, A/B=B; Pavement inside the building, B; Structure, A; Wall, B; Window &door, B; Color Painting, C; Roof, B	B, 26	
II-06	West Side Hall of Suichu Tang	Platform, A/B=B; Pavement inside the building, B; Structure, A; Wall, A; Window &door, B; Color Painting, A; Roof, A	A, 18	
II-07	West Ear Room of Suichu Tang	Platform, A; Pavement inside the building, B; Structure, A; Wall, A; Window &door, A; Color Painting, A; Roof, A	A, 14	
II-08	West Passage Room of Suichu Tang	Platform, A/C=B; Pavement inside the building, C; Structure, A; Wall, A; Window &door, C; Color Painting, D; Roof, A	B, 39	
III-01	Songxiu Ting Pavilion of Aloft Beauty	Platform, B/C=B; Pavement inside the building, A; Structure, A/C=B; Wall, No; Window &door, B; Color Painting, B; Roof, B	B, 25	
III-02	Cuishang Lou Building of Collection and Appreciation	Platform, B/C=B; Pavement inside the building, B; Structure, A; Wall, A; Window &door, A; Color Painting, A; Roof, A	B, 21	
III-03	Sanyou Xuan Pavilion of Three Friends	Platform, A/B=A; Pavement inside the building, B; Structure, A/B=A; Wall, A; Window &door, A; Color Painting, B; Roof, A	A, 19	

建筑残损统计

建筑编号	建筑名称	各部分残损等级	建筑残损评估	图纸编号
III-04	萃赏楼东耳房	台明，A；室内地面，B；大木结构，A；墙体，B；木装修，A；油饰彩画，A；屋面，A	A, 19	
III-05	延趣楼	台明，A/C=B；室内地面，C；大木结构，A；墙体，A；木装修，A；油饰彩画，B；屋面，A	B, 23	
IV-01	碧螺亭	台明，A；室内地面，A；大木结构，A；墙体，B；木装修，A；油饰彩画，A；屋面，A	A, 14	
IV-02	符望阁	台明，B；室内地面，B；大木结构，A/C=B；墙体，A；木装修，A；油饰彩画，B/D=C；屋面，C	B, 30	
IV-03	倦勤斋	台明，A；室内地面，A；大木结构，B；墙体，B；木装修，A；油饰彩画，A；屋面，B	A, 18	
IV-04	云光楼	台明，A/C=B；室内地面，B；大木结构，A；墙体，A；木装修，A；油饰彩画，B；屋面，A	A, 20	

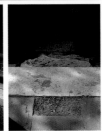

萃赏楼建筑各部位残损状况

三友轩建筑各部位残损状况

萃赏楼东耳房残损状况

延趣楼建筑各部位残损状况

符望阁建筑各部位残损状况

碧螺亭建筑各部位残损状况

Damage Survey of Buildings and Structures

No.	Building	Component Damage Grade	Damage Evaluation	Drawing Index
III-04	East Room of Cuishang Lou	Platform,A; Pavement inside the building, B; Structure, A;Wall, B; Window &door, A; Color Painting, A; Roof, A.	A, 19	
III-05	Yanqu Lou Building of Extended Delight	Platform, A/C=B; Pavement inside the building, C; Structure, A;Wall, A; Window &door, A; Color Painting, B; Roof, A	B, 23	
IV-01	Biluo Ting Pavilion of Emerald Conch	Platform, A; Pavement inside the building, A; Structure, A;Wall, B; Window &door, A; Color Painting, A; Roof, A	A, 14	
IV-02	Fuwang Ge Building of Wish and Reality in Accordance	Platform, B; Pavement inside the building, B; Structure, A/C=B;Wall, A; Window &door,A; Color Painting, B/D=C; Roof, C	B, 30	
IV-03	Juanqin Zhai Lodge of Retirement	Platform, A; Pavement inside the building, A; Structure, B;Wall, B; Window &door, A; Color Painting, A; Roof, B	A, 18	
IV-04	Yunguang Lou Building of Cloud Light	Platform, A/C=B; Pavement inside the building, B; Structure, A;Wall, A; Window &door, A; Color Painting, B; Roof, A	A, 20	
IV-05	Yucui Xuan Pavilion of Jade Purity	Platform, B; Pavement inside the building, B; Structure, A;Wall, A; Window &door, A; Color Painting, B; Roof, B	B, 22	

建筑残损统计				
建筑编号	建筑名称	各部分残损等级	建筑残损评估	图纸编号
IV-05	玉粹轩	台明，B；室内地面，B； 大木结构，A；墙体，A； 木装修，A； 油饰彩画，B； 屋面，B	B, 22	
IV-06	净尘心室	台明，A；室内地面，B； 大木结构，A； 墙体，A；木装修，A； 油饰彩画，A； 屋面，B	A, 18	
IV-07	竹香馆	台明，A/B=A； 室内地面，A； 大木结构，A；墙体，C； 木装修，B； 油饰彩画，A； 屋面，B	B, 21	
IX	第四进院落中游廊		平均A	
	第一至第三进院落中游廊		平均B	

倦勤斋建筑各部位残损状况

云光楼建筑各部位残损状况

5.6 内檐装修调查

5.6.1 内檐装修残损评估标准与统计

鉴于宁寿宫花园内檐装修的丰富性和复杂性，本规划特别将其作为现状勘察的最后一部分进行统计归纳。

尽管宁寿宫花园中的建筑比其他所有现存园林具有更加精美的室内装饰，但是不是每座建筑都有像楼阁、斋室中那样复杂奢华的内檐装修，其中游廊是装饰语汇使用最少的。而具有最复杂室内设计的殿宇的代表性的"室内配置"是这样的：空间由罩隔划分成为众多大小不一的空间；罩隔往往与床张组合成为更小的龛、室；空间中配置各式古典家具；墙上多悬匾联、屏、镜等，并在墙、顶之上裱糊壁纸，壁纸上裱糊贴落画；更有一些建筑中——如宁寿宫花园的第四进院落中，具有极其丰富的"线法"通景画和天顶画。

玉粹轩建筑各部位残损状况

竹香馆建筑各部位残损状况

Damage Survey of Buildings and Structures

No.	Building	Component Damage Grade	Damage Evaluation	Drawing Index
IV-06	Jingchenxin Shi Chamber of Heart Purification	Platform, A; Pavement inside the building, B; Structure, A; Wall, A; Window &door, A; Color Painting, A; Roof, B	A, 18	
IV-07	Zhuxiang Guan Chamber of Bamboo Fragrance	Platform, A/B=A; Pavement inside the building, A; Structure, A; Wall, C; Window &door, B; Color Painting, A; Roof, B	B, 21	
IX	Corridors in 4th courtyard		Average A	
	Corridors in 1st to 3rd courtyard		Average B	

5.6 Status Quo of Interior Features

5.6.1 General Interior Damage Assessment

The part of interior features of the buildings in Qianlong Garden is intentionally put in the last section of this chapter for its rich variety and extraordinary contents of each sort.

Interior spaces of pavilions usually have not as many interior screenings as that in lodges and closed buildings, and corridors are no more than linking units so that they are even less decorated. It is the similar case in the Qianlong Garden, though the way of decoration and interior features are far more sophisticated and delicate than those in any extant garden buildings elsewhere. Generally a most representative interior of the garden building may include a series of spatial screenings with beds or sitting beds at necessary places, some platforms in a niche or chamber, a traditional layout of furniture, hanging tablets or screens on walls, painting or calligraphy Tie'luo mounted on walls, wallpaper on ceiling and walls, and in the most interesting spaces in the fourth courtyard, many buildings have tromp l'oeil paintings on walls.

Interior feature survey is made according to requirement of the master plan and a series of damage survey principles as following,

(1) Grade A, for 0%-20% slight superficial damage, and structurally sound,

(2) Grade B, for 20%-40% superficial damage, and structurally sound,

本规划对于内檐装修残损现状的勘察和评估基于以下标准：

（1）残损A级，0%～20%的构件存在轻度表面残损，无构造形变；

（2）残损B级，21%～40%的构件存在表面残损，无构造变形；

（3）残损C级，41%～60%的构件存在显著残损，具有潜在形变等结构问题，或具有轻微结构问题；

（4）残损D级，大于60%的构件存在严重残损，或存在较严重结构问题。

总体来说对于内檐装修各组成部分——大边、屉心、镶嵌、衬板、夹纱等的残损等级确定为A到D四级，以反映构件组中1%至100%的构件的残损，并适当辅助以构件组成整体变化的因素。进而，每槽内檐装修的整体残损评估也使用同样的原则，辅助以整体结构形变的因素，为方便下文估算保护经费，以百分比表示各槽装修的残损率。

兹将宁寿宫花园中各座建筑的各种内檐装修语汇的勘察评估结果整理如下：

宁寿宫花园建筑内檐装修总体调查				
建筑编号	建筑名称	内檐装修	数量	平均残损系数
I-01	衍祺门	无		
I-02	古华轩	罩隔	8	C, 50 Max 50 Min 50
		楠木雕刻天花	1	B, 30
		匾额	7	A, 18
I-03	撷芳亭	无		
I-04	矩亭	无		
I-05	抑斋	罩隔	1	A, 15
		地平	3	A, 10
		壁板/饰	3	A, 10
		壁纸		D, 100
I-06	承露台	无		
I-07	井亭	无		
I-08	禊赏亭	无		
I-09	旭辉庭	罩隔	2	C, 40
		壁纸		D, 70
II-01	垂花门	无		
II-02	遂初堂	罩隔1	5 （1槽缺失）	B, 28 Max 32 Min 23
		壁纸		D, 100
II-03	遂初堂东配殿	有待研究复原		
II-04	遂初堂东配殿北耳	无		
II-05	遂初堂东耳	无		
II-06	遂初堂西配殿	有待研究复原		

古华轩内檐装修现存状况

故宫博物院宁寿宫花园历史研究与文物保护规划

抑斋内檐装修现存状况

(3) Grade C, for 40%-60% serious superficial damage, or facing obvious structural threat, or having slight structural failure, and

(4) Grade D, for above 60% superficial damage, or having structural failure.

In general the survey is listed according to extant interior features in a building, and the status quo of each item of a interior feature type is divided into 4 grades from A to D, with each grade covering a damage value ranging respectively from 1 to 20, 21 to 40, 41 to 60, and >60, and every damage value of a certain feature is calculated according to the average value of all individual items of the feature type. Then, the overall damage assessment of every single spatial partition / other interior decorative or functional element also follows the same principle and method, by both satistic record and judgement of strutural safety, resulting in percentage numbers, which to be further used in budget estimation. See the list below.

General Survey of Interior Features

No.	Building	Interior Features	Number	Avrg. Damage Evaluation
I-01	Yanqi Men, Gate of Extended Felicity	No		
I-02	Guhua Xuan, Pavilion of Ancient Flower	Screen	8	C, 50 Max 50 Min 50
		Carved Ceiling	1	B, 30
		Tablet	7	A, 18
I-03	Xiefang Ting, Pavilion of Embosoming Fragrance	No		
I-04	Ju Ting, Square Pavilion	No		
I-05	Yi Zhai, Chamber of Self Constraint	Screen	1	A,15
		Platform	3	A, 10
		Wall Tablet	3	A, 10
		Wallpaper		D, 100
I-06	Chenglu Tai, Dew Platform	No		
I-07	Jing Ting, Well Pavilion	No		
I-08	Xishang Ting, Pavilion of Floating Cup	No		
I-09	Xuhui Ting, Pavilion of Morning Splendour	Screen	2	C, 40
		Wallpaper		D, 70
II-01	Chuihua Men, Pendent-flora Gate	No		
II-02	Suichu Tang, Hall of Fulfilment of Original Wishes	Screen1	5 1 Missing	B, 28 Max 32 Min 23
		Wallpaper		D, 100
II-03	East Side Hall of Suichu Tang	Calls for Interior Reconstitution		
II-04	North Ear Room of East Side Hall of Suichu Tang	No		
II-05	East Ear Room of Suichu Tang	No		

宁寿宫花园建筑内檐装修总体调查

建筑编号	建筑名称	内檐装修	数量	平均残损系数
III-01	耸秀亭	无		
III-02	萃赏楼	罩隔	15	B, 22 Max 40 Min 13
		地平	2	A, 20
		楼梯	2	B, 30
		贴落	12	C, 50
		家具	27	A, 15
		壁纸		D, 80
III-03	三友轩	罩隔	5	B, 27 Max 37 Min 23
		地平	2	A, 20
		贴落	16	B, 20
		家具	16	A, 10
		壁纸		D, 80
III-05	延趣楼	罩隔	10	B, 33 Max 45 Min 14
		楼梯	1	B, 37
		贴落	1, 缺失情况不详	B, 30
		家具	17	A, 15
		壁纸		D, 80
IV-01	碧螺亭	天花	1	A, 10
IV-02	符望阁	罩隔	44 (历史上曾移动一槽1)	B, 27 Max 67 Min 10
		地平	3	A, 12
		楼梯	6	C, 42 Max 57 Min 37
		天花	2	B, 35
		贴落	缺失不详	
		家具	?	
		壁纸		D, 80

萃赏楼内檐装修现存状况

旭辉庭内檐装修现存状况

遂初堂内檐装修现存状况

三友轩内檐装修现存状况

萃赏楼内檐装修现存状况

延趣楼内檐装修现存状况

General Survey of Interior Features

No.	Building	Interior Features	Number	Avrg. Damage Evaluation
II-06	West Side Hall of Suichu Tang	Calls for Interior Reconstitution		
III-01	Songxiu Ting Pavilion of Aloft Beauty	No		
III-02	Cuishang Lou Building of Collection and Appreciation	Screen	15	B, 22 Max 40 Min 13
		Platform	2	A, 20
		Stair	2	B, 30
		Tie'luo	12	C, 50
		Furniture	27	A, 15
		Wallpaper		D, 80
III-03	Sanyou Xuan Pavilion of Three Friends	Screen	5	B, 27 Max 37 Min 23
		Platform	2	A, 20
		Tie'luo	16	B, 20
		Furniture	16	A, 10
		Wallpaper		D, 80
III-05	Yanqu Lou Building of Extended Delight	Screen	10	B, 33 Max 45 Min 14
		Stair	1	B, 37
		Tie'luo	1 (? Missing)	B, 30
		Furniture	17	A, 15
		Wallpaper		D, 80
IV-01	Biluo Ting Pavilion of Emerald Conch	Ceiling	1	A, 10
IV-02	Fuwang Ge Building of Wish and Reality in Accordance	Screen	44 (1 moved?2)	B, 27 Max 67 Min 10
		Platform	3	A, 12
		Stair	6	C, 42 Max 57 Min 37
		Ceiling	2	B, 35
		Tie'luo	Missing	
		Furniture	?	
		Wallpaper		D, 80

宁寿宫花园建筑内檐装修总体调查

建筑编号	建筑名称	内檐装修	数量	平均残损系数
IV-03	倦勤斋	罩隔		
		室内亭座	1	
		地平	3	
		楼梯	1	
		贴落	32	
		家具		
		壁纸		D, 65
IV-04	云光楼	罩隔	8	A, 17 Max 20 Min 14
		地平	4	
		通景画	2	
		天花天顶画		
		贴落	19	
		家具	28	
		壁纸		C, 60
IV-05	玉粹轩	罩隔	3	A, 17 Max 22 Min 10
		地平	5	
		通景画	1	
		贴落	3	
		家具	30	A, 10
		壁纸		D, 80
IV-06	净尘心室	地平	1	A, 20
IV-07	竹香馆	罩隔	14	B, 34 Max 47 Min 17
		镶嵌木壁板（下碱部分）	12	
		木刻贴落	7	
		壁纸		C, 60

1. 符望阁中西北进间的罩隔与同一空间中的其他罩隔做法不同；而形式和镶嵌做法均同于符望阁南边各间中的罩隔。我们判断此现象系因历史上拆改移动的结果。

符望阁内檐装修现存状况

云光楼内檐装修现存状况

乾隆遗珍
故宫博物院宁寿宫花园历史研究与文物保护规划

玉粹轩内檐装修现存状况

竹香馆内檐装修现存状况

General Survey of Interior Features

No.	Building	Interior Features	Number	Avrg. Damage Evaluation
IV-03	Juanqin Zhai Lodge of Retirement	Screen		
		Interior Pavilion	1	
		Platform	3	
		Stair	1	
		Tie'luo	32	
		Furniture		
		Wallpaper		D, 65
IV-04	Yunguang Lou Building of Cloud Light	Screen	8	A, 17 Max 20 Min 14
		Platform	4	
		Tromp l'oeil	2	
		Painted Ceiling		
		Tie'luo	19	
		Furniture	28	
		Wallpaper		C, 60
IV-05	Yucui Xuan Pavilion of Jade Purity	Screen	3	A, 17 Max 22 Min 10
		Platform	5	
		Tromp l'oeil	1	
		Tie'luo	3	
		Furniture	30	A, 10
		Wallpaper		D, 80
IV-06	Jingchenxin Shi Chamber of Heart Purification	Platform	1	A, 20
IV-07	Zhuxiang Guan Chamber of Bamboo Fragrance	Screen	14	B, 34 Max 47 Min 17
		Inlayed Wall Panel	12	
		Wooden Tie'luo	7	
		Wallpaper		C, 60

5.6.2 木作罩隔工艺与残损勘察

宁寿宫花园一些重要建筑具有尤其丰富和精美的内檐装修语汇，而另一些建筑则不然，因此在勘察和评估的标准中，有必要加上"工艺难度"一项和"材料做法"一项，并在保护措施的制定和保护经费的估算中参考此二项的评估指标。

各槽木作罩隔残损勘察与评估

建筑编号	建筑名称	工艺难度	材料做法	残损等级 [1]
I-02	古华轩	A, 90	楠木；黑漆油饰＋地仗；黑漆表面绘装饰纹样（材料做法待考）	A, 27
I-05	抑斋	C, 50	紫檀木；表面浮雕	A, 15
I-08	禊赏亭	C, 50	黑漆饰面木制屏风门；黑漆表面沥粉描金坐龙	B, 40
I-09	旭辉庭	C, 50	楠木大边和衬板；紫檀木雕刻纹样和花结	(2) B 40, B 40
II-02	遂初堂	C, 60	楠木大边和衬板；紫檀木雕刻纹样和花结；屉心夹纱；屉心书画贴落	(5) B 23, B 32, B 32, B 27, B 20
III-02	萃赏楼	A, 100	硬木大边衬板；硬木雕刻纹样和花结；竹节、驼骨拼装屉心；屉心夹纱、玻璃画；绦环板、群板漆饰描金／描彩	(15) B 40, B 37, B 28, B 30, B 34, A 20, B 23, A 17, A 20, A 20, A 18, A 17, B 23, A 23, A 23
III-03	三友轩	A, 100	硬木大边衬板；硬木雕刻纹样和花结；玉片镶嵌；竹丝镶嵌；屉心夹纱；屉心书画贴落	(5) B 23, B 23, B 26, B 37, B 25
III-05	延趣楼	A, 100	硬木大边衬板；硬木雕刻纹样和花结；瓷片镶嵌；屉心双面绣夹纱	(10) B 37, A 14, B 38, B 32, B 20, B 37, C 45, B 30, B 40, B 33
IV-02	符望阁	A, 100	硬木大边衬板；硬木雕刻纹样和花结；竹丝镶嵌；玉片镶嵌；珐琅镶嵌；鋄铜镶嵌；螺钿镶嵌；雕漆镶嵌；屉心绣片夹纱；屉心书画贴落	(44) B 30, B 30, B 27, B 38, B 24, B 35, A 15, A 20, A 18, A 18, B 33, A 19, A 10, A 20, D 63, C 53, A 20, A 20, B 28, B 40, C 55, C 53, B 24, A 17, B 21, A 15, B 21, B 27, B 36, B 27, B 28, B 28, B 32, B 25, B 32, A 10, A 10, A 10, B 23, B 23, B 30, B 30, B 30, B 30

各槽木作罩隔残损勘察与评估

建筑编号	建筑名称	工艺难度	材料做法	残损等级 [1]
IV-03	倦勤斋	A, 100 B, 60 （竹式药拦）	硬木大边衬板；硬木雕刻纹样和花结；竹丝、竹黄镶嵌；硬木镶嵌；玉片镶嵌；屉心双面绣夹纱；群板绦环板漆器描金／镶嵌彩色黄杨木	(65) （本规划不含倦勤斋内檐装修保护项目）
IV-04	云光楼	B, 60	楠木大边衬板；紫檀木雕刻纹样和花结；屉心夹纱	(8) A 18, A 14, A 14, A 18, A 20, A 18, A 15, A 15.
IV-05	玉粹轩	B, 60	楠木大边衬板；紫檀木雕刻纹样和花结；屉心夹纱	(3) B 22, A 18, A 10
IV-07	竹香馆	B, 80	硬木大边衬板；硬木雕刻纹样和花结；屉心夹纱	(14) C 47, A 15, B 27, B 33, B 40, B 40, B 40, A 17, B 30, C 50, C 47, A 17, B 33, B 40.

1. 每座建筑中木作木作罩隔的槽数记录于（ ）中，各槽罩隔的残损系数依次以"，"分隔，罩隔编号顺序参见保护规划图纸。

乾隆花园
故宫博物院宁寿宫花园历史研究与文物保护规划

Damage Survey of Interior Screens

No.	Building	Craftsmanship Evaluation	Material & Method	Damage Value[1]
IV-02	Fuwang Ge Building of Wish and Reality in Accordance	A, 100	Iron wood frame and board; Iron wood carving; Bamboo thread macquetry; Jade inlay; Enamel inlay; Hammered copper board inlay; Conch patchwork inlay; Carved lacquer inlay; Embroidered silk works; Calligraphy and painting Tie'luo on casement	(44) B 30, B 30, B 27, B 38, B 24, B 35, A 15, A 20, A 18, A 18, B 33, A 19, A 10, A 20, D 63, C 53, A 20, A 20, B 28, B 40, C 55, C 53, B 24, A 17, B 21, A 15, B 21, B 27, B 36, B 27, B 28, B 28, B 32, B 25, B 32, A 10, A 10, A10, B 23, B 23, B 30, B 30, B 30, B 30
IV-03	Juanqin Zhai Lodge of Retirement	A, 100 B, 60 (fence)	Iron wood frame and board; Iron wood carving; Bamboo thread macquetry; Iron wood inlay; Jade inlay; Embroidered silk works; Lacquer with gold painted pattern	(65)
IV-04	Yunguang Lou Building of Cloud Light	B, 60	Hard wood frame and board; Iron wood carving; Silk works	(8) A 18, A 14, A 14, A 18, A 20, A 18, A 15, A 15
IV-05	Yucui Xuan Pavilion of Jade Purity	B, 60	Hard wood frame and board; Iron wood carving; Silk works	(3) B 22, A 18, A 10
IV-07	Zhuxiang Guan Chamber of Bamboo Fragrance	B, 80	Hard wood frame and board; Iron wood carving; Silk works	(14) C 47, A 15, B 27, B 33, B 40, B 40, B 40, A 17, B 30, C 50, C 47, A 17, B 33, B 40

5.6.2 Craftsmanship and Damage Survey of Interior Screen

Now that interior screens some buildings were more sophisticated than those in others buildings, and some structures are simply decorated and have not interior spatial partition, introducing assessment of the craftsmanship required to make a screen is of the same importance with the damage survey, for when foreseeing into the conservation treatments, it is always true that the delicately decorated items call for more endeavors to maintain than the plain ones.

Damage Survey of Interior Screens

No.	Building	Craftsmanship Evaluation	Material & Method	Damage Value[1]
I-02	Guhua Xuan, Pavilion of Ancient Flower	A, 90	Nan wood; Lacquered surface; Painted Pattern	A, 27
I-05	Yi Zhai Chamber of Self Constraint	C, 50	Red Sandal wood; Carved surface	A, 15
I-08	Xishang Ting Pavilion of Floating Cup	C, 50	Wood door leaf panel with lacquer finishing; Decorated with dragon pattern	
I-09	Xuhui Ting Pavilion of Morning Splendour	C, 50	Hard wood frame and board; Iron wood carving	(2) B 40, B 40
II-02	Suichu Tang Hall of Fulfilment of Original Wishes	C, 60	Hard wood frame and board; Iron wood carving; Silk works; Calligraphy and painting Tie'luo on casement	(5) B 23, B 32, B 32, B 27, B 20
III-02	Cuishang Lou Building of Collection and Appreciation	A, 100	Iron wood frame and board; Iron wood carving; Bamboo patchwork with camel bone knot; Silk works/glass painting; Lacquer with gold /color painted pattern	(15) B 40, B 37, B 28, B 30, B 34, A 20, B 23, A 17, A 20, A 20, A 18, A 17, B 23, A 23, A 23
III-03	Sanyou Xuan Pavilion of Three Friends	A, 100	Iron wood frame and board; Iron wood carving; Jade inlay; Bamboo thread macquetry; Silk works; Calligraphy and painting Tie'luo on casement	(5) B 23, B 23 B 26, B 37, B 25
III-05	Yanqu Lou Building of Extended Delight	A, 100	Iron wood frame and board; Iron wood carving; Porcelain inlay; Double-side embroidered silk works	(10) B 37, A 14, B 38, B, 32, B 20, B 37, C 45, B, 30, B 40,B 33

5.6.3 通景画/天顶画残损勘察

正如本规划第二章中曾经分析讨论的，宁寿宫花园中现存的通景画主要集中在第四进院落的配殿和后殿中。

对于通景画残损状况的详细勘察需要仔细的材料检测、做法研究，且对于隐蔽的壁画下层构造等问题都是本规划尚无法涉及的。因此本节所做的勘察评估工作主要针对通景画的表面问题，并遵照以下评估标准：

(1) 残损A级，残损率0～20：0～20%表面轻微残损，未见底层构造问题；

(2) 残损B级，残损率21～40：21%～40%表面轻微残损，未见底层构造问题；

(3)残损C级，残损率41～60：41%～60%表面显著残损，或存在构造破坏倾向，或存在底层构造问题；

(4) 残损D级，残损率60～100：大于60%的表面严重残损，或存在严重构造破坏。

现存通景画统计

建筑编号	通景画分布	通景画内容	作者	残损评估	面积（m²）
IV-03 倦勤斋	西四间天花；西四间墙壁	天花：线法竹架、紫藤画；墙壁：线法园林景观	王幼学	保护中	160
IV-04 云光楼	首层天花；门口对面西墙1幅；南墙1幅	西墙：仕女婴戏图，园林景观；南墙：仕女婴戏图，建筑室内景观；天花：天蓝色	王幼学	D	19（天顶画面积不详）
IV-05 玉粹轩	明间西墙1幅	仕女婴戏图，建筑室内景观	姚文翰[1]	D	12
IV-07 竹香馆	位于竹香馆首层南部半开放龛形空间墙壁之上，仅余局部残迹				不详

5.6.4 帖落/匾联残损勘察

宁寿宫花园建筑中相当数量的贴落和匾联在历史上未受到人为扰动，仍然处于其原来的位置上；一些贴落已经从原位脱落，其中尚有部分贴落原位能够参照墙面痕迹辨认出来；一些贴落和匾额系近代补配或从他处移来。

故宫博物院退休专家傅连仲先生曾经亲身经历众多故宫文物的陈列、收藏、移动的过程，为本规划提供了非常重要的口述线索，如宁寿宫花园倦勤斋中的部分贴落系二十世纪七十年代为接待重要领导莅临参观而从库存文物中挑选移来的。

尽管花园建筑中现存贴落和匾联的历史情况十分复杂，本规划仍然认为全面统计和记录现存贴落、匾联的位置和内容是文物保护工作的基础，并做出如下统计（其中匾额、悬挂对联在括号中注明，贴落、张贴对联等纸制文物不另行注明）。

贴落/匾联勘察统计

建筑编号	贴落/匾联编号	内容	作者	残损率/%
I-01	TB-01	衍祺门（匾额）		
I-02 古华轩	TB-01	古华轩（匾额，复制）	乾隆书法摘选	A，10
	TB-02	御制诗（匾额）	乾隆	B，30
	TB-03	御制诗（匾额）	乾隆	B，30
	TB-04	御制诗（匾额）	乾隆	B，30
	TB-05	御制诗（匾额）	乾隆	B，30
	TB-06	御制诗（匾额）	乾隆	B，30
	TB-07	御制诗（匾额）	乾隆	B，30
I-05 抑斋	Special-01	罗汉像	不详	A，10
	Special-02	罗汉像	不详	A，10
	Special-03	礤礤佛龛	不详	A，20
I-08 禊赏亭	0	匾额缺失		
I-09 旭辉庭	0	匾额缺失		
II-02 遂初堂	0	匾额缺失		
III-01 耸秀亭	TB-01	耸秀亭（匾额）	乾隆	40
III-02 萃赏楼	TB-01	萃赏楼（匾额）	乾隆	10
	TL-01	水墨山水	袁瑛	80
	TL-02	御笔对联	嘉庆	30
	TL-03	御笔对联	嘉庆	30
	TL-04	水墨山水	顾铨	40
	TL-05	问路图	魏鹤龄	40
	TL-06	御笔对联	嘉庆	60
	TL-07	御笔对联	嘉庆	60
	TL-08	渔樵问答图	黄念	40
	TL-09	御笔对联	乾隆	40
	TL-10	御笔对联	乾隆	40
	TL-11	水墨山水	胡桂	80
	TL-12	御制诗	嘉庆	30
	TL-13	兰亭序	董诰	40

1. 在此幅通景画中，包含一些仿木作屉心贴落的绘画作品，其上更有乾隆时期宫廷画家署名，如方琮、董诰、贾铨、杨大章等。此类作品归入通景画一类，在贴落残损统计中不再重复。

Damage Survey of Tie'luo and Tablet

Building No.	Tie'luo/ Tablet No.	Contents	Write or Calligrapher	Damage Value
I-01	TB-01	衍祺门 , Name of the Building		
	TB-01	古华轩 , Name of the Building (Replica)	Cento from Qianlong's works	A, 10
	TB-02	Poem	Qianlong	B, 30
	TB-03	Poem	Qianlong	B, 30
I-02 Guhua Xuan	TB-04	Poem	Qianlong	B, 30
	TB-05	Poem	Qianlong	B, 30
	TB-06	Poem	Qianlong	B, 30
	TB-07	Poem	Qianlong	B, 30
	Special-01	Portraits of arhats	?	A, 10
	Special-02	Portraits of arhats	?	A, 10
I-05 Yi Zhai	Special-03	Niche + tablet for Buddha statues	?	A, 20
I-08 Xishang Ting	0	The tablet of the building is missing		
I-09 Xuhui Ting	0	The tablet of the building is missing		
II-02 Suichu Tang	0	The tablet of the building is missing		
III-01 Songxiu Ting	TB-01	耸秀亭 , Name of the Building	Qianlong	40
	TB-01	萃赏楼 , Name of the Building	Qianlong	10
	TL-01	Landscape painting	Yuan Ying	80
	TL-02	Couplet	Jiaqing	30
	TL-03	Couplet	Jiaqing	30
	TL-04	Landscape painting	Gu Quan	40
	TL-05	"Asking the Way"	Wei Heling	40
	TL-06	Couplet	Jiaqing	60
III-02 Cuishang Lou	TL-07	Couplet	Jiaqing	60
	TL-08	Dialogue between a fisher and an axman	Huang Nian	40
	TL-09	Couplet	Qianlong	40
	TL-10	Couplet	Qianlong	40
	TL-11	Landscape painting	Hu Gui	80
	TL-12	Poem	Jiaqing	30
	TL-13	Lan Ting Preface	Dong Gao	40
	TB-01	三友轩 , Name of the Building	Qianlong	30
	TL-01	Poem	Jiaqing	20
	TL-02	Poem	Jiaqing	30
III-03 Sanyou Xuan	TL-03	Landscape painting	FANG Cong	40
	TL-04	Poem	Jiaqing	40
	TL-05	Poem	Jianqing	20

5.6.3 Damage Survey of Tromp l'oeil

The extant tromp l'oeil paintings and the remaining strips of mural paintings reveal that the side buildings in the fourth courtyard in the Qianlong garden together forming a U-shape semi-envelope at the west part have tromp l'oeil paintings. This phenomenon indicates some original design concepts discussed in Chapter 2.

Damage assessment for the tromp l'oeil works calls for much in-depth investigation into the materials at the surface and at back as lining works, and the wall structures of wooden lattice or board that support the painting. At present stage of master plan, it is possible and logical survey covers superficial damages and the assessment of the damage according to the following standard,

(1) Grade A, value 0-20, for 0-20% slight superficial damage, and no structure failure detected;

(2) Grade B, value 21-40, for 21%-40% superficial damage, and no structure failure detected;

(3) Grade C, value 41-60, for 41%-60% serious superficial damage, or facing obvious tructural threat, or having slight structural failure;

(4) Grade D, value 61-100, for above 60% superficial damage, or having structural failure.

Damage Survey of Tromp l'oeil

Building No.	Distribution	Contents	Write / Calligrapher	Damage Value	Area (m²)
IV-03 Juanqin Zhai	Ceiling, Walls in the theatrical space	Perspective wisteria on the ceiling; Perspective scenery on the walls	Wang Youxue	In conservation	160
IV-04 Yunguang Lou	Blue silk ceiling on ground floor; One piece on the west wall facing the door; One piece on the south wall	Ceiling, simple blue paint; West wall, a family portrait with courtyard view; South wall, a family portrait with interior view	Wang Youxue	D	19
IV-05 Yucui Xuan	1 piece on the west wall facing the door	West wall, a family portrait with interior view	Yao Wenhan[1]	D	12
IV-07 Zhuxiang Guan	Only tiny remaining pieces show the existence of Tromp l'eil works, on the walls of a niche-like passage on the ground floor, contents unidentifiable. See drawing for more information				?

5.6.4 Damage Survey of Tieluo and Tablet

Some of the extant Tie'luo and tablets are in their original places on the walla or hung under eaves. There are some Tieluo that had been fallen off the wall coverd with wallpaper for a long time, and some walls still have traces indicating once attached Tieluo on wallpaper. And some tablets are replicas made recently.

贴落/匾联勘察统计				
建筑编号	贴落/匾联编号	内容	作者	残损率/%
III-03 三友轩	TB-01	三友轩（匾额）	乾隆	30
	TL-01	御制诗	嘉庆	20
	TL-02	御制诗	嘉庆	30
	TL-03	水墨山水	方琮	40
	TL-04	御制诗	嘉庆	40
	TL-05	御制诗	嘉庆	20
	TL-06	御制诗	嘉庆	20
	TL-07	御制诗	嘉庆	20
	TL-08	（卷装未开）	？	40
	TL-09	御制诗	嘉庆	20
III-03 三友轩	TL-10	水墨山水	周本	40
	TL-11	御制诗	嘉庆	20
	TL-12	御制诗	嘉庆	20
	TL-13	工笔博古	张启明	20
	TL-14	设色花卉	黄念	20
	TL-15	御制诗	嘉庆	20
	TL-16	设色花卉	周本	20
III-05 延趣楼	TB-01	延趣楼（匾额）	乾隆	10
	TL-01	御制诗	嘉庆	30
IV-01 碧螺亭	TB-01	碧螺亭（匾额）	乾隆	10
IV-02 符望阁	TB-01	符望阁（匾额）	乾隆	10
IV-03 倦勤斋	TB-01	倦勤斋（匾额）	乾隆	10
	TL-01	粉笺纸对联	陈官俊	移入
	TL-02	蓝粉笺纸字贴落	周系英	移入
	TL-03	粉笺纸对联	陈官俊	移入
	TL-04	设色山水画	顾铨	
	TL-05	御笔贴落	嘉庆帝	
	TL-06	御笔贴落	嘉庆帝	
	TL-07	设色山水画	谢遂	
	TL-08	蓝粉笺纸贴落	周系英	
	TL-09	高丽纸山水画	佚名	
	TL-10	黄绢书法贴落	果齐斯欢	

古华轩室内木刻御笔御制诗匾　承露台室内石刻御笔御制诗文匾

萃赏楼
室内御笔御制诗贴落　三友轩
室内御笔御制诗贴落　三友轩
室内臣工绘画贴落

萃赏楼室内御笔御制对联贴落　三友轩室内臣工绘画贴落

云光楼室内臣工书经

云光楼室内御笔御制对联贴落　　云光楼室内御笔御制对联贴落

云光楼室内御笔御制诗贴落　　云光楼室内臣工绘画贴落

Building No.	Tie'luo/ Tablet No.	Contents	Write or Calligrapher	Damage Value
		Damage Survey of Tie'luo and Tablet		
III-03 Sanyou Xuan	TL-06	Poem	Jianqing	20
	TL-07	Poem	Jianqing	20
	TL-08	?(scroll unopened)	?	40
	TL-09	Poem	Jianqing	20
	TL-10	Landscape painting	ZHOU Ben	40
	TL-11	Poem	Jianqing	20
	TL-12	Poem	Jianqing	20
	TL-13	Paintings of wares	ZHANG Qiming	20
	TL-14	Flower	HUANG Nian	20
	TL-15	Poem	Jianqing	20
	TL-16	Flower	ZHOU Ben	20
III-05, Yanqu Lou	TB-01	延趣楼 , Name of the Building	Qianlong	10
	TL-01	Poem	Jiaqing	30
IV-01, Biluo Ting	TB-01	碧螺亭 , Name of the Building	Qianlong	10
IV-02, Fuwang Ge	TB-01	符望阁 ,Name of the Building	Qianlong	10
IV-03 Juanqin Zhai	TB-01	倦勤斋 ,Name of the Building	Qianlong	10
	TL-01	Couplet on paper	CHEN Guanjun	Moved in
	TL-02	Calligrapy on blue paper	ZHOU Xiying	Moved in
	TL-03	Couplet on paper	CHEN Guanjun	Moved in
	TL-04	Colored landscape painting	GU Quan	
	TL-05	Imperial calligraphy on silk	Jiaqing	
	TL-06	Imperial calligraphy on silk	Jiaqing	
	TL-07	Colored landscape painting	XIE Sui	
	TL-08	Calligraphy on blue paper	ZHOU Xiying	
	TL-09	Landscape painting on Korean paper	Anon.	
	TL-10	Calligrapy on yellow silk	Guoqisihuan	
	TL-11	Colored flower painting	Anon.	
	TL-12	Imperial calligraphy on silk	Jiaqing	
	TL-13	Llandscape painting on yellow paper	JIANG Maolong	
	TL-14	Imperial calligraphy on silk	Jiaqing	
	TL-15	Llandscape painting on yellow paper	JIANG Maolong	
	TL-16	Calligraphy on yellow paper	WANG Yixian	
	TL-17	Painting of peony	Anon.	
	TL-18	Painting of family portrait	SHEN Qinglan	
	TL-19	Colored flower painting	SHEN Qinglan	

建筑编号	贴落/匾联编号	内容	作者	残损率/%
IV-03 倦勤斋	TL-11	设色花卉图	佚名	
	TL-12	御笔贴落	嘉庆帝	
	TL-13	黄地山水画	蒋懋龙	
	TL-14	御笔贴落	嘉庆帝	
	TL-15	黄地山水画	蒋懋龙	
	TL-16	黄粉笺纸贴落	汪廷珍	
	TL-17	牡丹图	佚名	
	TL-18	人物婴戏图	沈庆兰	
	TL-19	设色花卉图	沈庆兰	
	TL-20	御笔贴落	嘉庆帝	
	TL-21	设色花卉图	沈庆兰	
	TL-22	粉笺纸贴落	陈官俊	移入
	TL-23	蓝粉笺纸贴落	果齐斯欢	移入
	TL-24	粉笺纸贴落	陈官俊	移入
	TL-25	设色山水画	魏鹤龄	
	TL-26	蓝粉笺纸贴落	汪廷珍	
	TL-27	设色山水画	佚名	
	TL-28	蓝粉笺纸贴落	英和	
	TL-29	设色山水画	董诰	
	TL-30	蓝粉笺纸贴落	王以衔	
	TL-31	蓝粉笺纸贴落	王以衔	
	TL-32	设色荷花图	周本	
IV-04 云光楼	TB-01	养和精舍（匾额）	乾隆	30
	TL-01	水墨山水	蒋懋德	30
	TL-02	雪景山水	方琮	30
	TL-03	御制诗	嘉庆	20
	TL-04	御制诗	嘉庆	20
	TL-05	设色牡丹	佚名	10
	TL-06	水墨山水	贾铨	10

建筑编号	贴落/匾联编号	内容	作者	残损率/%
IV-04 云光楼	TL-07	水墨山水	朱宪章	10
	TL-08	水墨山水	魏	10
	TL-09	御笔对联	嘉庆	20
	TL-10	御笔对联	嘉庆	20
	TL-11	御笔书法	乾隆？	20
	TL-12	设色花卉	杨大章	70
	TL-13	设色花卉	佚名	80
	TL-14	御笔对联	嘉庆	30
	TL-15	御笔对联	嘉庆	30
	TL-16	御制诗	乾隆	20
IV-05 玉粹轩	TB-01	玉粹轩（匾额）	乾隆	10
	TL-01	水墨山水	贾铨	40
	TL-02	御制诗	嘉庆	20
	TL-03	御制诗	嘉庆	20
IV-07 竹香馆	TB-01	竹香馆（匾额）	乾隆	10
	TL-01	御制佛教主题诗	乾隆	30
	TL-02	御制佛教主题诗	乾隆	30
	TL-03	御制佛教主题诗	乾隆	50
	TL-04	御制佛教主题诗	乾隆	50
	TL-05	御制佛教主题诗	乾隆	30
	TL-06	御制佛教主题诗	乾隆	30
	TL-07	御制佛教主题诗	乾隆	50

5.6.5 家具残损勘察

近年来的研究表明，清宫营造室内空间、进行家具配饰时往往针对不同的空间尺度定做家具，主管部门就是内务府。对于宁寿宫花园各座建筑来说，历史档案表明，并非所有现在保存于宫室内的家具都是宫廷原状。统计勘察所有现存家具是开展保护工作和进行展陈设计的基础，兹罗列见下表。

Damage Survey of Tie'luo and Tablet

Building No.	Tie'luo/ Tablet No.	Contents	Write or Calligrapher	Damage Value
IV-05 Yucui Xuan	TB-01	玉粹轩 , Name of the Building	Qianlong	10
	TL-01	Landscape	JIA Quan	40
	TL-02	Poem	Jiaqing	20
	TL-03	Poem	Jiaqing	20
IV-07 Zhuxiang Guan	TB-01	竹香馆 , Name of the Building	Qianlong	10
	TL-01	Buddhist poem	Qianlong	30
	TL-02	Buddhist poem	Qianlong	30
	TL-03	Buddhist poem	Qianlong	50
	TL-04	Buddhist poem	Qianlong	50
	TL-05	Buddhist poem	Qianlong	30
	TL-06	Buddhist poem	Qianlong	30
	TL-07	Buddhist poem	Qianlong	50

80 year old Mr. Fu Lianzhong, a renownd retired expert from the Palace Museum, provided a very important piece of information that the Palace Museum had shifted some Tieluo into the Lodge of Retirement in the fourth courtyard in the Qianlong Garden on account of some visits of important bureau directors during 1970s.

Despite of all historical changes and messing, the present location and status of the Tieluo and tablets are listed in the following table.

5.6.5 Survey of Furniture

It was a tradition of the Imperial Household Department to order furniture with an exact style and dimension specially made for an interior space of an imperial palace. But according to available inventory made by the Palace Museum, furniture pieces now stored inside the buildings of Qianlong Garden were not all belong to the buildings in Qing dynasty. Furniture presently stored in the Qianlong Garden is summarized in the table below with its style of location.

Damage Survey of Tie'luo and Tablet

Building No.	Tie'luo/ Tablet No.	Contents	Write or Calligrapher	Damage Value
IV-03 Juanqin Zhai	TL-20	Imperial calligraphy on silk	Jiaqing	
	TL-21	Colored flower paintingt	SHEN Qinglan	
	TL-22	Calligrapy on paper	CHEN Guanjun	Moved in
	TL-23	Calligrapy on blue paper	Guoqisihuan	Moved in
	TL-24	Calligrapy on paper	CHEN Guanjun	Moved in
	TL-25	Colored landscape painting	WEI Heling	
	TL-26	Calligrapy on blue paper	WANG Tingzhen	
	TL-27	Colored landscape painting	Anon.	
	TL-28	Calligrapy on blue paper	Yinghe	
	TL-29	Colored landscape painting	DONG Gao	
	TL-30	Calligrapy on blue paper	WANG Yixian	
	TL-31	Calligrapy on blue paper	WANG Yixian	
	TL-32	Painting of colored lotus	ZHOU Ben	
IV-04 Yunguang Lou	TB-01	养和精舍, Name of the Building	Qianlong	30
	TL-01	Landscape painting	JIANG Maode	30
	TL-02	Snow Landscape	FANG Cong	30
	TL-03	Poem	Jiaqing	20
	TL-04	Poem	Jiaqing	20
	TL-05	Peony	Anon.	10
	TL-06	Landscape painting	JIAN Quan	10
	TL-07	Landscape painting	ZHU Xianzhang	10
	TL-08	Landscape painting	WEI	10
	TL-09	Couplet	Jiaqing	20
	TL-10	Couplet	Jiaqing	20
	TL-11	Calligraphy	Qianlong?	20
	TL-12	Flower	YANG Dazhang	70
	TL-13	Flower	Anon.	80
	TL-14	Couplet	Jiaqing	30
	TL-15	Couplet	Jiaqing	30
	TL-16	Poem	Qianlong	20

家具残损勘察

建筑编号	家具形式	件数	是否原物	残损率
III-02 萃赏楼	屏风	1	是	10
	宝座	1	是	10
	足榻	1	是	10
	绣墩	7	是	10, 10, 10, 10, 10, 10, 10
	佛台架	2	是	20
	书案	1	是	10
	供桌	4	是	10, 10, 10, 10
	扇架	4	是	20, 20, 20, 20
	条案	1	是	10
	炕琴	1	是	10
	羽扇	2	是	50, 50
III-03 三友轩	方桌	2	是	10, 10
	炕琴	4	是	10, 10, 10, 10
	方凳	5	是	10, 10, 10, 10, 10
	多宝格书案	1	是	10
	条案	1	是	10
	宝座	1	是	10
	屏风	2	是	10, 10
III-05 延趣楼	绣墩	10	是	10
	屏风	1	是	10
	宝座	1	是	10
	足榻	1	是	10
	多宝格书架	2	是	60, 50
	供桌	1	是	10
	条案	1	是	10
IV-02 符望阁	现状情况最为复杂，有待全面调查 内有云光楼罗汉像屏一套，景祺阁家具多件			
IV-03 倦勤斋	多宝格书架	2	是	30
	红木躺箱	2	是	10
	供桌	1	是	30
	紫檀木屏风	2	是	30
	紫檀木挂屏	2	是	10

萃赏楼室内现存家具

萃赏楼室内现存佛台佛像

三友轩室内现存家具

Damage Survey of Furniture

Building No.	Furniture Type	Piece	Original/not	Damage Value
III-02 Cuishang Lou	Screen	1	Y	10
	Imperial Seat	1	Y	10
	Foot Rest	1	Y	10
	Decorated Round Table	7	Y	10, 10, 10, 10, 10, 10, 10
	Buddha Shelf	2	Y	20
	Desk	1	Y	10
	Offering Table	4	Y	10, 10, 10, 10
	Fan Pedestal	4	Y	20, 20, 20, 20
	Long Table	1	Y	10
	Long Bed Table	1	Y	10
III-03 Sanyou Xuan	Fan	2	Y	50, 50
	Square Table	2	Y	10, 10
	Long Bed Table	4	Y	10, 10, 10, 10
	Square Stool	5	Y	10, 10 , 10, 10, 10
	Duobao GeReading Desk	1	Y	10
	Long Table	1	Y	10
	Imperial Seat	1	Y	10
	Stand Screen	2	Y	10, 10
III-05 Yanqu Lou	Decorated Round Stool	10	Y	10
	Stand Screen	1	Y	10
	Imperial Seat	1	Y	10
	Foot Rest	1	Y	10
	Duobao GeBook Shelf	2	Y	60, 50
	Offering Table	1	Y	10
	Long Table	1	Y	10
IV-02 Fuwang Ge	To be surveyed in future works Include screens from the Building of Cloud Light in Qianlong Garden, and pieces of furniture from the Building of Scenery and Felicity in the neighborhood courtyard			
IV-03 Juanqin Zhai	Duobao GeBook Shelf	2	Y	30
	Rosewood Lying Chest	2	Y	10
	Offering Table	1	Y	30
	Red Sandal Wood Standing Screen	2	Y	30
	Red Sandal wood Hanging Screen	2	Y	10

家具残损勘察

建筑编号	家具形式	件数	是否原物	残损率
IV-04 云光楼	供桌	2	是	10
	炕琴	3	是	10, 10, 10
	半八方桌	2	是	10, 10
	屏风	1	是	30
	宝座	1	是	30
	条案	1	是	10
	四分圆桌	8	是	10, 10, 10, 10, 10, 10, 10, 10
	圆炕桌	2	是	10, 10
	方凳	3	是	10, 10, 10
	高方桌	4	是	10, 10, 10, 10
	炕琴	1	是	10
IV-05 玉粹轩	条案	4	是	10, 10, 10, 10
	大方桌	3	是	10, 10, 10
	高方桌	1	是	10
	六角凳	8	是	10, 10, 10, 10, 10, 10, 10, 10
	多宝格书架	4	是	20, 20, 20, 20
	方凳	2	是	10, 10
	琴桌	2	是	10, 10
	炕琴	2	是	10, 10
	小柜	2	是	10, 10
	圆炕桌	2	是	10, 10

延趣楼室内现存家具

玉粹轩室内现存家具

故宫博物院宁寿宫花园历史研究与文物保护规划

符望阁室内现存家具（尚未完全统计，存有原阁内家具及周围建筑中移来之家具）

Damage Survey of Furniture

Building No.	Furniture Type	Piece	Original/not	Damage Value
IV-04 Yunguang Lou	Offering Table	2	Y	10
	Long Bed Table	3	Y	10, 10, 10
	Half Octangular Table	2	Y	10, 10
	Screen	1	Y	30
	Imperial Seat	1	Y	30
	Long Table	1	Y	10
	Quarter Round Table	8	Y	10, 10, 10, 10, 10, 10, 10, 10
	Round Bed Table	2	Y	10, 10
	Square Stool	3	Y	10, 10, 10
	High Square Table	4	Y	10, 10, 10, 10
IV-05 Yucui Xuan	Long Bed Table	1	Y	10
	Long Table	4	Y	10, 10, 10
	Large Square Table	3	Y	10, 10
	High Square Table	1	Y	10
	Hexagonal Stool	8	Y	10, 10, 10, 10, 10, 10, 10, 10
	Duobao GeShelf	4	Y	20, 20, 20, 20
	Square Stool	2	Y	10, 10
	Long Table for Musical Instrument	2	Y	10, 10
	Long Bed Table	2	Y	10, 10
	Small Chest	2	Y	10, 10
	Round Bed Table	2	Y	10, 10

无形文化遗产的保护

在第五章的勘察统计基础上，我们不仅可以更加深入地理解第二章所陈述的宁寿宫花园的文物价值、丰富、精美的园林、建筑、室内文物也更加清楚地揭示了清代宫廷所特有的非物质文化遗产。诚然，我们需要结合更多的历史研究来澄清这些非物质文化遗产赖以存在的人的因素——如生活习惯、禁忌、工作方式、信仰等以及物的因素——如书面记载、工具、器物等。我们至少可以将宁寿宫花园所反映出的非物质文化遗产的重要类型在本章列举出来，并将这些遗产的类型所从属的大的历史文化背景进行初步的描述。这些类型包括：清宫园林设计和造园理论与实践；清宫室内设计与内檐装修工艺；清宫园林叠石工艺；清宫各作建筑施工工艺。

上述各类型的非物质文化遗产中有一些得以流传至今，有一些濒临绝迹，还有一些已经失传，现只能通过现代技术的研究尝试复原。从这种意义上讲，宁寿宫花园项目的工作不仅应当充分利用现代科技对现存文物进行保护，而且应当"复活"或"标本式"地保存非物质文化遗产，并在制订文物保护方案和实施方案的时候将此作为重要因素进行考虑。

6.1 园林设计/造园的理论与实践

正如前文历史研究一章提到的，与西方传统方法不同，中国的传统造园方法是将植物、山水、建筑和谐地组织在一起，追求园林意境和对世界的理解的表达。乾隆皇帝为自己建的宁寿宫花园，园林要素则主要包括建筑、叠石、内檐装修。在这一点上，宁寿宫花园的造园是普遍意义上的中国造园，更是特殊意义上的皇家造园，而且带有清晰的"乾隆印记"。

宁寿宫花园是通过"拷贝"一些乾隆所钟爱的园林片段，结合叠石和植物配置而整体布局的。建筑布局是整体园林布局的基础。因此清宫样式房所绘制的园林平面也是叠石工匠现场设计创造园林景观的基础。无论以建筑设计为主体的"纸面设计工作"，还是以园林设施、景观为主体的"现场设计工作"都对今天继承和发扬中国传统造园和建筑文化具有深远意义。然而至今此类史料及相关研究对于当代的建筑师甚至建筑历史学者而言，还远不能称做研究深入、影响广泛。对于"传统设计方法"这一非物质文化遗产的保护，应当与"样式雷"档案的保护和其他古典园林设计研究相结合[1]。

手工造皮纸工艺调查与乾隆高丽纸复原尝试

1. 刘畅，清代宫廷内檐装修设计问题研究 [博士学位论文]。
   北京：清华大学建筑学院，2002

手工造皮纸工艺调查与乾隆高丽纸复原尝试

Based on surveys in the previous chapter, the question of intangible cultural heritage emerges and becomes more and more important. Though the heritage is facing threats of industrilization, the sudden local modernizationand and other effects of modern culture, those reflected in Qianlong Garden can still be traced with help of historical researches. We can list in this chapter some of the intangible cultural heritage, such as methodology of gardening, craftsmanship for interior furnishing, and laying rockery, in addition, some that have been commonly referred to in previous studies on historic Chinese buildings, such as mothodology and craftsmanship of timber structure, glazed tile and architectural color painting.

Among the above mention intangible heritage, some are still active today but need to be recorded and studied soon, while some are not active though yet surviving, and will be completely died out without deep and timely investigation and research using modern science and technologies. From this aspect, the conservation project of the Qianlong Garden should not only cover the tasks of preserving the cultural relics remaining in the site, but also cover the more profoundly important works of reviving or specimen-ization of the intangible cultural heritage. In constituting the genral conservation and implementation plan for Qianlong Garden, this should be stipulate as an essential point.

6.1 Methodology of Gardening and Garden Design

As discussed in many previous studies, Chinese gardening methodology is to harmonize many elements together, including plants, rocks, water and buildings, when comparing with western gardens. Moreover, Qianlong garden has her own trait of being a private garden for the emperor's retirement, which are mainly reflected in building arrangement, rockery works and the most representative, the interior design.

As for building layout of Qianlong Garden, it is reflected in the planning that the designer had dexterous skills in arranging buildings with rockeries and plants, and moreover in adapting exemplary previous building complexes into strictly restricted courtyard in Ningshou Gong. Both design and representation methodologies would benefit profoundly local modern garden planning and architectural design. But yet such historical information and tradition are not at all familiar to architects and even architectural historians nor influential among the architectual circle. Studies on historical design methodologies of China should better correspond with the studies on the Yangshi Lei collection of historical architectural representations, and with the specific studies on the art of designing and gardening in a more general view.

宁寿宫花园中的叠石与建筑的结合是丰富、和谐的。参考其他清代中期的宫廷、离宫中的园林，可以说高密度的叠山，和利用叠山及其与建筑之间的关系营造空间的做法是乾隆皇帝惯用的造园手法。在北方的皇家园林中，很多被称为"山房"的景区大多采用这种叠石密集的手法，而究其来源则应归于南方的文人园林。水作为园林的要素之一，没有在宁寿宫花园中得到充分利用，仅在禊赏亭中作为点缀用于曲水流觞。具体到宁寿宫花园中叠山设计的方法、技巧以及如何山水结合进行园林布置，则尚需在未来的研究中揭示。

内檐装修作为花园中最具装饰性、最为丰富多样的主题，堪称清代的代表，甚至在中国历代宫廷室内设计上也独树一帜。研究表明：

> 清代中期内檐装修的设计手段是同治后实例中所难以再现的，客观地讲，清代晚期实例所表现出来的内檐装修综合设计水平是低于乾隆时期的，而且这种设计水平的退步还明确地折射出以帝后为代表的宫室空间的使用者对于内檐空间的制度要求和审美要求的多样性和复杂性也趋于退步，呈现出僵化的态势。

至今，中国南方仍然存在一些世家，他们掌握一些传统的造园方法——尽管他们的技法已经在很大程度上受到了局限，他们的方法已不如前辈全面。事实上，传统造园中尤为重要的一点是要将不同人群的不同想法融入到园林设计当中，其中文人的观点尤其受到尊重。因此在今天提及保护传统造园方法的时候，我们所讨论的问题还包含了更加广泛的内容，即如何真正理解和保护中国深厚的人文传统。

6.2 内檐装修工艺

正如在本规划第四章第六节中提到的，两淮盐政李质颖承办了宁寿宫花园中部分内檐装修，而其余部分则在京由内务府造办处承做。江南制作的罩隔形式复杂、雕刻镶嵌精美；而在京造做者朴素大方，风格雅致。可以说，这座位于帝国中心的太上皇宫中的园林具有全国最具代表性、水平最高的内檐装修工艺。

乾隆时期内檐装修造作所使用的特殊材料工艺——尤其是江南地区的一些做法——对于今天的文物保护和工艺美术领域都还是比较陌生的。无论针对文物遗存实施保护措施，还是复兴传统的工艺美术做法，都必须建立在充分利用深入走访传统工匠、实验室技术和开展试验操作等工作的基础上。我们今天同样有可能时常面临匠作大师们不愿意透露工艺技术细节等诸多匠作传统问题。

宁寿宫花园中常见的内檐装修材料工艺主要涉及以下方面：
(1) 清中期的通景画工艺；
(2) 竹丝镶嵌工艺；
(3) 竹黄镶嵌工艺；
(4) 玉片、瓷片、珐琅、铜、螺钿、雕漆等镶嵌工艺；
(5) 双面绣纹饰和做法。

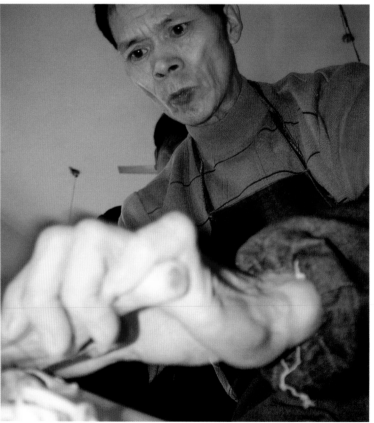

竹黄加工及镶嵌工艺调研与竹黄内檐装修文物保护

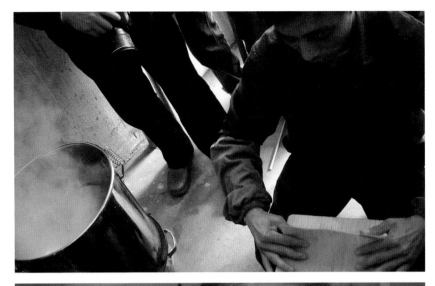

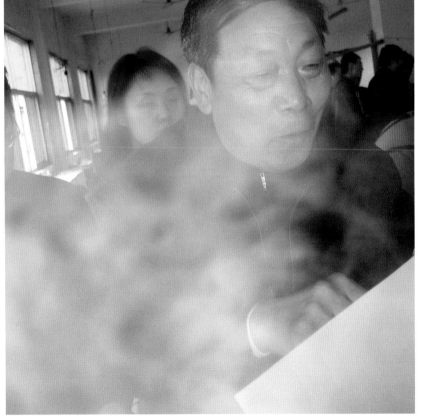

竹黄加工及镶嵌工艺调研与竹黄内檐装修文物保护

Rockery works in Qianlong Garden are harmonized perfectly with buildings, and in a wider scope of imperial gardens built in palaces and para-palaces, such high density rockery layout and close coordination of rockery and building must had been one of Emperor Qianlong's favourite design, which he might have learned during his inspection visit to the south and adopted then in many imperial garden settings called "mountain house" (山房) in his gardens in the suburb of Beijing. Though water was not a major subject in Qianlong Garden, the only water solution is the motif used in the Floating Cup Pavilion, it is explicit the emperor did want to embrace in the garden some water feature. What were the concept and design methods of rockery and water in gardens according to traditional ways still calls for further expounding.

Interior design, no doubt the most important topic, remain fabulously rich and extremely exquisite to discuss. It can be regarded as the highlight of interior design of Qing dynasty which period is actually the most sophisticatedly developed period of interior space of the whole history of China. As pointed out in recent researches.

Interior design skills in Mid-Qing were not reappeared in late Qing Dynasty, e.g. in Tongzhi period. Virtually speaking, interior design of late Qing court was inferior, which remains in most of the buildings of Qing dynast and is commonly regarded as typical Qing interior, than that of the middle period. This degeneracy, we are not speaking of its value in the whole history and value as important relics, reflects the changes in the cultural background of functional and aesthetic requirement, and the organization and expert-composition of the design circle.

There are still some families in southern China that grasp traditional gardening, though their skills have become more likely restricted in some specific fields other than omnipotence as their ancestors. As a matter of fact, it is also the most important way of planning a garden to bring into the design free ideas of different people, among which the literati's ideas were most respected. Today preservation of the traditional way of gardening has more general contents than preserving the garden substantially, which leads to better understanding and preservation of China cultural traditions of literati.

6.2 Craftsmanship for Interior Furnishings

As mentioned in Chapter 4 in previous text, Li Zhiying managed productions for the interior furnishings in Qianlong Garden in south province, while the rest works were made locally in Beijing that were relatively plain and modest in nature and also with elegant essence. Thus it can be said that the craftsmanship for interior furnishing in the lodge, as requited and achieved by emperor Qianlong, reflects the highest standard handiworks all over the country of that time.

In regard to craftsmanship of interior features, some craftsmanship treating the materials uncommon to both today's conservation and fine art are still to be revealed with the help of laboratory works and experimental facture, especially those made in south provinces in China where modern industry has been and is playing an overwhelming role. We should also be prepared today for the traditional probelems we had been used to, such as reluctancy and conservative attitude of the craftsmen when they are asked to thoroughly explicate their skills and recipies.

6.3 园林叠石工艺

  在此着重讨论一下园林中的叠石工艺。普遍认为，清代中国北方园林的叠石做法是继承当时已经成熟的南方园林中的叠石做法。时至今日，尽管尚有一些叠石世家幸运地延续了下来，但是纯正的传统的叠石工艺在中国江南地区也已经基本失传。

  在目前圆明园遗址的保护清理工作中，"山子韩"传人曾经被邀请参与山石泊岸、假山景观的复原工作。经过了若干代的心传口授，韩家仍然保留了相当多的叠石经验。然而从另一个角度来看，这种口耳相传的继承方式却由于缺乏系统记录，缺乏完整性和准确性，因此恰恰是今日纯正的传统工艺并未全面得以保护的原因。当今的迫切工作包括发掘这种文化遗产的本身—记录、采访、收集、整理；还包括通过采集遗留下来的叠石实例，辅助以检测检验工作，逐步揭示非物质遗产的赖以存在的"物质"因素。

  除园林中的叠山之外，利用形式独特的天然石料进行铺装的做法也是重要造园和建筑装饰手段。宁寿宫花园中五色石墙面地面、建筑花斑石地面是特色鲜明的做法。对于花斑石，尚有不少档案记载；而对于五色石铺装而言，其产地、表面处理工艺还都不甚清楚，增加了保护工作的难度。

  综上所述，在对宁寿宫花园开展保护工作之前，我们面临的课题又多了一个重要项目。这个课题是综合性的，因此对于文物保护实施方案的作用也是全方位的：我们需要了解物质层面的问题；我们还需要了解传统文化、传统工艺等问题；尔后我们才能确定合理的保护方案，并实施之。

竹丝加工及镶嵌工艺调研与竹丝内檐装修文物保护

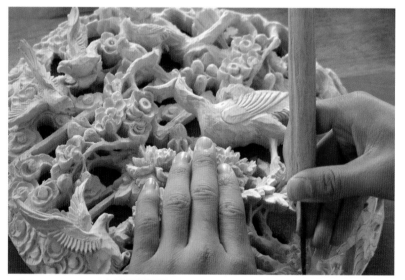

木雕工艺调研与内檐保护

壁纸工艺、裱糊工艺调研与内檐文物保护

We are facing the traditions and craftsmanship in conserving the Qianlong Garden, which include,

    (1) Mid-Qing mural paintings;

    (2) Bamboo thread macquetry;

    (3) Inner-bamboo skin carving and macquetry;

    (4) Jade, porcelain, enamel and copper relief inlay;

    (5) Double-sided embroidery used on interior screens.

6.3 Craftsmanship for Rock and Stone Works

It is widely accepted among the circle of architectural historians that craftsmanship of laying rockeries in the north China was developed from that in the south. Nowadays traditions for rockery laying can hardly be found in the north, while fortunately there are still families capable of this work in southern provinces.

At present in the conservation of Yuanming Yuan ruins, a family of Han (韩) was invited to contribute to the restoration of rockery works. After generations of oral transmission of skill and knowledge, Han family has many experiences in doing the work. But on the other hand, because of lack of basic recording and documenting measures, thoroughness and accuracy of the work became a major problem. In order to excavate and inherit the working methods of laying rockery, symposium and scientific analyses should be immediately organized.

Apart from the rockery laying, other traditions of decoration with stone are also of high significance. We can count in two representative examples, one is the five-color-stone pavement and wall, and the other is skewbald pavement inside buildings. The quarry of the five-color-stone is still unclear, and the traditional burnishing method of the later material remains mysterious.

A long-term subject is placed before the conservators today. The subject is comprehensive, including at least three major important parts. Material is one thing, traditional working method is another, and the proper conservation treatment is the other.

第七章
保护工作计划

目前故宫博物院与美国世界文化遗产基金会合作开展的倦勤斋保护工作可以作为宁寿宫花园保护工作的基本参考，其工作步骤、国内外文物保护专业协作等方式都是值得宁寿宫花园项目借鉴的。另外，参照第五章文物调查与现状评估中的内容，倦勤斋建筑中共保存65槽内檐装修罩隔（比花园中的符望阁的44槽还要多，就数量而言，倦勤斋居于首位，符望阁居其次），并保存有巨幅通景画和天顶画，32幅贴落，大面积的不同历史时期裱糊和修补过的壁纸，以及家具、亭座、匾联等附属文物。无论文物遗存的种类还是数量，无论传统工艺种类还是难度，都在整个宁寿宫花园中具有代表性。因此宁寿宫花园整体保护工作应当以倦勤斋内檐装修保护为基础，延展工作范畴，并添加园林设施、绿化系统、建筑群组等保护工作内容，实现系统保护的目的。

7.1 总体原则、分工与时间计划

7.1.1 总体原则

1 基本原则和方针

本规划以《中华人民共和国文物保护法实施条例》（2003）、《国务院关于加强和改善文物工作的通知》（1997）以及中国相关的法规制度为依据，尊重并参考《中国文物古迹保护准则》（2002）的体系和相关内容，同时借鉴有关国际宪章。本规划建议在宁寿宫花园保护工作完竣后整理出一整套关于中国内檐装修工艺美术保护的措施、工艺、材料方面的指导规范，以便于相关项目的借鉴。

2 工作范围

宁寿宫花园整体范围。包括所有建筑物、基础设施、内檐装修及室内书法绘画作品、庭院中的园林设施、绿化系统、叠石，及一切保护工作者可及的文物遗存。

3 确定保护工作优先级的原则

对于宁寿宫花园的保护工作的优先级别问题，应以下列四项标准为主要参考：文物价值，文物所面临的威胁，文物展示的策略与时机，从外围维护到室内遗存的顺序。

4 基本目标

本规划为整体保护工作确定以下三项基本目标：改善宁寿宫花园所有文物遗存的保存状况；保护并展示所有花园中现存的和可以被进一步研究发掘的历史信息；保护非物质文化遗产，充分利用并复原正在失传的匠作工艺和匠作文化。

5 记录工作

从规划到实施完成的过程中，所有保护和修复工作的所有步骤都必须得到详尽的记录。记录方式主要包括：图片记录、文字记录、影像记录、分析检测报告。

7.1.2 研究与保护人员分工

总体而言，实施方案制定阶段和实施阶段的保护工作涵盖以下范畴，保护工作应当由具有文物保护工作资质和经验的国内外单位和个人执行：

(1) 基础数据库组：建立文物信息数据库；建立并维护文物保护工作信息数据库；建立故宫环境检测数据库。

(2) 园林设施组：园林植物保育；山石/地面修缮与维护；庭院陈设管理（与文物保护部门协作）。

(3) 文物建筑组：木结构保护专业；砖石材料保护专业；彩画保护专业；环境控制专业（温度、湿度控制研究、设计与日常维护）；辅助专业设备系统（照明、安防、消防等设备设置与维护）。

(4) 特殊工艺技术组：木/竹作保护；绘画保护；织物保护。

(5) 展陈、讲解组：展览设计；导游讲解；印刷出版；互动软件；网络宣传。

4 Goal to Achieve

Improve heath status of the entire garden; maintain and display all vestiges of significant historic information that still can be found and that possibly can be studied in the future; preserve intangible heritage, use and revive disappearing craftsmanship.

5 Documentation

Restoration and conservation treatments should be fully documented throughout the procedures. Documentation methods include photography, text record, video record of the treatments, and technical analyses report of samples of all sorts.

7.1.2 Team Grouping & Education

Generally, team grouping should base on different division of work-field:

(1) Information System Group: Establish CHIS (Cultural Heritage Information System) for Qianlong Garden; Qianlong Garden CHIS data input and maintain; Establish and maintain the information system for the basic environment data of the Forbidden City.

(2) Gardening Group: Rejuvenate and protect horticulture items; Repair and maintain rockery and courtyard pavement; Repair and maintain courtyard displaying and pedestal (cooperate with conservation groups).

(3) Historic Architecture Group: Carpenter team; Masonry team; Color-painting team; Evironment team, in charge of research and design and maintain air handlers for interor spaces; Other teams, including lighting, theft alarm, fire alarm systems and other facilities required.

(4) Sepcial Craftsmenship Studios: Fine Carpenter's Studio (conserving wood and bamboo works); Paper Studio; Textile Studio.

(5) Interpretation Group: Interpretation design and plan; Site interpreter / Tourist guide; Publication; Interactive multi-media devices; Internet propaganda.

Present pilot project to preserve the Lodge of Retirement sets a good example for step-by-step conservation procedure and for international philosophy/technology cooperation. It is also important to be aware of that according to the survey and statistic works in Chapter 5, the Lodge of Retirement has 65 pieces of interior spatial partitions (far more that of the second place building Fuwang Ge, which is the biggest building in the garden and has 44 pieces), large pieces of tromp l'oeil on the walls and ceilings, many pieces of Tieluo on wallpapers, wallpapers mounted in different period in history and some pieces of furniture. It can be regarded as a most representative structure in the whole Qianlong Garden, for the conservation of it calls for cooperation of multi-craftsmanship and conservation science, and faces various challenges and problems. Thus the comprehensive work of preserving Qianlong Garden can be and should be based on the experience and working methods and team-construction of the project of the Lodge of Retirement, and should be then expanded in the aspects of working scope, which covers more generally the exterior features, such as the garden features, horticultural items and strucuture.

7.1 General Principle, Team Grouping and Schedule

7.1.1 General Principles

1 Fundamental Principles and Guidelines

The project abides by the Law of Cultural Relics Conservation of the People's Republic of China, and honors the principles Regulations of Cultural Relics Conservation of the PRC, as well as the Venice Charter, and Principles for the Conservation of Heritage Sites in China. It is also strongly proposed that after the comprehensive conservation project a series of technical guidelines for material and human interference be set up for conservation.

2 Restoration Scope

Entire Qianlong Garden, including all buildings in it, all types of infrastructure works, all interior works of handiworks and paintings and calligraphies, all courtyard displaying, horticultural items, and all rockery works, and all factors accessible to conservators.

3 Prioritization

Basing on four fundamental points, i.e. value, risk, strategical plan for opening, and exterior to interior sequence.

7.1.3 研究与保护人力资源

实施方案制定阶段和实施阶段的保护工作的参与者应当包括以下人员：

(1) 文物建筑的结构、构造问题的保护修缮、修复，基础设施工程主要承担部门：故宫博物院古建部。

(2) 叠石等特殊造园工艺：故宫博物院古建部，邀请中国南方传统工匠协助。

(3) 植物复壮工作：故宫古建部庭园科。

(4) 建筑内檐装修主要承担部门：

① 内檐装修罩隔和家具的保护由故宫博物院科技部木/竹器保护工作室承担，邀请中国南方工艺美术大师协助；

② 通景画、贴落画的保护由故宫博物院科技部书画装裱工作室承担（现该工作室正在承担倦勤斋通景画的保护工作）；

③ 壁纸保护由故宫博物院古建部和科技部书画装裱工作室合作承担；

④ 建立故宫科技部丝织品保护工作室，专门负责丝织品的保护。

(5) 故宫科技部工作以实验室、工作室工作为主，古建部主要主持和协调宁寿宫日常的现场工作。

此外，故宫博物院与美国世界文化遗产基金会在《故宫倦勤斋保护项目协议书》中曾经表达了这样的合作意向：

> 第九条
> 故宫博物院与美国世界文化遗产基金会均有开展倦勤斋以外的宁寿宫中文物建筑的意向。合作协议将另外签署。当前项目将尽可能在有关的保护问题方面对于未来项目形成技术帮助。
> 如果故宫博物院与美国世界文化遗产基金会确定开展宁寿宫花园或宁寿宫保护项目，故宫博物院将为该项目提供每年不少于 50 万美元的资金支持，作为美国世界文化遗产基金会捐赠资金的配套资金。（此配套资金不涉及目前开展的倦勤斋项目）

为了中美双方更好地形成专业互补，双方还初步商定，故宫博物院的配套资金将主要用于保护和修复建筑外檐部分、庭院部分及基础设施部分；而在以下领域，故宫将尽可能地寻求国外协作：

(1) 室内罩隔、家具等特殊工艺；

(2) 通景画贴落画等室内书画装饰；

(3) 壁纸；

(4) 室内照明；

(5) 室内温湿度环境控制；

(6) 生物破坏防治；

(7) 展陈与解说。

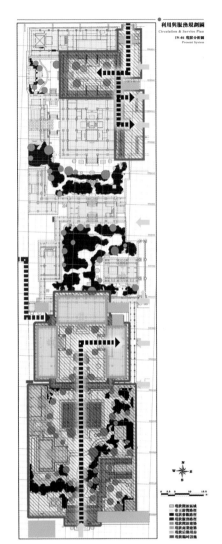

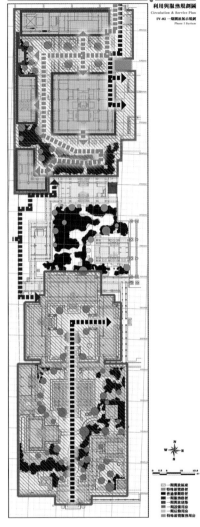

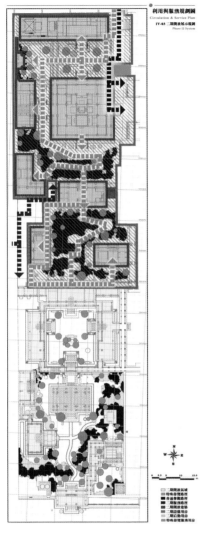

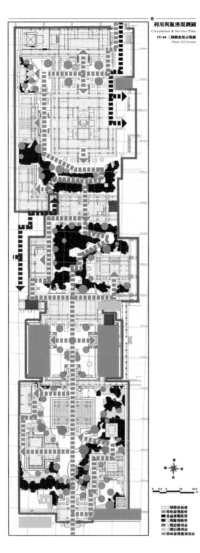

7.1.3 Research & Conservation Resources

Human resources of the teams can be described as follows.

(1) General structural and architectural restoration and infrastructure works will be mainly undertaken by the Department of Architecture of the Palace Museum.

(2) Invite craftsmen from south China to join the team of rockery work with local experts in the Palace Museum.

(3) Plant rejuvenation works will be undertaken by the horticulture group from the Department of Architecture of the Palace Museum.

(4) Furnishings and Fittings of the garden buildings will be allotted to two departments separately,

①Remedial treatments to Interior Screen and furniture are to be undertaken by Fine Carpenter's Studio (for wood and bamboo works) from the Department of Scientific Conservation Technology;

② Trompe l'oeil and Tie'luo treatments are to be undertaken by the Department of Scientific Conservation Technology with the experiences gained in the present work in the Lodge of Retirement;

③ Preservation and restoration of wallpapers are to be undertaken by the Department of Historic Architecture.

(5) Department of Scientific Conservation Technology will focus on studio works, while Department of Historic Architecture will be in charge for most of the site works.

Moreover, as stipulated in previous agreement on the conservation project in the Lodge of Retirement between World Monument Fund and the Palace Museum.

Item Nine

It is the desire of both Parties A (the Palace Museum) and B (World Monument Fund) to repair, restore and conserve other buildings in the Ning Shou Gong precinct other than the Lodge of Retirement. Separate agreement will be signed. Technical issues relevant to the restoration and conservation of the precinct should be tackled in the current Project if possible.

If Party A & Party B undertake additional projects in the Ning Shou Gong Garden or Precinct, Party A shall invest no less than $500 000US dollars each year in this project as matching funds（The matching funds are not available for the Lodge of Retirement project).

It was discussed that the matching fund of $500 000US dollars would most probably go to preserving and restoring the exterior features and infrastructure items. This premise further leads to closer international cooperation in the following fields,

(1) Interior Screen and furniture;

(2) Paintings including Tromp l'oeil and Tie'luo;

(3) Wallpaper;

(4) Interior lighting;

(5) Interior Environment Control;

(6) Anti-biodeterioration;

(7) and Design of the circulation in the interior spaces.

7.1.4 时间计划

1 保护分期

鉴于宁寿宫花园保护项目的综合性和复杂性，该项目必须分期实施，而且应当结合各个实施阶段逐步进行展陈布置，逐步对公众开放。保护分期主要考虑下列问题：

(1) 与现状开放路线的关系问题；

(2) 与当前倦勤斋保护项目的协调问题；

(3) 从局部到整体，从北部到南部的次序问题；

(4) 避免实施过程中开放/保护相互干扰的问题；

(5) 先基础设施，再建筑外部，而后建筑内部的工作次序。

参照上述原则，本规划制定了从2005年末至2016年的十二个年度的总体工作计划，本计划与当前倦勤斋保护工作形成技术层面和时间进度层面的衔接，并确定了一个前期研究阶段和三个实施阶段的工作分期计划。每两期工作之间同样考虑了技术任务的协调和衔接等问题。

一期工作前的研究阶段（2006.3–2006.12）：

(1) 继续修复倦勤斋，撰写纸张、木作、丝绸、油饰保护总结报告；

(2) 宁寿宫花园中现存文物材料学、工艺学调研，保护修复研究与试验；

(3) 编制宁寿宫花园现存文物总数据库及分支数据库；

(4) 制定一期工作计划和实施方案。

一期工作（2007.01–2010.12）：

(1) 全面整修宁寿宫花园排水系统，制定日常维护制度；

(2) 开展宁寿宫花园植物复壮与土壤改良工作；

(3) 实施对第四进院落（碧螺亭所在院落）的假山保护；

(4) 按照实施方案规定的进度修复竹香馆、玉粹轩、符望阁、云光楼内檐装修，对碧螺亭进行建筑保护；

(5) 制定第四进院落的展示和说明方案；

(6) 准备并实施第四进院落的展示和说明方案，开放第四进院落；

(7) 至2008年初，应当初步完成玉粹轩和竹香馆的室内外保护工作，为2008年中期开放第四进院落北半部做好准备；

(8) 建立和维护第四进院落现存文物总数据库及分支数据库；

(9) 制定第二期工作计划和实施方案。

故宫博物院宁寿宫花园历史研究与文物保护规划

7.1.4 General Schedule

1 Phase Laying

As a comprehensive and difficult project, the conservation of Qianlong Garden should be carried out in successive phases and be opened gradually according to the status of completion of the phases.

Phase laying is based on following principles,

(1) Close coordination with the present open routes;

(2) Close coordination with the present conservation project in the Lodge of Retirement;

(3) Being carried out from the north to the south;

(4) Avoiding inter-influence during implementation phases;

(5) Infrastructure first and then the exterior and interior of the structures.

According to above principles, the entire conservation project of Qianlong Garden should have a 12-year plan starting from the present stage of the conservation of the Lodge of Retirement (10 years after the proposed completion date), and the plan should be divided into a research phase plus 3 plan and implementation phases.

Research Phase, 2006.3-2006.12

(1) Implement and summarize the conservation in the Lodge of Retirement which serves as a pilot project for that of the entire garden;

(2) Study on basic technical solution and experimental processes for the relics in the entire garden;

(3) Organize and design of information system for Qianlong Garden relics.

(4) Prepare the conservation action plan for phase I.

Phase I, 2007.01-2010.12

(1) Renovate the drainage system;

(2) Start maintaining the plants and improve the soil in all courtyards;

(3) Preserve the rockery in the fourth courtyard;

(4) Restore the exterior and interior of 竹香馆（the Chamber of Bamboo Fragrance）, 玉粹轩（the Pavilion of Jade Purity）,符望阁 （the Building of Wish and Reality in Accordance）, 云光楼 （the Building of Cloud Light）;

(5) Interpret and exhibit exterior and interior features;

(6) Mobilize for opening of the fourth courtyard;

(7) Aim for 2008, restoration of the exterior and interior of 竹香馆（the Chamber of Bamboo Fragrance ） and 玉粹轩（the Pavilion of Jade Purity）would be possibly completed, to allow for the north part of the fourth courtyard would be ready to open for special visit during the Olympic Games;

(8) Establish, fill-in and maintain the Cultural Relics Information System (CHIS) of the fourth courtyard of the garden.

(9) Draw conservation action plan for phase II.

二期工作（2011.01–2013.12）：

(1) 各院落植物维护与土壤改良工作；

(2) 实施对第三进院落（耸秀亭所在院落）的假山保护；

(3) 按照实施方案规定的进度修复萃赏楼、延趣楼、三友轩内檐装修，对耸秀亭进行建筑保护；

(4) 制定第三进院落的展示和说明方案；

(5) 准备并实施第三进院落的展示和说明方案，开放第三进院落；

(6) 建立和维护第三进院落现存文物总数据库及分支数据库；

(7) 制定第三期工作计划和实施方案。

三期工作（2014.01–2016.12）：

(1) 各院落植物维护与土壤改良工作；

(2) 实施对第一、二进院落的假山保护；

(3) 按照实施方案规定的进度修复第一、二进院落中遂初堂、古华轩、旭辉亭、抑斋等建筑的内檐装修，对其他建筑进行保护；

(4) 制定第一、二进院落的展示和说明方案；

(5) 准备并实施第三进院落的展示和说明方案，开放第三进院落；

(6) 建立和维护第一、二进院落现存文物总数据库及分支数据库。

2 前期研究阶段的工作任务与时间表

结合倦勤斋项目全面开展内檐装修保护的工作进程，特详细规划前期研究阶段的各个主要任务和适于开展该研究的时间段落，切实将倦勤斋项目的研究成果与宁寿宫花园项目的研究选题结合起来。

倦勤斋保护／宁寿宫花园保护前期研究时间表

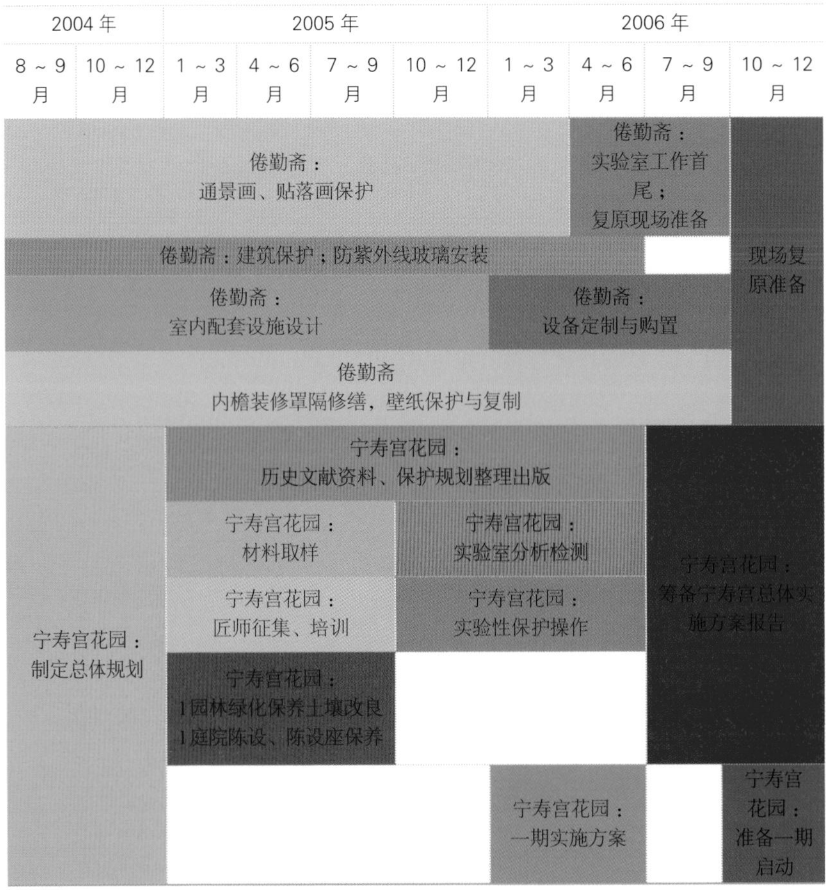

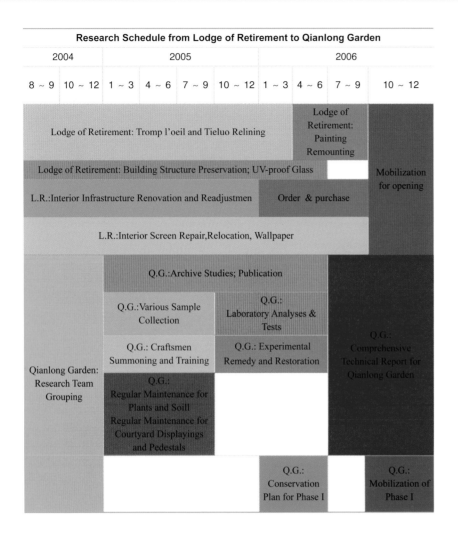

Research Schedule from Lodge of Retirement to Qianlong Garden

	2004		2005			2006			
	8 ~ 9	10 ~ 12	1 ~ 3	4 ~ 6	7 ~ 9	10 ~ 12	1 ~ 3	4 ~ 6	7 ~ 9	10 ~ 12

Lodge of Retirement: Tromp l'oeil and Tieluo Relining

Lodge of Retirement: Painting Remounting

Lodge of Retirement: Building Structure Preservation; UV-proof Glass

Mobilization for opening

L.R.:Interior Infrastructure Renovation and Readjustmen

Order & purchase

L.R.:Interior Screen Repair, Relocation, Wallpaper

Q.G.:Archive Studies; Publication

Q.G.:Various Sample Collection

Q.G.: Laboratory Analyses & Tests

Q.G.: Craftsmen Summoning and Training

Q.G.: Experimental Remedy and Restoration

Q.G.: Comprehensive Technical Report for Qianlong Garden

Qianlong Garden: Research Team Grouping

Q.G.: Regular Maintenance for Plants and Soill

Regular Maintenance for Courtyard Displayings and Pedestals

Q.G.: Conservation Plan for Phase I

Q.G.: Mobilization of Phase I

Phase II, 2011.01-2013.12

(1) Regularly maintain the plants and improve the soil in all courtyards.

(2) Preserve the rockery in the third courtyard.

(3) Restore the exterior and interior of 萃赏楼 (the Building of Collection and Appreciation), 延趣楼 (the Building of Extended Delight), 三友轩 (the Pavilion Three Friends) and 耸秀亭 (the Pavilion of Aloft Bueaty).

(4) Interpret and exhibit exterior and interior features.

(5) Mobilize for opening of the third courtyard.

(6) Establish, fill-in and maintain CHIS of the third courtyard of the garden.

(7) Draw conservation action plan for phase III.

Phase III, 2014.01-2016.12

(1) Regularly maintain the plants and improve the soil in all courtyards;

(2) Preserve the rockery in the first and second courtyard;

(3) Restore the exterior and interior of buildings in the first and second courtyards, including interior conservation of 遂初堂 (the Hall of Fulfillment of Original Wishes), 古华轩 (the Pavilion of Ancient Flower), 旭辉亭 (the Pavilion of Morning Splendo) and 抑斋 (the Chamber of Self-Constraint) should be stressed;

(4) Interpret and exhibit exterior and interior features;

(5) Mobilize for opening of the first and second courtyards;

(6) Establish, fill-in and maintain CHIS of the first two courtyards of the garden.

2 Tentative Schedule for Research and Preparation

The schdule below is set up concerning the implementation time schedule for the substantial conservation tasks of the pilot project in the Lodge of Retirement after removing the interior painting works.

3 实施前期应完成的保护研究 / 课题一览

结合倦勤斋项目的各项检测、实验、研究、试操作等工作，宁寿宫花园的研究课题可以进一步拓展范围、加深研究。兹列举前期研究各主要课题及其计划如下。

编号	课题	研究者	时间	预期成果
01	生物破坏防治	科技部； 罗伯特·凯斯勒	2004～2006	研究报告； 长期检测方式、计划
02	建筑大木彩画的分析检测与保护	科技部； 境外（盖蒂？）	2004～2006	研究报告； 颜料成分、产地； 建议保护措施
03	叠石修整与保护	古建部	2004～2006	三维激光测量存档； 保护加固工艺
04	木竹作、镶嵌工艺等工艺美术的保护	科技部	2004～2006	研究报告； 建立样本库； 组织工美匠师
05	漆器保护	科技部； 马里昂·麦克林伯格	2004～2006	研究报告； 材料分析； 环境控制建议
06	总结室内绘画文物保护经验	科技部	2004～2006	研究报告

7.2 基础设施的修复

7.2.1 排水系统

至少是清覆以来，紫禁城内地下排水系统每岁疏浚的惯例便已经不存在了。尽管排水系统的工作状况并不良好如初，但是至今仍然起到了渲泄雨水的作用，保证了紫禁城内暂无严重积水问题。

数十年来，紫禁城地下排水系统的问题由于长期不受重视而日益严峻，亟待制定和实施保护措施。这些问题包括：

(1) 所有地下雨水沟需要全面调研和修缮，一些沟帮、沟盖已经塌陷；

(2) 地下雨水沟内淤积亟待清除，沟底标高需要根据原排水方向和坡度进行调整和恢复，以确保排水效果；

(3) 现故宫博物院内环卫工人将尘土和垃圾清扫入地下排水沟的做法必须严令禁止；

(4) 必须恢复每年农历三月疏浚地下雨水沟的惯例。

延趣楼地下排水沟入水孔　　　延趣楼台基下过水沟沟孔

玉粹轩台基下过水沟沟孔　　　竹香馆地下排水沟入水孔

萃赏楼台基下过水沟沟孔

抑斋地炕烧火口

遂初堂地炕烧火口

三友轩地炕烧火口

萃赏楼地炕烧火口　玉粹轩地炕烧火口

倦勤斋地炕烧火口　延趣楼地炕烧火口

3 Task List for Conservation Research Phase before Implementation

The research can find basic assistance when being carried out in good coordination with the implementation phase of the conservation project of the Lodge of Retirement.

No.	Task	Executant	Time	Envisaged Goal
01	Anti-biodeterioration	Conservation Tech. Dept. SCMRE	2004-2006	Study Report; Long-term observation plan
02	Preserving architectural color painting	Conservation Tech. Dept. Getty Inst.?	2004-2006	Study Report; Material & section analyses; Suggestion for treatment
03	Preserving rockery	Architecture Dept.	2004-2006	3D laser scanning; Reinforcement plan
04	Preserving wood/bamboo and inlay works	Conservation Tech. Dept.	2004-2006	Study Report; Material database; Conservator+artisan teams
05	Preserving lacquer objects	Conservation Tech. Dept. SCMRE	2004-2006	Study Report; Material & section analyse; Suggestion for protection
06	Review of Tromp o'eil conservation	Conservation Tech. Dept.	2004-2006	Study Report

7.2 Infrastructure Restoration

7.2.1 Drainage System

Drainage system inside and outside Qianlong Garden has been out of regular repair for almost a century after the abdication of the last Qing Emperor. It is fortunate that this system is still working to conduct today rainwater into the Inner Golden River, though it is not functioning perfectly.

After decades of neglecting, problems have accumulated acceleratedly, and measures should be urgently taken.

(1) All drain lines should be surveyed and preserved, including some of fallen sidewalls and collapsing cover that call for restoration.

(2) Debris in the drains should be removed, and sedimentation at the bottom should be corrected in order to guarantee a smooth drain.

(3) Activities including sweeping dust and debris into the drains should be strictly prohibited, and improper objects that covers the water inlet should be removed.

(4) All drain lines should be regularly cleaned and maintained once a year, as it was done in Qing dynasty, once in the third month according to lunar calendar.

7.2.2 地炕系统

规划研究组在现存资料中无法找到关于清代如何使用宁寿宫花园地下取暖设施的直接材料。我们只能通过乾隆、嘉庆皇帝确实造访宁寿宫花园并题写诗篇的时间来推断皇帝更多的是在冬日来此（夏季往往是在御园中度过的），而当时，地炕一定是在使用的。

对于地炕系统的保护修缮需要首先清除烧火口地穴中大量积土，进而应在需要的部位拆开室内地面，暴露地炕和火道，进行修整后重墁地面。尽管在宁寿宫花园的前导项目——倦勤斋保护项目中，勘察发现了一些的地炕残损现象，但是基于保护处理的必要性与迫切性的判断，并未实施地炕修缮。

本规划建议在宁寿宫花园保护工作中，普遍进行烧火口地穴积土的清理工作，同时在室内地面较严重残损的建筑中（以第三进院落的延趣楼为试点，建筑编号）结合室内地面的修缮工程，揭开地下火道，进行维护。一方面记录、揭示和修缮地下取暖设施；另一方面探询结合地下火道安置照明、电力、空调等系统的管线。

7.3 园林设施的保护

7.3.1 叠石

如本规划第5章所述，宁寿宫花园庭院叠石总体而言是稳定、安全的，同时存在一些构造和表面问题，如叠石松动走闪、失位坠落，铸铁拉扯裸露，栏杆望柱残损不全，山脚淤积厚重等。

本规划认为，必须针对上述残损现象进行治理，防止病害发展，保护叠石景观的历史面貌，同时开展以下工作：

(1) 利用三维激光扫描技术逐步确定叠石的形象，形成基础档案；

(2) 以5年为周期重复扫描，进行数据比较，确定假山结构形变问题；

(3) 分析叠石填充和勾缝灰浆成分，选择适宜材料封护裸露铸铁拉扯，加固灰缝流失部位；

(4) 通过照片对比、现状判断等方法确定散落山石的原始位置，将散落山石复位；

(5) 清理山脚淤积杂物，重新露出原始铺地材料，保持山脚低洼处的干燥；

(6) 恢复、补配循山径栏杆望柱，恢复木寻杖。

7.3.2 庭院地面铺装

1 砖墁地面

经过几个世纪的修缮改造和自然损坏，宁寿宫花园庭院砖地面最为显著的残损现象是沉降、磨损和破碎。为确保地面排水功能，应对沉降、破碎严重者予以更换。并确立每年定期除草的惯例。

叠石小径栏杆现存石望柱、望柱遗留痕迹及散落石望柱

紫禁城瑰宝
故宫博物院宁寿宫花园历史研究与文物保护规划

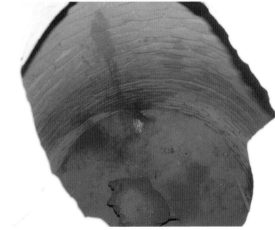

宁寿宫园第四进院内古井

7.2.2 Underground Heating System

There are almost no documents about using the underground heating system in the buildings in Qianlong Garden in Qing dynasty. We can only infer from some records that this system had been used sometimes when Qianlong and Jiaqing came to the garden during winter.

Restoring underground heating system calls for removing dust and debris in the furnace pit and partially re-paving of interior brick floor. Such work has not yet done nor planned in the pilot conservation project of the Lodge of Retirement, though some damage and sedimentations are detected.

The Master Plan suggests that dust-removal and some interior-pavement-relay be done (Trial work in the Building of Extended Delight, building ID III-05) wherever underground heating are, not only to restore the system but also finding possibilities of using the underground tunnels for either laying electric power supply or air condition pipes.

7.3 Garden Feature Preservation

7.3.1 Rockery Works

As the survey shows in Chapter 5, most rockeries are largely stable, and problems mainly include:

(1) Some fallen rocks from tops can be found, and the original location can hardly be determined.

(2) Some iron ties are exposed to the air and rain.

(3) Most stone posts for barriers are broken or lost.

(4) At foot of the rockeries, earth is thickly accumulated, which leads to rising moisture that might be hazardous to aged lime joints.

It is proposed to take measure to prevent further damage and restore the basic features of the rockeries. The master plan stresses on the following points.

(1) Use 3D laser scanning technique to establish basic 3D record of the rockery.

(2) Re-scan rockery in five-year cycle to detect deformation of the rockery-complex.

(3) Analyze mortars applied in the joints and as pointing, and use authentic and durable material to cover the exposed iron holders and reinforce the rocks.

(4) Research to determine original location of the fallen rocks and relocate them to the place with proper mortar.

(5) Remove earth and debris at the foot of the rockeries in order to re-expose the ground pavement and keep the foot of building clean to prevent moisture accumulation.

(6) Restore the broken and missing stone balustrade post and restore wood rails between balustrade posts.

保护规划设计图
Drawings for Conservation Plan
III-01 基础设施保护
方针示意图
Guidelines for
Infrastructure Rehabilitation

2 石子铺墁

花园第一进院落中的石子铺墁近期经历了修缮，其他院落中的石子铺墁则保持了原有状态。鉴于石子现存铺墁的缺失和松散现象比较严重，应解剖各部位代表性的构造做法，聘请/培训专门匠师对各院石子地面进行修补，并针对破损最为严重者进行局部重墁。

3 五色石铺墁

五色石材料保存现状表明，该材料多生细小裂缝，具有较高的孔隙率，耐磨性较弱。因此对于这种做法的保护应尝试借助现代化学保护材料进行加固。实施保护的前提是利用实验室技术进行材料分析和实验性处理。

7.3.3 庭院陈设及陈设座

一些现存庭院陈设及其石陈设座并非原位摆放，一些陈设座也已经折断或拆解搁置。本规划列举以下保护复原措施：

(1) 保留现状完好的陈设和陈设座；

(2) 选取风化严重的石座进行化学加固实验，列出加固计划；

(3) 使用树脂材料修补折断/破损的陈设座；

(4) 根据历史档案和现有库存情况制定恢复庭院陈设的方案并予以实施。

7.4 绿化系统复壮

7.4.1 土壤改良

目前的研究分析表明，土壤有适中的渗透性土壤显碱性无盐渍化现象。在结合实施方案的研究中，还应对土壤即时状况和更多的土样进行分析，以取得最及时、最全面的材料。土壤改良应制定实施方案，方案内容应当包括：

(1) 保持土壤现有的渗透性；

(2) 将现状的碱性土壤改良成中性或微酸性土壤。

7.4.2 病虫害防治

关于宁寿宫花园内的昆虫存在情况，研究认为谷婪步甲为捕食性昆虫，以其他的昆虫为食，是益虫，需要我们加以保护，这可能也是1号院福婆鳃金龟虫口密度低的原因之一。福婆鳃金龟为植食性种类，其幼虫以植物的根部为食，成虫取食植物的叶片，可对植物造成严重伤害，需要加以监测和控制。从福婆鳃金龟在各院的分布情况来看，除1号院虫口密度较低不需要防治外，第2～5号院虫口密度均在30头/m²以上。为保证古树的健康生长，有必要对福婆鳃金龟实施防治措施。具体防治方法是：用20%甲基异柳磷乳油或50%辛硫磷乳油800～1000倍液灌根，每株根据树坑大小25～50kg不等。

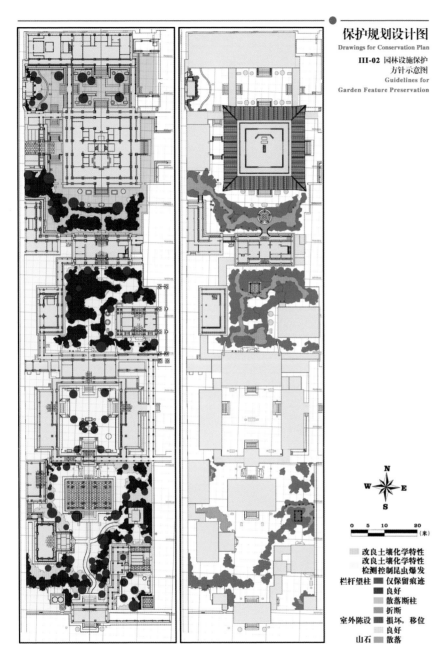

保护规划设计图
Drawings for Conservation Plan
III-02 园林设施保护
方针示意图
Guidelines for
Garden Feature Preservation

改良土壤化学特性
改良土壤化学特性
检测控制昆虫爆发
栏杆望柱　仅保留痕迹
　　　　　良好
　　　　　散落断柱
　　　　　折断
室外陈设　损坏，移位
　　　　　良好
山石　　　散落

7.3.2 Courtyard Pavement

1 Brick Pavement

After centuries of human impacts and environmental changes, brick pavement in Qianlong Garden is mainly facing problems of sedimentation and abrasion and cracking. It is proposed to replace the serious broken bricks with traditional bricks and re-lay the parts that are serious subsided.

2 Scree Pavement

In the first courtyard, some scree paths and ground pavement had been recently re-paved, and in other courtycards most of the pavement are original. Partial repaving and consolidation should be carried out where the screes are lost or loose. Capable traditional craftsman in this field in this fiell should be invited for this job.

3 Five-color-slate Pavement

Five-color-slate has relatively high porosity, and has low anti-abrasion property. It is proposed that modern chemical protection material should be applied. The primary task for this treatment is to do comprehensive experiments and tests before wide using a treatment.

7.3.3 Courtyard Displaying and Pedestal

Courtyard displaying and pedestals remaining today are not all their original place, and there are also many broken pieces lying in the corners.

It is planned that in the next phase of conservation plan that direct implementation,

(1) Preserve the remaining stone pedestals.

(2) Select samples of serious damaged stone pieces for chemical consolidating treatment, draw consolidation plan.

(3) Repair and stick the broken with proper epoxy resin solution.

(4) Basing on archives and remaining in collection, draw a layout plan to re-exhibit all courtyard displaying objects, or use replicas.

7.4 Plant Rejuvenation

7.4.1 Soil Improvement

Based on sampling and analyses at present stage, also requiring further proving and researches, soil condition can be basically described as, having moderate plasticity, being alkalescent and not salt-affected.

Suggestions for soil improvement are,

(1) Maintain water penetration property of the soil;

(2) Meliorate the soil to non-alkalescent.

7.4.3 竹根控制疏导

所有现状存在竹林的院落都需要对竹根的恣意生长进行控制。控制方法主要有：(1)进一步发掘史料，在历史资料证明原状并无竹林生长的地方清除竹林；(2)针对竹林周边建筑的基础和台帮进行处理，并加深台帮深度，杜绝竹根生长影响建筑基础，或造成局部构造破坏。

7.5 建筑保护措施

7.5.1 建筑保护的一般方法

对应第三章中建筑现状勘察所发现的构造和结构问题，选择适宜的常规建筑保护修缮方法如下，以供各座建筑确定规划保护原则、制定实施方案时选择参照。

建筑部位	典型残损现象	保护处理初步意见	所需开展的研究／保护措施
台明台帮	砖体风化	I-a	采用化学方法对风化程度较重的砌块进行加固
	砖体风化与片状剥落 砖体破裂／砖体缺失	I-b	对深度风化的砌块进行挖补
室内地面	砖体轻微风化	II-a	选择性化学加固
	砖体中度以上风化 砖体磨损／砖体破裂 砖体缺失	II-b	局部挖补； 选择性化学加固
大木结构	轻微老化／腐朽	III-a	除尘清理、修补； 实施防虫防腐处理
	生物破坏（腐朽／虫蛀等） 挠曲／木材开裂／拔榫	III-b	抽换失效构件； 使用同样材质复制、替换失效构件； 实施防虫防腐处理
	结构严重形变或重要承重构件折断	III-c	局部解体、更换失效构件； 打牮拨正
墙体	抹灰老化脱落 墙体灰缝流失 砖体酥碱	IV-a	按照传统做法重新抹灰饰面； 对砖石砌块进行选择性的化学加固
	显著裂缝	IV-b	采用结构加固处理
室内木壁板	轻度老化	V-a	除尘清理、局部修补； 实施防虫防腐处理
	生物破坏 翘曲／开裂／拔榫	V-b	修整变形构件，更换残损严重者； 实施防虫防腐处理
	严重残破或缺失 严重生物破坏	V-c	使用同样材质复制，更换残损严重部分

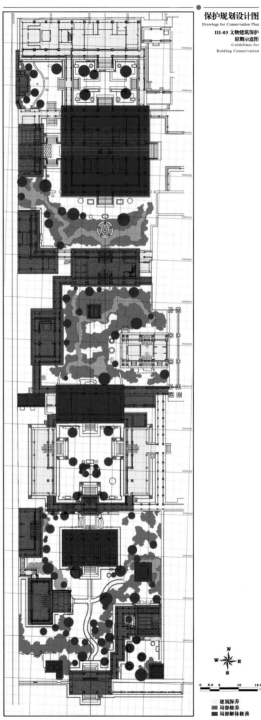

保护规划设计图
Drawings for Conservation Plan
III-03 文物建筑保护原则示意图
Guidelines for Building Conservation

建筑除养
局部修养
局部解体修善

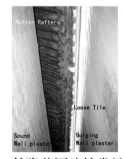

乾隆花园建筑常见残损，以倦勤斋为例

7.4.2 Insect Control

Research shows that harpalus calealus is preyer of other insects therefore is beneficial to plants, as we can see from the insect density in Courtyard I that there is very low density of brahmina faldermann because of the existence of harpalus calealus. Protecting harpalus calealus should be one of the goals of insect control. Brahmina faldermann lives on plants, imago on leaf and larva on root, which should be carefully dectected and controlled. Basing on the survey, apart from that brahmina faldermann in the first courtyard is very low, the other samples show that brahmina faldermann density in other courtyards is higher than 30 per m^2. Suggested treatment is,

Pesticide, 20% emulsifiable solution of 甲基异柳磷 or 50% emulsifiable solution of phoxim.

Usage & Dosage, dilution 800 ~ 1000,irrigating basing on delve size, range from 25 ~ 50kg.

7.4.3 Bamboo Root Control

All courtyards that have bamboo are facing problems of the over-thriving growth of the bamboo roots. Measures should be taken either remove bamboos which are not authentic to the site or keep the bamboo which could be proved according to historic archives and treat the foundation with isolation layers to prevent the roots from growing into the fundation of structure.

7.5 Envisaged Tasks for Structure Maintenance

7.5.1 General Structural and Architectural Treatment

In accordance with the damage survey of the garden buildings, general guideline of remedial treatment for structures in Qianlong Garden is listed below.

Chief Component	Representative Damage	Remedy ID	Research Task / Remedy
Platform Stone & Brick	Efflorescence	I-a	Preserve stone and brick works with modern technique
	Efflorescence & exfoliation Broken / Missing	I-b	Replace seriously-damaged parts with traditional materials and methods
Pavement inside building	Efflorescence	II-a	Preserve stone and brick works
	Efflorescence Abrasion / Broken Missing	II-b	Replace seriously-damaged parts with traditional material and methods Repair the slightly damaged pieces
Structure Timber	Minor aging	III-a	Dedust and apply minor treatments Apply pesticide and antiseptic treatments
	Bio-deterioration Bending / Breaking Disjunction (quoin & mortise)	III-b	Disassemble damaged part Replace seriously-damaged parts with original material Apply pesticide and antiseptic treatments
	Structure failure or serious distortion	III-c	Part disassembly Correct distortion

建筑部位	典型残损现象	保护处理初步意见	所需开展的研究/保护措施
天花	轻度老化	VI-a	除尘清理、局部修补；实施防虫防腐处理
	生物破坏 翘曲 开裂 拔榫	VI-b	修整天花支条，更换挖补残损部分；实施防虫防腐处理
木装修及栏杆、药栏	轻度老化	VII-a	除尘清理、局部修补；实施防虫防腐处理
	生物破坏 开裂或缺失 拔榫	VII-b	局部解体；采用同样材质局部挖补、更换原构件；实施防虫防腐处理
	严重腐朽/老化 严重破损或缺失	VII-c	使用同样材质复制，更换失效构件
	经现代改造	VII-d	根据历史线索复原旧有形式；实施防虫防腐处理
大木彩画	近期修复	VIII-a	除尘清理、局部修补
	（原始彩画老化问题：） 地仗空鼓脱落 褪色 起甲剥落	VIII-b	取样，检测颜料、地仗成分；除尘；回帖；使用化学材料进行选择性封护
屋面	灰缝轻度老化、流失 瓦件轻度缺失	IX-a	屋面除草；捉节夹陇
	瓦件脱釉 瓦件缺失 瓦件破损	IX-b	屋面除草；捉节夹陇、更换破碎瓦件
	瓦件严重破损 雨水渗漏	IX-c	局部揭瓦，添配瓦件
防尘处理		X-a	密封窗隔扇缝隙；恢复传统门扇掩缝做法
新添电力设备系统		XI-a	消防、安防报警系统；通风、温湿度控制系统；照明系统

乾隆花园建筑常见残损，以倦勤斋为例

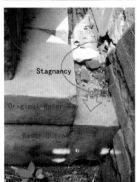

乾隆花园建筑常见残损，以倦勤斋为例

Chief Component	Representative Damage	Remedy ID	Research Task / Remedy
Wall Stone & Brick	Minor aging Plastering desquamating Efflorescence	IV-a	Re-plastering with traditional material and method Preserve stone and brick works with modern technique
	Serious cracking	IV-b	Apply reinforcement
Interior Wooden Wall Board	Minor aging	V-a	Dedust and apply minor treatments Apply pesticide and antiseptic treatments
	Bio-deterioration Bending Breaking Disjunction (quoin & mortise)	V-b	Reform the boards and replace the damaged components Apply pesticide and antiseptic treatments
	Serious damage or missing Serious bio-deterioration	V-c	Replace with replicas
Ceiling frame	Minor aging	VI-a	Dedust and apply minor treatments Apply pesticide and antiseptic treatments
	Bio-deterioration Bending Breaking Disjunction (quoin & mortise)	VI-b	Reform the frames and replace the damaged components Apply pesticide and antiseptic treatments
Window & Door, Balustrade and Fence	Minor aging	VII-a	Dedust and apply minor treatments Apply pesticide and antiseptic treatments
	Bio-deterioration Breaking or missing Disjunction (quoin & mortise)	VII-b	Disassemble damaged part Replace seriously-damaged and missing parts with original material Apply pesticide and antiseptic treatments
	Serious efflorescence Serious broken or missing	VII-c	Replace failed components with replica
	Being modernized	VII-d	Restore according to original style Apply pesticide and antiseptic treatments
Color Painting	Recently restored	VIII-a	Dedust
	Aging of original pieces Efflorescence Fading Peeling-off	VIII-b	Sample and pigment-Analyze Dedust Attach-back Apply chemical-protection
Roof	Minor aging Slight missing tiles	IX-a	Weeding and re-jointing the tiles
	Glaze-desquamation Slight missing tiles Medium broken tiles	IX-b	Weeding and re-jointing the tiles and replace damage tiles
	Serious broken tiles Water leakage	IX-c	Partial tile-re-laying
Dust proofing		X-a	Seal gapes between casements Use traditional cloth-cotton stripes at door leafs
Electrical Devices		XI-a	Alarm system against fire and theft Ventilation devices / Lighting

7.5.2 工作量估算

宁寿宫花园各座建筑保护措施工作量估算

编号	建筑名称	残损等级	建议保护措施（编号参见表5-03）	措施类型
I-01	衍祺门	B, 25	I-b, II-b, III-b, IV-b, VI-b, VII-a, VIII-b, IX-a, XI-a	B
I-02	古华轩	B, 27	I-b, II-b, III-b, VIII-b, IX-b, XI-a	B
I-03	撷芳亭	B, 30	I-b, II-a, III-c, VIII-b, IX-b	C
I-04	矩亭	B, 22	I-a, II-b, III-b, VI-b, VII-a, VIII-b, IX-a	B
I-05	抑斋	B, 21	I-b, II-b, III-a, VI-a, V-a, VI-a, VII-a, VII-c, VIII-b, IX-c	B
I-06	承露台	B, 21	I-b, II-a, III-a, IV-a, VII-a, VII-c, X-a	B
I-07	井亭	B, 34	I-b, II-b, III-b, IV-b, V-c, VII-c, IX-c	C
I-08	禊赏亭	A, 20	I-a, II-a, III-b, IV-a, VII-a, VIII-b, IX-b, XI-a	B
I-09	旭辉庭	B, 21	I-a, II-a, III-a, VI-b, VII-b, VIII-b, IX-b, X-a, XI-a	B
II-01	垂花门	B, 23	I-b, II-a, III-c, VI-a, VII-a, VIII-b, IX-b	B
II-02	遂初堂	B, 28	I-b, II-b, III-c, IV-a, V-a, VI-a, VII-b, VIII-b, IX-c, X-a, XI-a	C
II-03	遂初堂东配殿	A, 16	I-a, II-a, III-a, IV-a, V-a, VI-a, VII-b, VIII-a, IX-b, X-a, XI-a	A
II-04	遂初堂东配殿北耳房	B, 21	I-a, II-a, III-a, IV-a, V-a, VI-a, VII-b, VIII-b, IX-b, X-a, XI-a	B
II-05	遂初堂东耳房	B, 26	I-a, II-a, III-a, IV-a, V-a, VI-b, VII-a, VIII-b, IX-c, X-a, XI-a	C
II-06	遂初堂西配殿	A, 18	I-a, II-a, III-a, IV-a, V-a, VI-a, VII-b, VIII-a, IX-c, X-a, XI-a	A
II-07	遂初堂西耳房	A, 14	I-a, II-a, III-a, IV-a, V-a, VI-a, VII-a, VIII-a, IX-a, X-a, XI-a	A
II-08	遂初堂西穿堂	B, 39	I-b, II-a, III-b, IV-a, V-b, VII-a, VIII-a, IX-c, X-a, XI-a	C
III-01	耸秀亭	B, 25	II-b, III-b, VII-b, VIII-b, IX-b	B
III-02	萃赏楼	B, 21	I-b, II-a, III-b, IV-a, V-a, VI-b, VII-a, VIII-b, IX-a, X-a, XI-a	B
III-03	三友轩	A, 19	I-b, II-a, III-b, IV-a, V-a, VI-a, VII-b, VIII-b, IX-a, X-a, XI-a	A
III-04	萃赏楼东耳房	A, 19	I-a, II-a, III-a, IV-a, V-a, VI-a, VII-a, VIII-a, IX-a, X-a, XI-a	A
III-05	延趣楼	B, 23	I-a, II-a, III-c, IV-a, V-a, VI-a, VII-b, VIII-a, IX-a, X-a, XI-a	B
IV-01	碧螺亭	A, 14	II-a, III-b, VI-a, VII-b, VIII-b, IX-b	A
IV-02	符望阁	B, 30	I-b, II-a, III-c, IV-a, V-a, VI-c, VII-b, VIII-b, IX-c, X-a, XI-a	C
IV-03	倦勤斋	A, 18	I-a, II-a, III-a, IV-a, V-a, VII-a, VIII-a, IX-a, X-a, XI-a	A
IV-04	云光楼	A, 20	I-a, II-a, III-a, IV-a, V-a, VI-a, VII-a, VIII-a, IX-a, X-a, XI-a	B
IV-05	玉粹轩	B, 22	I-a, II-a, III-a, IV-a, V-a, VI-a, VII-a, VIII-a, IX-a, X-a, XI-a	B
IV-06	净尘心室	A, 18	I-a, II-a, III-a, IV-a, V-a, VII-a, VIII-a, IX-a, X-a, XI-a	A
IV-07	竹香馆	B, 21	I-a, II-a, III-a, IV-a, V-b, VI-a, VII-b, VIII-a, IX-a, X-a, XI-a	B
IX	四进院游廊	A	I-a, II-a, III-a, IV-a, VII-a, VIII-b, IX-a	A
	一至三进院游廊	B	I-a, II-b, III-c, IV-a, VII-b, VIII-b, IX-c	B

7.6 内檐装修的保护

宁寿宫花园建筑内檐装修由各不同类型的装饰做法组成，即通景画、贴落、壁纸、内檐彩画、木作罩隔、家具等。对于这些内檐装修类型应实施不同保护做法。同时，本规划特别强调，内檐装修保护工艺流程和做法都是极其复杂的，必须在每个工艺步骤之前和之后都进行图象和文字记录，必要阶段取样进行实验室分析检测。

7.6.1 内檐装修保护的一般方法

1 内檐装修保护一般措施

内檐装修保护一般措施

内檐做法类型	材料/工艺	典型残损现象	研究/保护任务	残损系数	工作量
通景画	纸托绢画心	生物破坏 老化/撕裂 污染	揭取/去褙裱褙 全色/回贴	30～99	*****
贴落	纸托纸画心	生物破坏 老化/撕裂 污染	揭取/去褙裱褙 全色/回贴	10～70	***
贴落	纸托绢画心	生物破坏 老化/撕裂 污染	揭取/去褙裱褙 全色/回贴	10～40	**
硬木作罩隔等	普通雕饰/装饰	老化/开裂 缺失/变形	现场拆卸解体 修复（研究原做法；选择工艺；修复；烫蜡）/复位	10～60	**
硬木作罩隔等	中等雕饰/装饰	老化/开裂 缺失/变形	现场拆卸解体 修复（研究原做法；选择工艺；修复；烫蜡）/复位	10～30	***
硬木作罩隔等	精细雕饰/装饰	老化/开裂 缺失/变形	现场拆卸解体 修复（研究原做法；选择工艺；实验性修复；正式修复；烫蜡）复位	10～40	*****
家具	硬木雕刻	积尘 构件缺失 构件破损	局部拆卸 除尘（保留部分包浆）修复/烫蜡/复位	10	*

7.6 Proposed Remedial Treatments for Interior Relics

Envisaged tasks for interior feature include treatment to tromp l'oeil, Tieluo, wallpaper, color painting on structural components, interior screenings and furniture. Moreover, the master plan specifically stresses that the methodologies, working procedure and material are all complicated factors that affect standard and result of conservation and are part of cultural heritage themselves, thus detailed recording and documentation should be made thoroughly throughout the research and treatments, and necessary laboratory analyses and tests should be applied whenever necessary.

7.6.1 General Remedial Treatments for Preserving Interior Features

1 General Treatments

Treatments for Interior Relics

Chief Component	Construction Feature	Representative Damage	Research Task / Remedy	Damage Inventory	Work-load
Tromp l'oeil	Silk with paper lining	Bio-deterioration Aging Tearing Contamination	Removal Relining In-painting Remounting	30-99	*****
Tieluo	Paper with paper lining	Bio-deterioration Aging Tearing Contamination	Removal Relining In-painting Remounting	10-70	***
	Silk with paper lining	Bio-deterioration Aging Tearing Contamination	Removal Relining In-painting Remounting	10-40	**
Screens and etc.	With plain decoration	Aging Cracking Missing Distortion	Removal Repair Relocation	10-60	**
	With medium decoration	Aging Cracking Missing Distortion	Removal Repair Relocation	10-30	***
	With delicate decoration	Aging Cracking Missing Distortion	Removal Repair Studying inlay and macquetry methods Relocation	10-40	*****
Furniture	Carved iron wood	Dust Missing component Broken component	Removal Dedust Repair Waxing Relocation	10	*

7.5.2 Envisaged Workload for Buildings

Proposed Remedies for Individual Buildings

ID	Building	Damage Value	Working Methods	Grade of Restoration
I-01	Gate of Extended Felicity	B, 25	I-b, II-b, III-b, IV-a, VI-b, VII-a, VIII-b, IX-a, XI-a	B
I-02	Pavilion of Ancient Flower	B, 27	I-b, II-b, III-b, VIII-b, IX-b, XI-a	B
I-03	Pavilion of Embosoming Fragrance	B, 30	I-b, II-a, III-c, VIII-b, IX-b	C
I-04	Square Pavilion	B, 22	I-a, II-b, III-b, VI-b, VII-a, VIII-b, IX-a	B
I-05	Chamber of Self Constraint	B, 21	I-b, II-b, III-a, VI-a, V-a, VI-a, VII-a, VII-c, VIII-b, IX-c	B
I-06	Dew Platform	B, 21	I-b, II-a, III-a, IV-a, VII-a, VII-c, X-a	B
I-07	Well Pavilion	B, 34	I-b, II-b, III-b, IV-b, V-c, VII-c, IX-c	C
I-08	Pavilion of Floating Cup	A, 20	I-a, II-a, III-b, IV-a, VII-a, VIII-b, IX-b, XI-a	B
I-09	Pavilion of Morning Splendour	B, 21	I-a, II-a, III-a, VI-b, VII-a, VIII-b, IX-b, X-a, XI-a	B
II-01	Pendent-flora Gate	B, 23	I-b, II-a, III-c, VI-a, VII-a, VIII-b, IX-b	B
II-02	Hall of Fulfilment of Original Wishes	B, 28	I-b, II-b, III-c, IV-a, V-a, VI-a, VII-b, VIII-b, IX-c, X-a, XI-a	C
II-03	East Side Hall of Suichu Tang	A, 16	I-a, II-a, III-a, IV-a, V-a, VI-a, VII-b, VIII-a, IX-b, X-a, XI-a	A
II-04	North Ear Room of East Side Hall of Suichu Tang	B, 21	I-b, II-b, III-b, IV-a, V-a, VI-a, VII-a, VIII-b, IX-b, X-a, XI-a	B
II-05	East Ear Room of Suichu Tang	B, 26	I-b, II-b, III-b, IV-a, V-b, VI-b, VII-b, VIII-b, IX-c, X-a, XI-a	C
II-06	West Side Hall of Suichu Tang	A, 18	I-a, II-a, III-a, IV-a, V-a, VI-a, VII-b, VIII-a, IX-c, X-a, XI-a	A
II-07	West Ear Room of Suichu Tang	A, 14	I-b, II-a, III-a, IV-b, V-a, VI-a, VII-a, VIII-a, IX-a, X-a, XI-a	A
II-08	West Passage Room of Suichu Tang	B, 39	I-b, II-b, III-b, IV-b, V-b, VII-b, VIII-b, IX-b, X-a, XI-a	C
III-01	Pavilion of Aloft Beauty	B, 25	II-b, III-b, VII-b, VIII-b, IX-b	B
III-02	Building of Collection and Appreciation	B, 21	I-b, II-b, III-b, IV-b, V-a, VI-b, VII-b, VIII-b, IX-c, X-a, XI-a	B
III-03	Pavilion of Three Friends	A, 19	I-b, II-a, III-b, IV-a, V-a, VI-a, VII-a, VIII-b, IX-a, X-a, XI-a	A
III-04	East Room of Building of Collection and Appreciation	A, 19	I-b, II-b, III-a, IV-a, V-a, VI-a, VII-a, VIII-a, IX-a, X-a, XI-a	A
III-05	Building of Extended Delight	B, 23	I-b, II-b, III-c, IV-a, V-b, VI-a, VII-b, VIII-b, IX-a, X-a, XI-a	B
IV-01	Pavilion of Emerald Conch	A, 14	II-a, III-b, VI-a, VII-b, VIII-b, IX-b	A
IV-02	Building of Wish and Reality in Accordance	B, 30	I-b, II-b, III-c, IV-a, V-b, VI-c, VII-b, VIII-b, IX-c, X-a, XI-a	C
IV-03	Lodge of Retirement	A, 18	I-b, II-b, III-b, IV-a, V-a, VI-a, VII-a, VIII-a, IX-a, X-a, XI-a	A
IV-04	Building of Cloud Light	A, 20	I-a, II-b, III-a, IV-a, V-b, VI-c, VII-a, VIII-a, IX-a, X-a, XI-a	B
IV-05	Pavilion of Jade Purity	B, 22	I-a, II-b, III-a, IV-a, V-a, VI-a, VII-b, VIII-a, IX-b, X-a, XI-a	B
IV-06	Chamber of Heart Purification	A, 18	I-a, II-a, III-a, IV-a, V-b, VI-b, VII-a, VIII-a, IX-a, X-a, XI-a	A
IV-07	Chamber of Bamboo Fragrance	B, 21	I-b, II-b, III-a, IV-b, V-b, VI-b, VII-b, VIII-a, IX-a, X-a, XI-a	B
IX	Corridors, 4th courtyard	A	I-a, II-a, III-a, IV-a, VII-b, VIII-b, IX-b	A
	Corridors, 1st to 3rd courtyards	B	I-a, II-b, III-c, IV-a, VII-b, VIII-b, IX-c	B

内檐做法类型	材料/工艺	典型残损现象	研究/保护任务	残损系数	工作量
家具	硬木雕刻 + 普通镶嵌工艺	积尘 构件缺失 构件破损 镶嵌残破	局部拆卸 除尘（保留部分包浆） 修复 烫蜡 复位	10～20	★
	硬木雕刻 + 特征镶嵌工艺	积尘 构件缺失 构件破损 镶嵌残破	局部拆卸 除尘（保留部分包浆） 修复（须实验性修复） 烫蜡 复位	10～30	★★★

2 通景画保护初步方案

在宁寿宫花园倦勤斋室内通景画保护成功的经验基础上，在故宫博物院和美国世界文化遗产基金会专家共同研究的基础上，达成以下对通景画保护的一般流程做法。

通景画保护建议流程

步骤	操作/措施	注意事项
揭取	画面揭取准备（确定幅面、初步除尘）； 隐蔽结构除尘； 先用竹起子剥离画片一边，再逐步剥离另二边缘，缓慢揭取至第四边，最后实现整幅揭取； 粘接顽固初采用蒸汽、酒精软化措施； 无法揭取部位方可借助刀具； 揭取过程中多人协作，随时注意用胶带在背纸后粘接断裂部位，以保证裂缝不扩大； 将揭取画面编号、拍照； 原始画面的粘贴小件随主体画面揭取、编号	在揭取过程中尽量减少水份的使用； 在揭取的前一周期（约两星期）中，由美国世界文化遗产基金国际专家组和故宫博物院组织的中方专家共同参与工作
运输和保存	揭取后就地铺展； 进行正、背面初步除尘； 画心正面铺盖一层薄绵质辅助衬纸； 用大型塑料布衬里、包裹； 用大型车辆运送至工作室	确定负责每幅画面的专业人员妥善保管； 在工作室进行二次排序，并进行照相、测量和文字记录
工作室除尘	使用毛刷和毛巾卷、筱面团清除画面灰尘； 对顽固灰渍处采用少量化学药剂进行清除； 对使用药剂者，反复使用毛刷等沾蒸馏水擦拭； 采用 pH 检测至消除残留药剂，即 pH 值呈中性	如有必要少量使用蒸馏水，尽量避免使用化学药剂

通景画保护一般建议工作流程一

Chief Component	Construction Feature	Representative Damage	Research Task / Remedy	Damage Inventory	Workload
Furniture	Carved iron wood with inlays	Dust Missing component Broken component Inlay failure	Removal; Dedust; Repair; Waxing; Relocation	10-20	*
	Carved iron wood with inlay and macquetry	Dust Missing component Broken component Inlay failure	Removal; Dedust; Repair; Waxing; Relocation	10-30	***

2 Proposed Preservation Treatment for Trompe l'oeil

Based on previous and present works on tromp l'oeil paintings in the Lodge of Retirement, a revised working guide line is drawn by the Palace Museum experts and guest experts invited by WMF.

Proposed Preservation Procedure for Tromp l'oeil

Step	Working Methods	Points for Attention
Removal	Surface preparation. Dedusting from the above structure. Dismounting and separating the Trompe-l'oeil from the substrata respecting the old joints and mends. Use bamboo picks to gradually separate the sheets. Use tapes to enforce from the back and stop the crack whenever unexpected crack or fold occurs, especially at the damaged sheets, because of the great size and the fragility at the edges. Original patches should be detached together with the main sheet.	Minimize use of water in removal. International conservation team (WMF and Palace Museum) to work during the first two-week phase of removal to refine the process.
Transportation and Storing	Packing and transporting to studio. Tansport the paintings in loose rolls, and store in flat state.	Be properly stored before and after studio treatment. Re-measured and photographed in studio.
De-dusting	Paintings to be cleaned with paintbrush or towel roll or flour dough to remove the dust and dirt before separating silk from backing paper Minimum use of chemical medicament as the final resort to remove the persistent dirt.	Clean with distilled water to avoid possible long-term damage of chemical medicament wherever it is used.
Sterilizing	Paintings to be sterilized before separating silk from backing paper. (Argon is suggested).	
Consolidating	Color Consolidating with thin seaweed glue (0.5%□1.5%) according to the experience gained in the project of the Lodge of Retirement.	Avoid using alum; Redo experimental application in any other new paintings.

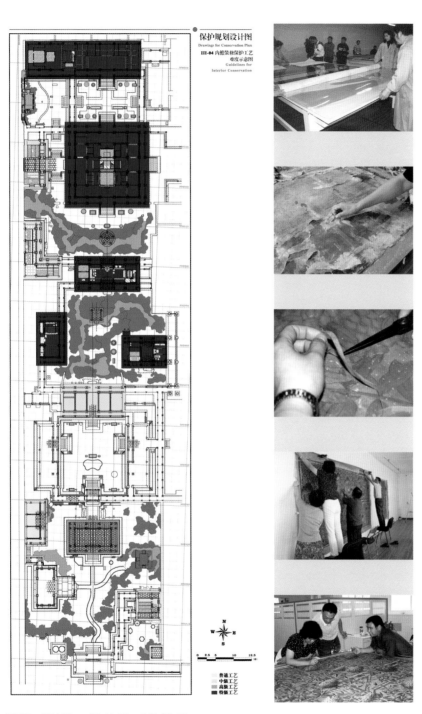

保护规划设计图
Drawings for Conservation Plan
III-04 内檐装修保护工艺难度示意图
Guidelines for Interior Conservation

通景画保护一般建议工作流程二

步骤	操作 / 措施	注意事项
消毒	拟采用氩气法对画面进行除虫处理	
颜料加固	使用浓度为 0.1%~1.5% 的动物胶液进行颜料加固	避免使用传统的明矾材料,以消除其对画绢的破坏作用; 对每张通景画均应采取试验
固定画心	使用化纤纸固定画心	
翻面	使用聚酯薄膜承托翻转画心	
去褙	聘用具备丰富经验的专家揭取画面褙纸	
补绢、加固断裂	选用与画面材料相同的绢丝进行仿旧处理在画面缺损、断裂处补齐缺损	选用绢丝的经纬密度、厚度均须与原件严格一致
托心	裱糊一层仿乾隆高丽纸褙,四周留边; 裱糊一层宣纸褙,四周留边	注意纸张帘路方向的交错层次; 注意加强画面抗拉强度
回翻	使用聚酯薄膜承托翻转画心 去除加雇画心用化纤纸	
全色	照相记录画意缺损; 分部分绷平全色; 在全色色彩与原画意实现画面统一与可识别性;	拟订修补画意稿子,经审核批准方可实施; 控制温度湿度,防止画面绷裂
平整与校验	平整并重新测量画心尺寸; 初步考察拼揭变化	详细记录每一步骤的尺寸变化
墙基层准备	加固修整木格栅及板墙; 实施防虫防腐处理; 木基层构造上裱糊夹堂苎布和 2~3 层乾隆高丽纸	
上墙	湿润画面; 按照原始拼接顺序裱糊画心; 拼缝并修补画意	自通景画天顶画中心部位向四周逐步拼接裱糊
防虫防腐处理	拟熏蒸法除虫处理	借助 WMF 邀请专家的帮助
监督与验收	每个工作项目在过程中和完成后由故宫博物院和美国世界文化遗产基金会领导小组、特邀专家组进行监督和验收	

特殊残损通景画保护潮湿法揭取

特殊残损通景画保护潮湿法揭取

Step	Working Methods	Points for Attention
Mounting Fixation Paper	Use rayon papers to fixate the silk.	
Turning	Using mylar to turn the painting over for lining removal.	
Removing Old Backing Paper	Inviting most skilled workers to remove the old backings.	
In-filling Lost Silk	Making up lost silk with the same material of the same micro texture.	Match carefully warps and wefts of patch with the original.
Attaching Backing Paper	Attach 1 layer of New Qianlong Korean paper, with margins at the edges; Attach 1 layer of Xuan Paper, with margins at the edges; Turning back with mylar; Remove the fixating paper.	Be fully respect to original linings of each single piece of painting. Be fully aware of influence of the backings' expanding and shrinking to the painting.
Flattening and Experimental Rejoining	Re-measure painting sheets and prepare for the rejoining; Experimental rejoining.	Document the size.
In-painting Lost Painting	Voids will be in-filled so that new work will be discernable to scholars or on close inspection, but not necessarily to viewer; Work to be readable as a whole.	Strictly follow the procedure of reporting and approval.
Wall Preparation	Re-fine wall lattice or board; Anti-deterioration treatment; Wall backing with 2 to 3 layers of new Qianlong Korean paper, and 1 layer of gauze.	
Remounting onto the Wall	Spray water onto the sheets of Trompe l'oeil. Remount according to the original location. Mend the joints.	As there will be possible stretching out and drawing back of the sheets, it is planned to remount from the joint in the middle of wall.
Final Anti-biodeterioration Treatment	Fume with pesticide.	With help of WMF experts.
Check and Accept	By expert panel formed by WMF & the Palace Museum.	

3 贴落保护初步方案

<table>
<tr><td colspan="3" align="center">贴落保护建议流程</td></tr>
<tr><td align="center">步骤</td><td align="center">操作 / 措施</td><td align="center">注意事项</td></tr>
<tr><td>揭取</td><td>将裱糊于壁纸表面的贴落揭离：先用竹起子剥离画片一边，再逐步剥离另二边缘，缓慢揭取至第四边</td><td>揭取过程中尽量减少水份的使用；
在揭取的前一周期（约两星期）中，由美国世界文化遗产基金会国际专家组和故宫博物院组织的中方专家共同参与工作</td></tr>
<tr><td>运输和保存</td><td>进行正、背面初步除尘；
画心正面铺盖一层薄绵质辅助衬纸；
运送至工作室编号保存</td><td>工作室进行照相、测量和文字记录</td></tr>
<tr><td>工作室除尘</td><td>使用毛刷和毛巾卷、莜面团清除画面灰尘；
在顽固灰渍处采用少量化学药剂进行清除</td><td></td></tr>
<tr><td>消毒</td><td>拟采用氩气法对画面进行除虫处理</td><td></td></tr>
<tr><td>颜料加固</td><td>必要者使用浓度为 0.1% ~ 1.5% 的动物胶液进行颜料加固</td><td>避免使用传统的明矾材料，以消除其对画绢的破坏作用；
对每张通景画均应采取试验</td></tr>
<tr><td>固定画心 / 翻面</td><td>使用化纤纸固定画心
使用聚酯薄膜承托翻转画心</td><td></td></tr>
<tr><td>去褙</td><td>聘用具备丰富经验的专家揭取画面褙纸</td><td></td></tr>
<tr><td>隐补</td><td>采用同种材料隐补缺失画心</td><td></td></tr>
<tr><td>托心</td><td>托裱两层宣纸
清除多余糨糊</td><td>注意纸张帘路方向的交错层次；
注意加强画面抗拉强度</td></tr>
<tr><td>回翻</td><td>使用聚酯薄膜承托翻转画心
去除加雇画心用化纤纸</td><td></td></tr>
<tr><td>全色</td><td>照相记录画意缺损；
分部分绷平全色；
在全色色彩与原画意实现画面统一与可识别性；</td><td>拟订修补画意稿子，经审核批准方可实施；
控制温度湿度，防止画面绷裂</td></tr>
<tr><td>上墙</td><td>湿润画面；
在修复好的壁纸表面裱糊贴落</td><td></td></tr>
<tr><td>防虫防腐处理</td><td>拟熏蒸法除虫处理</td><td>借助 WMF 邀请专家的帮助</td></tr>
<tr><td>监督与验收</td><td>每个工作项目在过程中和完成后由故宫博物院和美国世界文化遗产基金会领导小组、特邀专家组进行监督和验收</td><td></td></tr>
</table>

贴落画保护成果示意图

内檐装修保护工作流程，以倦勤斋为例

内檐装修保护工作流程，以倦勤斋为例

3 Proposed Preservation Treatments for Tie'luo

Proposed Preservation Procedure for Tie'luo

Step	Working Methods	Points for Attention
Removal	Dismounting and separating Tielou from the wallpaper. It is supposed to use bamboo picks to gradually separate the sheets.	Minimize use of water in removal. International conservation team (WMF and Palace Museum) to work during the first two-week phase of removal to refine the process.
Transportation and Storing	In situ dedusting both sides. Cover the painting with a thin soft paper. Number, transport and store.	Re-measur and photograph in studio.
De-dusting	Paintings to be cleaned with paintbrush or flour dough roll to remove the dust and dirt before separating painted paper from backing.	
Sterilizing	Paintings to be sterilized before separating painted paper from backing.	
Pigment Consolidation	Consolidate painting surface regarding to pigment powdering status with animal glue from 0.1% to 1.5%.	Avoid using alum. Do trial works before treatment to every single piece.
Turning over	Use rayon paper to fixate the painted surface. Using mylar to turn the painting over.	
Removing Old Backing Paper	Invite most skilled workers to remove the old backings.	
In-filling Lost Surface Paper	Making up lost painted paper with the same material of the same micro texture.	
Attaching Backing Paper	Attach 2 layers of Xuan paper, staggering the edges. Remove surplus paste.	Be fully aware of the influence of the backings' expanding and shrinking to the painting.
Turning back	Using mylar to turn the painting back.	
In-painting Lost Painting	Voids will be in-filled so that new work will be discernable to scholars or on close inspection, but not necessarily to viewer. Achieving readability of the in-painting.	In-paint should be carefully discussed and implemented. Temperature and humidity environment of the studio should be carefully controlled.
Remounting onto the Wall	Spray water onto the back of the painting sheet. Remount according to the original location on wallpaper.	
Final Anti-biodeterioration Treatment	Fume with pesticide.	With help of WMF experts.
Check and Accept	By expert panel formed by WMF & the Palace Museum.	

4 木作罩隔/家具保护初步方案

（1）竹黄与竹丝镶嵌工艺：以倦勤斋现进行中保护工作为蓝本，继承与保护以浙江东阳何复礼大师的工艺技术为代表的无形文化遗产，形成工艺做法报告，在宁寿宫花园保护项目中推广。

（2）其他镶嵌工艺：由传统小木作匠师组成专门化小组，在倦勤斋工作完成后形成工艺做法报告，在宁寿宫花园保护项目中推广。

（3）丝织品文物保护：在倦勤斋工作完成后形成工艺做法报告，在宁寿宫花园保护项目中推广。

7.6.2 工作量估算

宁寿宫花园建筑内檐装修保护难度与工作量统计

建筑编号	建筑名称	残损率	难度系数	数量
I-02	古华轩	罩隔：C, 50	90	8
		雕刻天花：B, 30	90	1
		匾联：A, 18	100	7
I-05	抑斋	罩隔：A, 15	50	1
		地平：A, 10	50	3
		壁饰：A, 10	100	3
		壁纸：D, 100	50	—
I-09	旭辉庭	罩隔：C, 40	50	2
		壁纸：D, 70	50	—
II-02	遂初堂	罩隔：B, 28	60	5, 缺失一槽
		壁纸：D, 100	50	—
III-02	萃赏楼	罩隔：B, 22	100	15
		地平：A, 20	30	2
		楼梯：B, 30	50	2
		贴落：C, 50	50	12
		家具：A, 15	80	27
		壁纸：D, 80	50	—
III-03	三友轩	罩隔：B, 27	100	5
		地平：A, 20	30	2
		贴落：B, 20	50	16
		家具：A, 10	80	16
		壁纸：D, 80	50	—

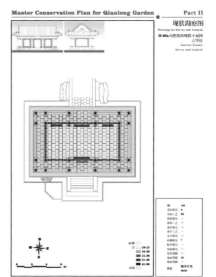
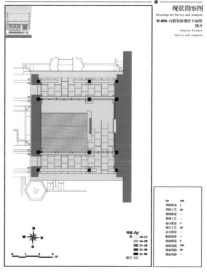
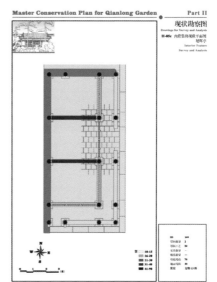
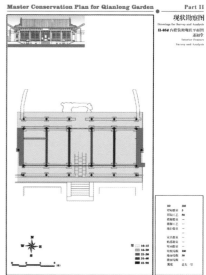

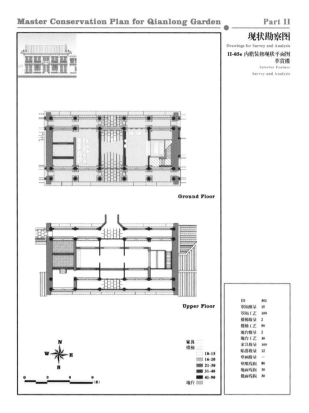

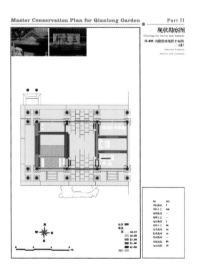

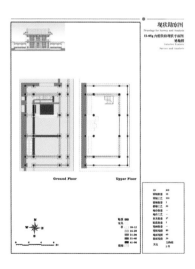

4 Interior Fine Crafts

(1) Bamboo Macquetry: to be studied and renovated basing on inheriting the craftsmanship represented mainly by Master He's workshop from Dongyang county in Zhejiang province. The working flow will be finalized in the Technical Report after the trial work in the Lodge of Retirement, and will be applied in preserving Qianlong Garden.

(2) Inlay, to be carried out by the workshop of carpenters. The working flow will be finalized in the Technical Report after the trial work in the Lodge of Retirement and will be applied in preserving Qianlong Garden.

(3) Textile, to be finalized in Technical Report after the trial work in the Lodge of Retirement.

7.6.2 Envisaged Workload for Interior Features of Buildings

ID	Building	Damage Value	Difficulty Value	Working Contents
		Treatments for Interior Feature of Buildings		
I-02	Pavilion of Ancient Flower	Screen: C, 50	90	8
		Carved Ceiling: B, 30	90	1
		Tablet: A, 18	100	7
I-05	Chamber of Self Constraint	Screen: A,15	50	1
		Platform: A, 10	50	3
		Wall Tablet: A, 10	100	3
		Wallpaper: D, 100	50	—
I-09	Pavilion of Morning Splendour	Screen: C, 40	50	2
		Wallpaper: D, 70	50	—
II-02	Hall of Fulfilment of Original Wishes	Screen: B, 28	60	5 (1 Missing)
		Wallpaper: D, 100	50	—
III-02	Building of Collection and Appreciation	Screen: B, 22	100	15
		Platform: A, 20	30	2
		Stair: B, 30	50	2
		Tie'luo: C, 50	50	12
		Furniture: A, 15	80	27
		Wallpaper: D, 80	50	—
III-03	Pavilion of Three Friends	Screen: B, 27	100	5
		Platform: A, 20	30	2
		Tie'luo: B,20	50	16
		Furniture: A, 10	80	16
		Wallpaper: D, 80	50	—

宁寿宫花园建筑内檐装修保护难度与工作量统计

建筑编号	建筑名称	残损率	难度系数	数量
III-05	延趣楼	罩隔：B, 33	100	10
		楼梯：B, 37	50	1
		贴落：B, 30	50	1, 缺失数量不详
		家具：A, 15	100	17
		壁纸：D, 80	50	—
IV-02	符望阁	罩隔：B, 27	100	44, 一槽历史移位
		地平：A, 12	80	3
		楼梯：C, 42	80	6
		天花：B, 35	100	2
		贴落	50	缺失数量不详
		家具	?	调研未及
		壁纸：D, 80	50	—
IV-03	倦勤斋	参见《倦勤斋保护研究报告》		
IV-04	云光楼	罩隔：A, 17	60	8
		地平	30	4
		通景画	100	2
		蓝绢天花	50	—
		贴落	50	19
		家具	100	28
		壁纸：C, 60	50	—
IV-05	玉粹轩	罩隔：A, 17	60	3
		地平	30	5
		通景画	100	1
		贴落	50	3
		家具：A, 10	80	30
		壁纸：D, 80	50	—
IV-06	净尘心室	地平：A, 20	30	1
IV-07	竹香馆	罩隔：B, 34	80	14
		拼镶木墙裙：B, 37	80	12
		木壁板贴落：B, 39	90	7
		壁纸：C, 60	50	—

乾隆花园
故宫博物院宁寿宫花园历史研究与文物保护规划

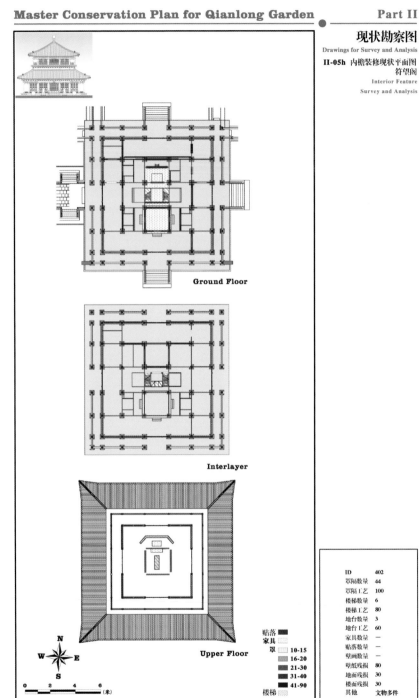

Master Conservation Plan for Qianlong Garden　Part II

现状勘察图
Drawings for Survey and Analysis
II-05h　内檐装修现状平面图
符望阁
Interior Feature
Survey and Analysis

Ground Floor

Interlayer

Upper Floor

贴落
家具
罩　10-15
　　16-20
　　21-30
　　31-40
　　41-90
楼梯

N
W　E
S
0　2　4　6
（米）

ID	402
罩隔数量	44
罩隔工艺	100
楼梯数量	6
楼梯工艺	80
地台数量	3
地台工艺	60
家具数量	—
贴落数量	一
壁画数量	一
壁纸残损	80
地面残损	80
楼面残损	30
其他	文物多件

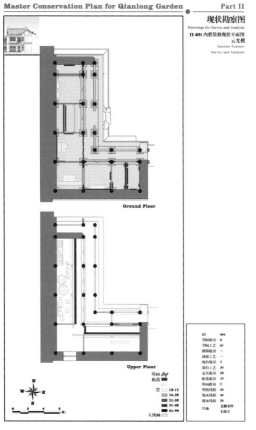

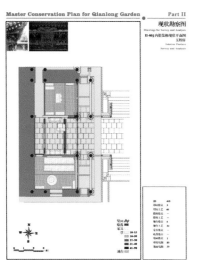

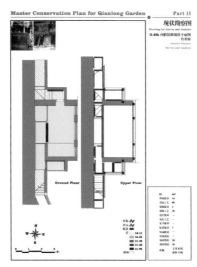

ID	Building	Damage Value	Difficulty Value	Working Contents
III-05	Building of Extended Delight	Screen: B, 33	100	10
		Stair: B, 37	50	1
		Tie'luo: B, 30	50	1 (X Missing)
		Furniture: A, 15	100	17
		Wallpaper: D, 80	50	—
IV-02	Building of Wish and Reality in Accordance	Screen: B, 27	100	44 (1 moved?1)
		Platform: A, 12	80	3
		Stair: C, 42	80	6
		Ceiling: B, 35	100	2
		Tie'luo	50	X Missing
		Furniture	?	X to be investigated
		Wallpaper: D, 80	50	—
IV-03	Lodge of Retirement	*See Conservation Plan for the Lodge of Retirement*		
IV-04	Building of Cloud Light	Screen: A, 17	60	8
		Platform	30	4
		Tromp l'oeil	100	2
		Painted Ceiling	50	—
		Tie'luo	50	19
		Furniture	100	28
		Wallpaper: C, 60	50	—
IV-05	Pavilion of Jade Purity	Screen: A, 17	60	3
		Platform	30	5
		Tromp l'oeil	100	1
		Tie'luo	50	3
		Furniture: A, 10	80	30
		Wallpaper: D, 80	50	—
IV-06	Chamber of Heart Purification	Platform: A, 20	30	1
IV-07	Chamber of Bamboo Fragrance	Platform	30	1
		Screen: B, 34	80	14
		Inlayed Wall Panel	80	12
		Wooden Tie'luo	90	7
		Wallpaper: C, 60	50	—

第八章
文物展示与说明

8.1 开放路线现状

目前宁寿宫花园局部对游人开放。在花园的四进院落中，位于南侧的第一、二进院落，以及位于北端的第四进院落的北半部是开放的。而这种开放状态主要是开放庭院，假山山径不允许游人登临，除开敞的门座、轩廊之外古建筑内部一般是不对外开放的。前两进院落中的建筑属于内部用房或文物库房，第四进院落所有建筑均为文物库房占用，而园中不开放的区域更是全部属于博物院内部用房。开放建筑部分用于展示门座、轩廊内外环境，部分用于游客服务。这样相对封闭的状态始于溥仪退位之时，在此期间仅接待过个别特殊的参观、视察。

宁寿宫花园现有开放路线是经宁寿宫后的衍祺门，穿行第一进院落，至第二进院落中东折而进入宁寿宫后中路；直行至中路北部，西偏于宁寿宫北门贞顺门内与花园第四进院落北部相连。

8.2 开放路线规划

以乾隆为代表，清代帝王在宁寿宫和花园中的游览路线与今日开放路线截然不同——当时花园是作为后路"西花园"而使用的，中路建筑群中随处设有入园通道——或通过南端正门，或经任何一座中路重要殿宇均可到达。然而，鉴于今日宁寿宫花园自身的突出特点及其亟待特殊护理的保存状态，继续封闭或日常开放或如清代全面连通宁寿宫与花园的做法都是不适当的。需要确定一种建立在长期、有效地保护花园文物基础上的，合理、有序的开放模式。

8.2.1 游线特点

本规划认为，宁寿宫花园的未来开放模式应当实现以下目标：

(1) 宁寿宫花园的开放路线应当相对独立于一般的开放游览路线，应具有自身的完整性，并设有独立的出入口。

(2) 此路线应当能够最好地揭示皇家花园的内在特点及乾隆时期内檐装修所代表的工艺美术水平，因此路线应当尽可能地联系所有适宜开放的建筑室内环境。

(3) 为了更加全面地给参观者提供对宁寿宫及花园原始空间结构的直观感受，应当用说明牌或石刻小品等形式将花园通往宁寿宫后中路的所有路径标识出来。

(4) 路线应当适当分合，起点、中间点和终点适宜处应设多于1处（建议3处）观众会合区、休息停留区，并在此区域内利用建筑室内空间进行展示、说明等辅助展览手段。

(5) 参观路线上必须避免形成拥挤的人流，应完善设计参观时间段落，并如(4)条所述，将一队观众继续划分成小组分路线行进。

(6) 虽然参观路线并不采用历史上皇帝所走的所有路线，但是为了全面介绍历史情况，应当在所有帝王出入口处设立显著标志，并在解说中明确介绍。

8.2.2 建议参观路线

本规划对于参观路线的关注不仅在于全面完成宁寿宫花园保护规划之后的系统展示，而且认为应随着逐步实施的保护工作逐步将花园丰富的历史遗存展示出来。本规划将此开放展示计划与实施阶段的三期计划结合考虑。

1 第一期保护工作完竣后

花园的第一、二进院落保持现有开放范围和形式。

第四进院落的庭院和建筑内部空间应作为特殊展览完整开放。鉴于现有开放路线能够满足宁寿宫参观路线，且途经符望阁、倦勤斋的局部路线为通往宁寿宫北门贞顺门的唯一路线，因此应当得到保持，直至宁寿全宫统一完成保护并制订新的开放计划。

规划建议同时保留并局部调整分隔普通开放路线和宁寿宫花园特展区域的木制栅栏。建议将符望阁西北游廊内栅栏移至符望阁东北游廊，以保证宁寿宫花园空间的相对完整性，同时仍将符望阁东北游廊作为一般开放区观众游览路径使用。这种调整的缺点在于可能造成宁寿宫参观路线北端的局部不畅，因此须经由故宫博物院组织多方研究再最终确定。

乾隆花园
故宫博物院宁寿宫花园历史研究与文物保护规划

buildings and large caves in rockeries used for regathering, and more than one, recommendingly, three tourist guides are required.

(5) Crowding must be avoided along the visit routes, and visit should be arranged to set time range and during each visit guests should also recommended to be divided into groups as described in item (4).

(6) In order to provide visitors more information on the original spatial structure of the garden and Ningshou Gong princinct, original imperial accesses to theQianlong Garden should be indicated clearly on plaques and in guidebook or brochure or leaflet.

8.2.2 Proposed Circulation

The master plan proposes a main visiting route in Qianlong Garden, and in accordance to the three implementation phases the circulation is arranged into three steps of development.

1 After Phase I

The first and second courtyards remain the present way of visiting.

After completion of conservation of the fourth courtyard buildings, both exterior and interior, the courtyard will be opened as a special exhibition. The present open area in this courtyard is a compromise of various possible choices of circulation that makes visitor convenient to exit the precinct through the rear gate, and this solution will be continued until the entire Ningshou Gong precinct is open to visitors, and the passage linking the west route to the Gate of Obedience and Pudicity can be used as a tourist path. This circulation will lead to stagnancy of visitors for that north exit of Ningshou Gong precinct is used as the general visitor exit and that of the Qianlong Garden, so it should be further dicussed and decided by the Palace Museum.

It is proposed in this master plan that the present access block of lattice fence will still be used and moved to the northeast corridor separating common visit and special visit. This change will enable the integrity of the garden, and still use a sect of corridor serving as the exit passage from middle route.

8.1 Present Circulation

Qianlong Garden is now partly open to the public. Among the four courtyards of the garden complex, exterior spaces in the first and second courtyards and 2/3 of interior spaces are open, while the third and most part of the south part of the fourth courtyard have been closed after the abdication of the last emperor, and have only received very limited people of assigned missions since then.

The opening first courtyard is connected with the rear middle route of Ningshou Gong at the front entrance and the passage leading to the second courtyard in the middle route. The rear opening part of the garden is also used as a rear access of the whole precinct at the Gate of Obedience and Pudicity, which had been serving as the rear gate of all the three routes in the east, middle and west.

8.2 Circulation Proposal

By tracing Emperor Qianlong's wandering routes inside Ningshou Gong as a whole, it can be found that the emperors used the garden as a side gardend, which was adjacent and within reach. The accesses were convenient, either from the main entrance at the Gate of Extended Felicity, or from the halls along the rear middle route of Ningshou Gong. Because of the delicacy and fragility of the garden and interior features, and that today the garden would serve as a public site rather than a private resort, the visiting route should not be the same as it was in the imperial time, but should be designed in accordance with the goals to serve the visitors and to achieve full interpretation.

8.2.1 Characteristics of the Visit

The Master Plan proposed that the characteristics of Qianlong Garden visit should stress on the following points,

(1) Open route in Qianlong Garden should be set apart from the general open area in Ningshou Gong Precinct, and should be one that has its own integrality and own entrance(s) and exit(s).

(2) There should be proper stops along the visit route, before and during visit, which can provide the guests interpretation of the complex and imperial life.

(3) The visit should embody the nature of privacy of the garden as it had been in Qing dynasty, the visit routes should link as many as buildings and interiors as possible.

(4) Since the route is inevitable to separate and re-converge, there should be identified spots such as

规划建议开放第四进院落南部的山石洞穴。安全起见，建议不开放登临假山的路径，登山路径仅对工作人员和研究者开放。

2 第二期保护工作完竣后

花园的第一、二进院落保持现有开放范围和形式。

第三进院落的庭院和建筑内部空间应继续作为特殊展览完整开放。规划建议开放第三进院落南部的山石洞穴。安全起见，建议不开放登临假山的路径，登山路径仅对工作人员和研究者开放。

建议复原萃赏楼原有穿堂空间模式，作为主要参观通道；将现经过萃赏楼西连廊的工作人员继续作为工作人员通道和辅助通道使用。

3 第三期保护工作完竣后实现宁寿宫花园的全面开放

花园的第一、二进院落保护全部完竣后，将宁寿宫花园整体作为特殊展览完整开放。整体开放是以上述一、二期开放方式的基础上，与花园一、二进院落的进一步开放相结合。开放路线始于花园南门衍祺门，结束于宁寿宫北门贞顺门，其间解说、展览和观众休息空间布置在衍祺门外值房、遂初堂东西配殿和/或贞顺门外的某适宜附属建筑中。

前二进院落的开放调整主要反映在以下三个方面。

其一，建议在禊赏亭流杯渠上方适宜位置铺设架空玻璃走廊，通往禊赏亭北游廊，连接并开放旭辉庭室内空间，旭辉庭室内陈设专题展览。

其二，开放抑斋及承露台下山洞房。安全起见，建议不开放登临假山的路径，登山路径仅对工作人员和研究者开放。

其三，开放遂初堂正殿和东西配殿，并将东西配殿作为专门演示和观众服务的空间使用。东西配殿中应装备实物展示、音像设施和网络设施，为观众全面、深入地了解宁寿宫花园及其历史背景提供有效服务。此二配殿空间的设计和使用应纳入宁寿宫花园全面解说系统的计划中。

8.2.3 开放策略

鉴于上述开放路线曲折绵长，路线所连接的建筑室内原状展览众多，建筑室内空间尺度变化复杂，难以容纳较大的参观团队，因此结合开放路线应当制定适宜的开放策略，实现合理利用的目的。以下针对开放策略提出规划性建议，今后应在此建议的基础上结合国际成功经验和观众意见调查统计进行修正，制定具体措施。

一是建议采用定时、有限开放的策略。建议年开放时段为每年故宫博物院开放日，如遇特殊暴雨、沙尘暴等极端恶劣天气及内部维护工作时，应行关闭。建议采用预约方式限制人数的日开放策略，预约应在参考前期预报的情况下提前一周提交完成，当日接待只限于预约人数不足的情况；按照参观用时2小时，每院平均停留半小时，逐院依次组织参观团队的模式计算，每队间隔30

分钟，每日上、下午（上午9时至12时、下午1时至4时）各6组，每组12人，分3个游览路线，每路4人。每日共提供预约参观名额144人。此策略适合每小组2名参观导引的规模要求，同时满足环境与气氛的需求。

二是建议保证专业人员的特殊预约。专业人员应比普通预约参观提前一周，即预定参观时间前二周提交完成。建议在保证专业参观的前提下安排普通参观。专业参观同样应当符合天气条件允许的前提。

三是建议对预约参观收取适当的门票。门票收入应主要用于维护展陈、解说系统，提供专门化服务，提高文化教育质量。

8.3 文物展示说明的手段

8.3.1 印刷品

印刷品是宁寿宫花园特展应当提供的最基本说明材料，包括大型图书、小册子、散页。材料内容除最基本的花园描述之外应当涵盖以下方面。

(1) 花园布局、建筑、内檐装修、装饰的独特性所在；

(2) 清代帝王生活与宁寿宫花园的关系；

(3) 花园中所有文物及其反映出的清代匠作工艺；

(4) 花园中所有文物及其反映出的其他非物质文化遗产；

(5) 宁寿宫花园保护项目，文物保护理论及技术方法。

8.3.2 影像方式

如本规划节所述，拟将衍祺门外值房、遂初堂东西配殿和或贞顺门外某适当建筑用于集中多媒体演示、解说和观众休息服务空间。鉴于衍祺门外值房和可能落实的贞顺门外某小型建筑的室内空间受到限制，均不适合相对人员和演示内容集中的影像放映，建议将遂初堂东西配殿中开辟专门化的、专题化的影像放映空间，建议人员规模为12~20人，影片长度15分钟。

in comparison with foreign experiences.

(1) Limited Period and Limited Admission Policy. It is proposed at present phase that open time would mainly be the same with that of the Palace Museum in general except maintenance and extreme weather conditions such as extraordinary heavy rain and sand storm. Bespeak should be make in a week's advance; daily temporaty visit is accepted only number of bespeak has not been reached. In every open day, visits should be arranged in groups. Intervals between every two groups should be 30 minutes, so that in every open day from 9 am to 12 am in the morning and 1 pm to 4 pm in the afernoon the garden will be able to receive 12 groups. The best size of a group is 12 people, for it can be further divided into three teams of four people each, which size would be better for two docents to manage, and which size does neither conflict the small spaces in the garden nor the tranquil atmosphere that other teams would enjoy at the same time.

(2) Professional First Policy. It is proposed that general visitors be admitted but on the circumstance that there is no confliction with professional visiting group who has asked to make appointment in advance of two weeks, i.e. one week earlier than general registery correspondingly. Besides, admission of professional bespeak will be granted when weather and other visiting provisions are met.

(3) Additional Admission Fee Policy. The additional admission fee policy makes it possible to maintain, repair or reform reception office and to achieve the goal of providing more personalized service and of raising the educational quality of the visit.

8.3 Interpretation Means

8.3.1 Printed Material

Printed material is essential for general visitors, including book, brochure and leaflet. The contents of them should not restrict to overall descriptions of the site and treasures in buildings, it is suggested to cover the fields as,

(1) Uniqueness of the garden, building, interior, and decoration.

(2) Lives of the emperor and their relationship with Qianlong Garden.

(3) Craftsmanship reflected in the complex.

(4) Intangible cultural heritage.

(5) The conservation project, conservation philosophy, methodology and techniques.

In the special open area to the south of the Building of Wish and Reality in Accordance, cave path in the rockery will be open to visitors, while for the sake of safety of the visitors and rockeries, the path on the top of the rock is recommended to remain closed except for the researchers and working labors.

2 After Phase II

The first and second courtyards remain the present way of visiting until the end of this phase the first two courtyards will be closed for conservation treatments.

After completion of conservation of the third courtyard and buildings in this region, both exterior and interior, the courtyard will be opened as an extended part of the tour to the fourth courtyard. Cave path in the rockery is planned to be opened to visitors, while for the sake of safety of the visitors and rockeries, the path on the top of the rock is recommended to remain closed except for the researchers and working labors.

It is also proposed that the orginal passage through the Buidling of Collection and Appreciation be restored. Thus visitors will be able to walk through the building, and the present path should be used as service path.

3 After Phase III, the final visiting route should be achieved.

After completion of conservation treatment in the first and second courtyards, a general open route can be achieved. The general route is a combination of the routes in Phase I and Phase II, with an improved open route in the front courtyards, starting at the Gate of Extended Felicity and ending at the Gate of Obedience and Pudicity. There will be interpretation stops, exhibition rooms, visitor reception room and souvenir shop in proper buildings. For the front two courtyards the following three ideas should be specially mentioned.

First, apply stilted glass on the floating cup channels so that a path can be formed leading to the corridor further north and the Pavilion of Morning Splendor on the top of rockery, and in the Pavilion of Morning Splendor, a subject-exhibition is suggested to be set up.

Second, open the interior space of the Chamber of Self Constraint and the arched space under the Dew Platform. For the sake of safety of the visitors and rockeries, the path leading to the Dew Platform at the top of the rock is recommended to be closed.

Third, open the main hall of the second courtyard, and to use the two side halls as tourist service center in which an exhibition of objects, a bookstore, a souvenir shop, video/audio device and multimedia facilities should be provided for the visitors so as to achieve a vivid interpretation and omni-possibility of inquiry into the knowledge and background of the Qianlong Garden. More details will be further developed in the master interpretation plan for Qianlong Garden.

8.2.3 Open Policy

Taken into account that the sinuation of the visit routes, intricate courtyard spaces, and scale and fragility of the building interiors, albeit different routes for the visitors are provided, it is essential to establish a limited admission of visiting policy. Hereafter proposals are presented for future decision with respect to visitorship and

8.3.3 录音导游

建筑声环境在当代建筑设计中的重要性日益凸显。将宁寿宫花园作为博物馆进行利用，其原状陈列的游览方式也应当充分利用录音导游手段。建议在国际范围内邀请有经验的专家进行录音导游系统设计，同时邀请国际/国内游客参与意见。建议根据以下原则确定录音导游的基本功能和内容：

(1) 系统应包括涵盖所有展陈要点的录音导游人声说明、现场说明和背景声。导游人员作为现场引导和问题解答者同样应当参与导游工作。

(2) 现场说明和背景声应当同时具备自动的和手控的开启/渐弱/关闭功能。

(3) 录音导游应具有多语言、多功能的系统设计，其中功能应涵盖提示、警示等。

8.4 拟添加的设施与设备

在保证文物安全的前提下，为达到理想的展陈效果，应合理设计、适当增加必要的设施与设备，做到既避免干扰参观视线，又便于检查、维修和更新改造。因此，

(1) 安全监控设施应设于所有院落门座（衍祺门、垂花门和拟作为花园后门使用的符望阁东北游廊栅栏门），及所有室内设展的建筑。

(2) 所有木结构建筑物均须安装火灾警报系统。

(3) 室内文物密集的建筑应添加适当的温湿度控制调节系统。

(4) 所有室内展览均应添加照明系统，特殊展览应添加多媒体解说系统。

(5) 重要建筑外檐装修应参考光学测量结论适当安装防紫外线玻璃。

(6) 多媒体演示、观众休息用房内部应集中设置多媒体解说系统。

8.3.2 Video Program

Since that there is not a proper space for a preface of introduction of the garden outside the complex, it is proposed to accomodate this function in the side halls of the second courtyard which had been renovated as shops in recent decades. It is also recommended to play a 15-minute video program in the room for a group of 12 to 20 visitors.

8.3.3 Controlled Audio Interpretation

Audio environment is becoming more and more stressed in latest architectural design, and should be invited into the exhibition in the Qianlong Garden. Experienced designer in the scope of the world should be invited to form a careful plan. The technique and the program of the audio-tour of the audio system may vary, but it should have the following functions at least,

(1) This system should be programmed with a genreal tour guide, detailed interpretations of architectural and artistic features in accordance with the situ, and a background sound which works with special sites; docents' interpretation is also indispensable.

(2) The interpretation voice should be manual controllable.

(3) The background should have multi-language, and multi-function that covers reminding, warning etc.

8.4 Facilities and Utilities

As backing-up system, facilities and utilities in Qianlong Garden should be further designed, aiming at keeping beyond visible range of visitors and being easy to check and repair and improvement.

(1) Security devices against theft should be built in all gates (the Gate of Extended Felicity, the Pendent Floral Gate, and the rear fence gate in the north east corridor of the Building of Wish and Reality in Accordance) and all rooms of interior exhibits.

(2) Fire alarm should be installed in all wood structured buildings.

(3) Interior space that has dense environment sensitive objects and multi-material wall/roof finishes should have properly designed to have control of temperature and relative humidity.

(4) All interior spaces should have lighting system and multi-media interpretation system fitted in.

(5) Installation of UV-free glass in important buildings should be considered.

(6) Multi-media displaying and interpretation facilities should be used in the visitors' center.

第三篇 | Part 3

保护规划图 | Graphics of Master Plan

图纸目录

Contents of Drawings

参考文献

i.历史研究文献

1. 于敏中.日下旧闻考
2. 庆桂.国朝宫史续编
3. 章乃炜.清宫述闻
4. 单士魁.清代档案丛谈
5. 内务府奏销档
6. 内务府奏案
7. 内务府堂谕堂交
8. 汉文录副奏折
9. 内务府活计档
10. 旨意底档
11. 旨意题头底档
12. 内务府陈设档
13. 总管内务府现行则例.清刻本.清华大学藏
14. 圆明园现行工程则例（十四、十五、十六、十八卷本）.清抄本
15. 热河工程则例.存十七卷.清抄本.中国国家图书馆藏
16. 热河园庭现行则例（十二卷）.清抄本.中国国家图书馆藏华大学藏
17. 万寿山工程则例（十九卷）.清抄本.中国国家图书馆藏
18. 圆明园万寿山内庭汇同则例（三十五卷）.抄本.中国国家图书馆藏
19. 内庭圆明园内工诸作现行则例.中国文物研究所藏
20. 圆明园万寿山内庭三处汇同则例.北京大学藏
21. 散帙,于高家档案中.清抄本.清华大学建筑学院藏
22. 散帙,于样式雷档案中）.清抄本.中国国家图书馆藏
23. 史贻直.工部则例.清乾隆刻本
24. 乾隆京城全图
25. 圆明园四十景图
26. （圆明园坦坦荡荡）素心堂半亩院地盘画样.中国国家图书馆藏
27. 建福宫花园立样.故宫博物院藏
28. （长春园）含经堂地盘画样.中国国家图书馆藏，故宫博物院藏
29. 天津大学建筑系.清代内廷宫苑.天津：天津大学出版社，1986
30. 赵光华.禊赏亭之"禊"源流小考.故宫博物院院刊，1979（3）
31. 于倬云，傅连兴.乾隆花园的造园艺术.故宫博物院院刊，1980（3）
32. 徐启宪，周南泉.大禹治水图玉山.故宫博物院院刊，1980（4）
33. 傅连仲.乾隆花园点滴.故宫博物院院刊，1980年（4）
34. 万依.乾隆花园的园囿.故宫博物院院刊，1984年（2）
35. 许以林.宁寿宫的花园庭院.故宫博物院院刊，1987（1）
36. 朱杰.长春园淳化轩与故宫乐寿堂考辨.故宫博物院院刊，1999（2）
37. 罗文华.清宫六品佛楼模式的形成.故宫博物院院刊，2000（4）
38. 聂崇正.故宫倦勤斋天顶画、全景画探究.见：区域与网络——近千年来中国美术史研究国际学术讨论会论文集（抽印本）.台湾大学艺术史研究所，2001
39. 刘畅.清代宫廷和苑囿中的室内戏台述略.故宫博物院院刊，2003（2）
40. 张淑娴.倦勤斋建筑略考.故宫博物院院刊，2003（3）
41. 倦勤斋工作组，刘畅等执笔.倦勤斋保护工作阶段报告.故宫博物院院刊，2004（1）
42. 李福敏整理.故宫《倦勤斋陈设档》之一.故宫博物院院刊，2004（2）
43. 李福敏.关于倦勤斋陈设档的几点认识.故宫博物院院刊，2004（2）

ii.文物保护文献

1. 中华人民共和国文物保护法
2. 国际古迹遗址理事会中国国家委员会.中国文物古迹保护准则

iii.规划设计文献

1. 建设部.历史文化名城保护规划编制要求
2. ICOMOS.威尼斯宪章
3. ICOMOS.华盛顿宪章
4. ICOMOS.佛罗伦萨宪章
5. ICOMOS.关于保护乡土建筑的国际宪章
6. ICOMOS.关于文化旅游的国际宪章（第八稿）
7. UNESCO.国际遗产保护公约实施守则

内 容 简 介

乾隆花园（官方称宁寿宫花园）是由清朝乾隆皇帝直接指挥兴建的，融会了皇家园林与私家花园、北方与南方的工艺、传统文化与当代成就，体现了乾隆皇帝深厚的文化修养与丰富才情。作者从解读清官样式房图档与实地斟察入手，对乾隆花园园林与建筑设计进行了细致的剖析和深入的研究，在此基础上制定了乾隆花园文物保护规划，并列入了实施计划。

本书是对古典皇家园林建筑的研究与保护规划进应的一次探索，适合广大历史文化爱好者、建筑学研究者、建筑师和房地产策划人员、古建筑研究与保护人员阅读。

图书在版编目(CIP)数据

乾隆遗珍：故宫博物院宁寿宫花园历史研究与文物保护规划（汉、英）/

刘畅，王时伟，张淑娴著. —北京：清华大学出版社，2010.9

ISBN 978-7-302-23786-0

Ⅰ. ① 乾… Ⅱ. ① 刘… ② 王… ③ 张… Ⅲ. ① 故宫—花园—文物保护—研究—汉、英

Ⅳ. ① K928.74 ② TU-87

中国版本图书馆CIP数据核字(2010)第170071号

责任编辑：徐晓飞 李 嫚
责任校对：赵丽敏
责任印制：孟凡玉

出版发行：清华大学出版社　　　　　　　　　　地　　址：北京清华大学学研大厦 A座
　　　　　http://www.tup.com.cn　　　　　　　邮　　编：100084
　　　　　社　总　机：010-62770175　　　　　邮　　购：010-62786544
　　　　　投稿与读者服务：010-62776969, c-service@tup.tsinghua.edu.cn
　　　　　质　量　反　馈：010-62772015, zhiliang@tup.tsinghua.edu.cn
印　装　者：北京雅昌彩色印刷有限公司
经　　销：全国新华书店
开　　本：330×240　　印　张：23.5　　字　　数：518千字
版　　次：2010年9月第1版　　　　　　　　印　　次：2010年9月第1次印刷
印　　数：1～1500
定　　价：288.00元

产品编号：023759-01